COLLINS PHOTOGUIDE TO THE

WILD FLOWERS

of the Mediterranean

COLLINS PHOTOGUIDE TO THE

WILD FLOWERS
of the Mediterranean

Ingrid and Peter Schönfelder

Translated from the German by
CLIVE J. KING

COLLINS
Grafton Street, London

Fig. 1 (Page 2) Spanish Broom on the coast at Saint-Tropez (S. France).

Fig. 2 (Page 7) Sea Squills on a pasture in autumn at Brucoli (Sicily).

William Collins Sons & Co Ltd
London · Glasgow · Sydney · Auckland ·
Toronto · Johannesburg

© Ingrid and Peter Schönfelder, 1984
Originally published in Germany by
Kosmos-Verlag, Stuttgart
© in the translation, William Collins Sons & Co Ltd, 1990

Typesetting: Ace Filmsetting Ltd, Frome, Somerset

ISBN 0 00 219863-0

Printed and bound by Wm. Collins Sons & Co Ltd, Glasgow

Contents

Preface

Millions of holiday-makers visit the Mediterranean coasts every year, but they are mainly concentrated in the many tourist centres. This is a good thing from the point of view of wildlife, for it still leaves many areas – often only a few miles away from the hordes of sedentary sun-bathers – where you can find the Mediterranean plant-world in all its abundant variety. You have to go out into the surrounding countryside and wander through fields and olive groves, through garigue and maquis, and into the forests, but even where there is abundant proof that a place has been inhabited – in some cases for thousands of years – you can still find many interesting flowers among the Greek and Roman ruins or mediaeval walls. And if you can manage to travel in spring, between March and May, when it is still quiet even in the tourist centres, then you will begin to really appreciate the Mediterranean flora. You will come across evergreen shrubs with scented flowers covering large areas, especially rock-roses which can dominate whole stretches of land with their pink or white flowers. Of course most of the plants do not flower quite so brilliantly – it is only in gardens and parks that you will find conspicuous, large-flowered ornamental plants from various subtropical countries gathered together – but it is sometimes primarily these that the amateur naturalist is thinking of when he talks about the flowers of the Mediterranean region. Only the most important of these are mentioned in this book, and then mainly because they have penetrated the neighbouring wild vegetation.

Other seasons too, of course, have their botanical charm. At the height of summer many coastal plants are beginning to flower, the evergreen shrubs of the maquis and garigue creating a colourful impression with their colourful fruits, and only now is the mountain flora fully developed. Even in autumn there are still a few species from widely different plant-families sending up their inflorescences, often when the surrounding vegetation has become completely withered. With the arrival of rain-showers in October, the Mediterranean life-cycle begins all over again. The variety of the flora is considerable, with approximately 20,000 species, but about half of these are restricted to the east and south, from Asia Minor to North Africa, and many occur only in small or very small regions and in the mountains. So although in the end the 1000 or so species described and the 506 illustrated in this book represent only a selection, the plant enthusiast will be able to recognise and identify the more common plants. Occasionally, of course, he will come across a plant that is not illustrated, and so discover something new, but this still happens to us too every time we visit a part of the Mediterranean region.

Ingrid and Peter Schönfelder

Hints on using this book

In choosing the species we have tried to produce a cross-section, as evenly balanced as possible, of the most common representatives of all the plant-families from the ferns to the orchids, and to take as much account of the less striking ones, for example the grasses, as of those that are attractive. First and foremost are the widely distributed species that are found throughout the whole Mediterranean region. Then there are plants that are characteristic of a particular part of the region, occurring perhaps only in the west or east. Finally there are examples of species restricted to quite small areas, e.g. the Balearic Islands, Corsica or Crete, and these are known as endemics. We have concentrated mainly on the evergreen plants of the Mediterranean zone, and have also taken into account a considerable number of deciduous species of the sub-Mediterranean zone, but have mentioned only a few representatives of the Mediterranean mountain vegetation.

With few exceptions, the arrangement of the book and the scientific nomenclature used follow that of *Flora Europaea*, and show the natural relationship of plant-families from ferns to gymnosperms and angiosperms, and from dicotyledons to monocotyledons, so similar and related species are therefore found close to each other even if their flower-colour is different. We have added in brackets after the accepted Latin name those synonyms that are often used in other books, and have also given the author or authors of each name, which is necessary for the unambiguous naming of a species. The English names, where they already exist, have been taken from books written in English about the Mediterranean flora (see Bibliography).

There are several ways of finding a particular plant in this book. If you already know the family, genus or species you can look in the Index of scientific and English names (p. 304), or, in the case of family names only, you can consult the list of contents (p. 5). If you do not know the name you can find out the family by using the Key to identification (p. 34), and in the process get to know some of its most important features with the help of the line drawings. Lastly you can make a direct comparison with the coloured photographs and accompanying descriptions, and this will enable you to identify 506 species with certainty and a further 442 with a good chance of success. At the beginning of each description are details of height, and the average for ordinary locations will be found to lie round about the middle of the range given, or slightly above. In the case of flowering times too, only an average period of variation has been given, for in the extreme south and east flowering can begin somewhat earlier and on the northern boundary can end rather later. The usual signs for life-forms are explained on p. 53.

The description begins with the structure of the stem and leaves, followed by details of the inflorescence, flowers and fruit. Special emphasis is placed on those characters which can be used to distinguish a species from related plants that may be mentioned here or illustrated elsewhere in the book. This section will sometimes be concluded with references to subspecies or a mention of its being a poisonous, medicinal, or economic plant of some kind. The botanical terms used in this section are explained on p. 28 by means of diagrams.

The various types of Mediterranean vegetation, such as maquis or garigue etc., mentioned in the lines devoted to habitat, are discussed on pp. 16–27.

To conserve space, details of the distribution are usually given in a line or two like those of the habitat. While many species occur throughout the entire Mediterranean region (see map on p. 13), others are found only in the western part, i.e. the Iberian peninsula, generally also parts of north-west Africa and southern France. In the Apennine peninsula western and eastern Mediterranean species overlap, while the number of central Mediterranean ones is smaller, with an area of distribution that includes Italy and usually also the surrounding islands. The distribution of the numerous east Mediterranean species can differ considerably, sometimes covering only the southern Balkan peninsula together with the Aegean, sometimes extending across Turkey or Cyprus to Israel and northern Egypt. If the distribution includes the Atlantic islands only the Canary Islands are named, since it is here that most connections with the Mediterranean flora exist, and at the same time it is these islands that are visited most frequently. The use of the name 'Canary Islands' does not of course mean that the species in question is present on all of these. The more or less extensive spread of many Mediterranean plants into south-west Asia is normally indicated by the general term 'S.W. Asia'. Differences between the plant described and other similar species which are not illustrated are given here, wherever possible with some of their more important characteristics.

Notes on nature conservation

Up to now nature-lovers travelling in the Mediterranean region will have found a sign 'Nature Conservation Area' just as rare as a reference to protected species. In these countries nature conservation stands on a much weaker footing than in Britain, and is often still at an early stage, although in the coastal regions during the last 20 years more vegetation worthy of protection has fallen victim to building development and tourism than anywhere else in Europe. The main threat to many Mediterranean plant communities, including endemic species with only small areas of distribution, lies in the widespread opening up of more and more places to holiday-makers. In addition of course, factors similar to those in northern Europe have had an influence on the threat to plants (and animals), especially changes in the use of land for agriculture and forestry. By contrast, the direct threat to individual species by picking and uprooting is certainly less, even if it is centred on a few groups of plants of special interest to the garden-lover. The situation in Great Britain was recognised some years ago, and in 1981 Parliament passed the Wildlife and Countryside Act. Under the terms of this Act it is an offence to uproot any wild plant in this country without the permission of the owner or occupier of the land. In addition, there are a number of species that are strictly protected, the picking of any part of these plants being prohibited unless for educational, conservation or scientific purposes, when a licence is required. Even earlier it had become clear that some legally-backed agreement between nations was necessary in order to control international trade in wild plants, and in 1975 the Convention on International Trade in Endangered Species (CITES), often referred to as the Washington Convention, came into force after being ratified by ten countries. Since then the importance of this convention has become more and more apparent, and it has now been ratified by 90 countries around the world. Like Britain, many countries now have legislation to protect their native flora, but in the Mediterranean region where there are numerous endemics under threat, especially amongst the coastal and mountain vegetation, and conservation measures are less advanced, all that remains for visitors to the Mediterranean is to regard all species that do not occur in large numbers as protected species, and to resist the temptation to add to their collections rather than contribute to the extinction of endangered species.

Climate and plant life-forms

The Mediterranean floral region can be defined in various ways, either according to the occurrence of characteristic plant species and formations, or according to the range of the typical Mediterranean climate. Since the occurrence and form of Mediterranean plants is determined to a large extent by the climate, we will begin with a short description of this.

The total annual **rainfall** throughout large areas of central Europe is about 500–900mm (e.g. Stuttgart 673mm, Hamburg 712mm, Munich 866mm), with a considerable difference between the wetter western part or rainy mountain districts and the southern boundary formed by the Mediterranean region. However, the season of maximum rainfall is quite different. While in the northern part most of the year's rainfall occurs during the summer, in the south it is concentrated in the winter season, from about October to April – the summer months are dry, July and August being almost completely rainless. This can be seen in the diagrams in Fig. 3, in which the rainfall of Rome and Tunis is compared with that of Stuttgart. The total amount for Rome (881mm annually) is considerably higher than that for Tunis, which has an annual average of 415mm, but whereas in Rome the maximum rainfall occurs at the beginning of the winter period in October, in Tunis the peak is not reached until December. The graph shows that Stuttgart has typical central European conditions with the maximum rainfall in mid-summer.

Temperature is the second important element in the Mediterranean climate. The winter is mild, with average temperatures even in January, the coldest month, usually lying between 5° and 10°C. Short periods of frost occur only in northern parts of the region; in the south they are almost entirely absent. In summer, too, average temperatures are considerably higher than in northern Europe. In July and August the maximum daily air temperature can often exceed 30°C,

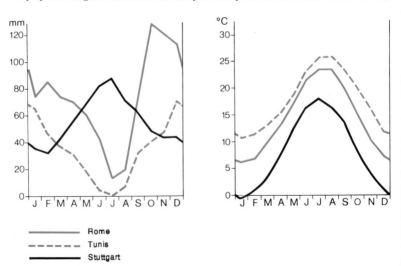

	Rome
	Tunis
	Stuttgart

Fig. 3 Seasonal variation in rainfall (left) and temperature (right).

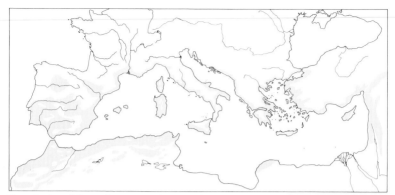

Fig. 4 Region of the Mediterranean climate and sclerophyllous vegetation.

while ground temperatures in open places rise to about 70°C. If you look at the graph on the right, which shows average temperatures by month, you will see that for all 3 places the maximum occurs in July/August, that for Tunis of course being distinctly higher than Rome, and on average almost 10°C above Stuttgart.

This typically Mediterranean climate with moderately moist winters and hot dry summers is caused by areas of low pressure which in winter move from Iceland southwards across the continent of Europe into the Mediterranean region, bringing with them the winter rains. In summer, high pressure from the Azores spreads into the Mediterranean region, forcing the low pressure areas into central and northern Europe. The Mediterranean region, then, lies in the dry subtropical zone, and this is much more noticeable in the continental east and south than in the Atlantic west and north.

The region governed by the Mediterranean climate is also the region of sclerophyllous vegetation and growth-forms typical of this zone. Trees and shrubs are usually adapted to these climatic conditions by having firm evergreen leaves which can withstand the summer period of drought and last for two or more years. Because of this they can continue to grow throughout the whole year unless a shortage of water restricts their activity. In most of the Mediterranean region the characteristic tree of natural vegetation is the Holm Oak (*Quercus ilex*), but this is replaced in parts of the west and east by other species of oak. Many shrubs forming the undergrowth of these forests have similar types of leaves, e.g. species of strawberry tree (*Arbutus andrachne* and *A. unedo*), Laurustinus (*Viburnum tinus*) or the Mediterranean Buckthorn (*Rhamnus alaternus*). Many woody plants have evergreen leaves which are narrowed to an elliptic or linear shape, like the characteristic tree of cultivated land, the Olive (*Olea europaea*), Rosemary (*Rosmarinus officinalis*), Myrtle (*Myrtus communis*), Phillyrea latifolia and *P. angustifolia*, or Oleander (*Nerium oleander*), or even reduced to scales as in *Thymelaea hirsuta*, the tamarisks (*Tamarix* spp.) or species of heath (e.g. *Erica arborea* or *E. multiflora*). In the summer drought some species lose many of their older leaves, like the Sage-leaved Cistus (*Cistus salviifolius*), but complete loss of leaves as in, e.g., the Tree Spurge (*Euphorbia dendroides*) is exceptional. Even some of the characteristic thorny shrubs, which have only very small leaves anyway, lose them in summer, like various species of broom (*Genista corsica* or *G. acanthoclada*) and thorny broom (*Calicotome villosa* and *C. spinosa*), the spurges (*Euphorbia acanthothamnos* and *E. spinosa*) the Thorny

13

Burnet (*Sarcopoterium spinosum*), or switch-shrubs like species of *Ephedra*, Spanish Broom (*Spartium junceum*), *Lygos sphaerocarpa* and *Coronilla juncea*. There are also a large number of plants that are woody only at the base and are termed subshrubs.

Many herbaceous plants are adapted to the Mediterranean climate by surviving the dry summer period underground in the form of tubers, bulbs or corms, and then in the spring they delight us with a profusion of flowers. These plants, called geophytes, include orchids, plants of the Lily family such as asphodels (*Asphodelus* spp.) and the Yellow Asphodel (*Asphodeline lutea*), tulips (*Tulipa* spp.), fritillaries (*Fritillaria* spp.), star of Bethlehem (*Ornithogalum* spp.), squills (*Scilla* spp.), grape hyacinths (*Muscari* spp.), species of *Allium*, and also members of the Daffodil family and the Iris family. Only a few of the members of these families flower in the autumn.

Lastly there are numerous plants, especially those growing in open country, which have an annual life-cycle. These annuals survive the unfavourable dry season as seeds, which germinate in autumn and winter, come into flower from late winter to spring, and then produce seeds once more. This life-form is represented in many groups in the Mediterranean region, which in the northern European flora consists only of perennials, as for example *Biscutella didyma*, Lupin (*Lupinus angustifolius*), *Coronilla scorpioides*, Horseshoe Vetch (*Hippocrepis unisiliquosa*), Sun Rose (*Helianthemum salicifolium*), species of Plantain (*Plantago afra*), Daisy (*Bellis annua*) and species of Carline Thistle (*Carlina racemosa*).

While flowering in most of our northern European plant communities takes place from spring through to autumn, in the Mediterranean climate it is concentrated much more in the spring, especially in the months of March, April and May. Many plants only flower during the summer if they are in coastal areas which are better supplied with water, or if they grow by one of the few lakes or rivers. In the drier localities, but also in the forests, flowering gradually begins again with the first heavy rains.

Vegetation zones

As climatic conditions change, both with the geographical latitude from south to north and also with altitude in the mountains, so there is variation in the composition of the various zones of vegetation. The Mediterranean zone containing evergreen oaks and olive trees is confined to a narrow coastal strip in the northern Mediterranean region, e.g. S. France, N. Italy and Yugoslavia, and spreads only a few hundred metres up the mountainsides. In the south of course it reaches even further upwards and extends into the interior, e.g. into southern Spain. Here, in addition to the evergreen forests, there are characteristic evergreen shrub formations known as maquis and garigue. Towards the north and at a higher altitude is the adjoining submediterranean zone, whose natural vegetation consists largely of deciduous oaks, in particular the Downy Oak (*Quercus pubescens*). These forests, often open and rich in shrubs and undergrowth, extend to the southern foot of the Alps, and also westward and eastward round the Alps as far as the Kaiserstuhl and into Lower Austria. Some individual species have spread further, forming outlying communities in central Europe. In this submediterranean zone the summers are not nearly so hot and dry, the winters have a more northern character, and at higher altitudes there are more frequent periods of frost, to which the trees have adapted by shedding their leaves in autumn. Here, the characteristic tree of cultivated land, especially in the west, is the Sweet Chestnut (*Castanea sativa*), also grape-vines are widely grown. Towards the north and in the mountains, as in the Apennines and the Balkan peninsula, are the adjoining central European beechwoods and mixed deciduous forests. While the northern boundary of the beech zone in S. Sweden is restricted to the lowlands, it rises progressively across central Europe until at its southern boundary, in Sicily, it is situated in the montane zone where it forms the timber-line. This sequence of vegetation is found mainly in the damper and more northerly areas of the Mediterranean region. In drier parts, from the Mediterranean to the montane zone, there are coniferous forests, composed of various species of pine, and at higher altitudes firs, cypresses and cedars as well. Above the timber-line are the subalpine and alpine zones, which are partly characterised by thorn-cushion vegetation, but which have considerable regional differences and contain numerous endemic species. Towards the south, where amounts of rain become gradually smaller and the summer dry period becomes even longer, the Mediterranean sclerophyllous vegetation becomes more sparse, changing first into open garigue-like shrub formation and then into steppe and semi-desert zones.

The most important plant communities

Rocky and sandy coasts, saltmarshes

It is the coastal plant communities that many visitors to the Mediterranean first come across. It is true that many sections of rocky coastline have been neatly smoothed with concrete, and that the sands of the main bathing beaches from the northern edge of the Mediterranean to the N. African coast have been levelled by bulldozers and cleared of 'nasty' plants, but there are still to be found those few, often fleshy species that occupy the spray zone along rocky coasts. Amongst these are the Rock Samphire (*Crithmum maritimum*), members of the Sea Lavender family represented by the locally variable genus *Limonium* or by *Limoniastrum monopetalum*, and also *Lotus cytisoides* and *Senecio bicolor*.

The sandy beaches are more varied, with many different plants coming into flower from spring until late summer. In the splash zone just above the line not reached by even the higher waves, there is a scattered plant-community growing amongst material washed up on the shore, which consists mainly of two more or less succulent annuals, Sea Rocket (*Cakile maritima*) and Saltwort (*Salsola kali*). Then come the first small primary dunes, continually altered by the wind and strengthened by grasses like *Elymus farctus* and *Sporobolus pungens*, whose roots creep along through the sand and grow through to the surface whenever their stems are covered up. The higher secondary dunes are colonised by Marram Grass (*Ammophila arenaria*), and in between are numerous plants which are adapted in various ways to sandy places, whose surface dries out and heats up from time to time. Here, in spring, one can find Sea Bindweed (*Calystegia soldanella*) with thickish leaves and large funnel-shaped flowers, and also cushions formed by various members of the Pea family, especially *Lotus creticus* and the Sea Medick (*Medicago marina*) which is covered in silvery white hairs to lessen evaporation. The Cottonweed (*Otanthus maritimus*) and Sea Stock (*Matthiola sinuata*) are also protected by a covering of white felt. Two prickly members of the Carrot family create a special impression on those running about barefoot on the shore; Sea Holly (*Eryngium maritimum*) with umbels of flowers contracted into heads and with bracts tinged steel-blue, and *Echinophora spinosa*, both of which begin to flower in mid-summer like the Sea Daffodil (*Pancratium maritimum*) with its enormous white flowers. Unfortunately this member of the Daffodil family has been repeatedly picked so that in some places it has become rare. Tufts of long twisted leaves can be seen in spring, and large, pitch-black seeds are visible until late in the autumn. There are also many annuals like Hare's-tail (*Lagurus ovatus*) or certain species of restharrow, e.g. *Ononis variegata*. On dunes that have been established over a long period there is an increasing number of subshrubs, herbaceous plants which become woody at the base, e.g. *Crucianella maritima* or *Helichrysum stoechas*. Soon taller shrubs appear in some places, especially *Juniperus oxycedrus* ssp. *macrocarpa*, which although limited in dune localities is often found in the garigue and maquis. Sometimes a coastal garigue will form on sandy and particularly on rocky coasts, which without interference by man soon changes into evergreen forest.

Behind the dunes, where lagoons with more or less salty water are gradually drying up, one finds saltmarshes. Like all plant communities in extreme habitats they are often poor in species, dominated frequently by the succulent, shrubby *Arthrocnemum glaucum* or *A. fruticosum*. *Limonium angustifolium* is also one of

Fig. 5 Coastal dunes with Sea Daffodils, Sea Holly and Marram Grass at Marbella (S. Spain).

the characteristic plants here. As more dry land forms and becomes richer in species, the landscape is often determined by coarse tufts of Sharp-pointed Rush (*Juncus acutus*) which may grow taller than a man. Amongst these one may find *Linum maritimum*, various species of *Centaurium*, or the Golden Samphire (*Inula crithmoides*) in flower.

Evergreen Forests

Nowadays evergreen oak forest, which is characteristic of the Mediterranean zone, has become rare. The most widespread tree-species which forms forests is the Holm Oak (*Quercus ilex*), but after thousands of years of man's influence ancient Holm Oak forests are rather rare and not very extensive. It is more com-

17

mon to see low-growing forests consisting of tree-stumps with stems rising from them, which were previously cut off regularly for firewood and charcoal. Holm Oak forests have comparatively thick foliage but a number of shrubs can thrive in their shade, and these appear again as important components of the maquis. They include the Mastic Tree (*Pistacia lentiscus*), Turpentine Tree (*Pistacia terebinthus*), Tree Heath (*Erica arborea*), Strawberry Tree (*Arbutus unedo*), *Phillyrea latifolia*, and the Wild Olive (*Olea europaea* var. *sylvestris*); also a few climbing plants such as Wild Madder (*Rubia peregrina*), *Asparagus acutifolius* and *Smilax aspera*. On the other hand the number of herbaceous plants is small, the most common being the Acute-leafed Spleenwort (*Asplenium onopteris*) and *Cyclamen repandum*. In the south of the Mediterranean region, where there is less rain, Holm Oak forests are more open and have a richer undergrowth.

In the west *Quercus ilex* is replaced by the closely related *Q. rotundifolia*, and forests are also formed by the semi-evergreen Portuguese Oak (*Q. faginea*). Where rainfall is higher the Cork Oak (*Q. suber*) is found on siliceous soils. As most of these trees are used as a source of cork, the forests are more open, and consequently herbaceous plants are more abundant. In some areas Bracken (*Pteridium aquilinum*) is found in massive quantities.

In the eastern Mediterranean region, forests are occasionally formed by *Quercus calliprinos*, the tree-form of the Kermes Oak (*Q. coccifera*) and by the semi-evergreen Valonia Oak (*Q. macrolepis*). In damp gorges, and also in the somewhat more rainy coastal areas such as the Dalmatian coast, the Laurel (*Laurus nobilis*) may be present, though it rarely occurs in large numbers.

A number of conifers also form evergreen forests, and in the Mediterranean zone there are chiefly two species of pine, the Stone Pine (*Pinus pinea*) and the Aleppo Pine (*P. halepensis*). Since the crowns of pine trees remain less dense than those of evergreen oaks, pine forests generally have a more abundant undergrowth than oak forests, and indeed form the primary habitat of many species which nowadays are concentrated in the maquis and garigue. The Stone Pine has been cultivated since ancient times for its edible seeds ('pinioli'), and its original distribution cannot be established for certain, but it probably used to occur wild on sandy soils near the coasts of the western Mediterranean region. The Aleppo Pine is the most widespread conifer of the evergreen zone, grows mainly on limestone, and because it has no special requirements and is a source of good timber is often planted nowadays. Plants found in its undergrowth include *Daphne gnidium*, the Sage-leaved Cistus (*Cistus salviifolius*), the Mastic Tree (*Pistacia lentiscus*) and Rosemary (*Rosmarinus officinalis*). In the eastern Mediterranean region westwards to Mt. Athos and Crete, *Pinus halepensis* is replaced by *P. brutia*, which is also found at higher altitudes, while in the western part of the region the Maritime Pine (*Pinus pinaster*) occurs on dry, acid soils composed of primitive rock and sandstone. In the Iberian peninsula and on Corsica this also spreads far up into the mountain zone.

Subspecies of the Black Pine (*Pinus nigra*), which are only found in certain areas of the Mediterranean region, form extensive forests in the mountain zone and their often bizarre shapes have a distinct effect on the tree-line. Amongst our native species the Scots Pine (*Pinus sylvestris*) extends southwards to some of the mountains in central Spain, and one of its subspecies grows in the Sierra Nevada in southern Spain. And of the firs, the Silver Fir (*Abies alba*) – usually accompanied by the Beech – extends into the Pyrenees, Apennines, and the mountains of the northern and central Balkan peninsula. In Sicily it is replaced by the closely related *Abies nebrodensis*, which is severely threatened in its native habitat. Other firs that are endemic or have a restricted distribution are the Spanish Fir (*Abies pinsapo*), found in S.W. Spain, especially in the Serrania de Ronda, where it forms open forests in the mountains, and *A. maroccana*, a related species now present only in small areas in the Rif section of the Atlas mountains.

Fig. 6 Holm Oak forest at Patrimonio (Corsica).

The Greek Fir (*Abies cephalonica*) occupies a larger area in the mountains of southern Greece.

In the eastern Mediterranean region westwards to Crete and the island of Rhodes in the eastern Aegean, the Italian Cypress (*Cupressus sempervirens*) together with *Pinus brutia* form open forests with abundant undergrowth in the mountain zone as far as the timber-line. Finally, in the far east of the region it is replaced by the Cedar of Lebanon (*Cedrus libani*) and in the far south-west in the Atlas mountains by the Atlas Cedar (*Cedrus atlantica*). The isolated occurrence of these trees in the mountains means that they are regarded as relict species which in ancient times had a much wider distribution.

Deciduous forests

Beyond the zone of sclerophyllous vegetation and in the adjacent area to the north where the summer water-supply is greater and more certain, evergreen forests are replaced by deciduous oak forests and the Mediterranean zone changes into the submediterranean zone. These relatively open forests, which prefer

Fig. 7 Downy Oak forest with Cyclamen and Paeonies, Foresta Umbra/Monte Gargano (Italy).

Left Fig. 8 Maquis with Strawberry Trees and Tree Heath at Porto (Corsica).

warm situations and stretch from northern Spain and southern France across the Apennines as far as the Balkan peninsula, are dominated by the Downy Oak (*Quercus pubescens*), but other species of oak may take its place, e.g. the Pyrenean Oak (*Q. pyrenaica*) in the Iberian peninsula. The semi-evergreen Turkey Oak (*Q. cerris*) may form pure forests or may be mixed with other tree-species, e.g. the Oriental Hornbeam (*Carpinus orientalis*), Hop Hornbeam (*Ostrya carpinifolia*), Nettle Tree (*Celtis australis*), Montpelier Maple (*Acer monspessulanum*) and Manna Ash (*Fraxinus ornus*). In the undergrowth are deciduous shrubs, e.g. *Pyrus amygdaliformis*, Scorpion Senna (*Coronilla emerus*), Bladder Senna (*Colutea arborescens*), the Wig Tree (*Cotinus coggygria*), and also evergreen species such as *Rosa sempervirens*, Mediterranean Buckthorn (*Rhamnus alaternus*) and Butcher's Broom (*Ruscus aculeatus*). Herbaceous vegetation in these forests is abundant, some of their typical representatives spreading into the warmest areas of central Europe and forming outlying communities there. Amongst these are Bastard Balm (*Melittis melissophyllum*), Purple Gromwell (*Buglossoides purpurocaerulea*), Black Bryony (*Tamus communis*), *Doronicum orientale*, and also orchids such as Limodore (*Limodorum abortivum*) and *Dactylorhiza sulphurea* ssp. *pseudosambucina*.

Lastly, on the subject of deciduous forests, we must mention beech woods, which occur in some places in the mountain zone, for these are quite familiar to those of us who live in the cooler countries of Europe. In structure and composition they are almost identical to our native woods. Although most of the species

present are also found in temperate parts of Europe, there are a few that have a predominantly Mediterranean distribution, such as the Blue Wood Anemone (*Anemone apennina*), some species of hellebore (*Helleborus* spp.), *Cyclamen* spp., and Butcher's Broom (*Ruscus aculeatus*).

Shrub formations, Maquis, Garigue

In the Mediterranean region as a whole, shrub formations are nowadays more widespread than evergreen forests. Most of these are not of ancient origin but have arisen by the clearing or burning of forests followed by grazing, but originally they only occurred on the natural boundaries of forests and woods, i.e. on coasts. Today one can occasionally find a narrow strip of shrubland on long-established, fixed dunes which will eventually be occupied by oak and pine forest, but on stormy, rocky coasts, much of the coastal garigue with its unique and characteristic flora is considered to be in its original state. It also occurs on the dry margins of evergreen forests in the southern Mediterranean region, e.g. in dry areas of S. Spain and N. Africa, where tree-growth gradually thins out and comes to an end. Several names have been applied to these regionally very diverse shrub formations. In this book we have given the name 'maquis' to all those communities of mainly evergreen shrubs of usually 2–5m in height, while those consisting of lower shrubs and subshrubs, usually less than 1.5m high, have been called 'garigue'. Apart from the few natural formations, maquis and garigue represent stages in the process of degeneration, during which the effects of axe, fire and grazing in turn have transformed evergreen forests first into maquis and garigue, then into the grassy pastures desired by shepherds, and finally into bare, stony ground. Connected with this degeneration is the removal and impoverishment of the soil, so that the reverse process – regeneration to maquis and forest – can only be very slow, where it is possible at all.

The term 'maquis' is derived from a Corsican word used to describe the extensive, dense and often impenetrable shrub formation found on the island and dominated by the Tree Heath (*Erica arborea*) and Strawberry Tree (*Arbutus unedo*, Fig. 8). Many plants that are present in evergreen oak forests, but which prefer more open habitats, grow even more abundantly in the maquis, e.g. the Myrtle (*Myrtus communis*) and species of rockrose (*Cistus monspeliensis*, *C. salviifolius*). In other parts of the Mediterranean region different plants are dominant, resulting in very varied aspects, for in any particular region it may be the Mastic Tree (*Pistacia lentiscus*), species of *Phillyrea*, Spanish Broom (*Spartium junceum*) or the Eastern Strawberry Tree (*Arbutus andrachne*) which determine their appearance. This dense, tall maquis is dependent on a relatively high rainfall or degree of dampness, and is therefore found mainly on the western and northern slopes of mountains, and especially in those parts of the western and central Mediterranean region which receive a greater amount of rain. The garigue (also spelt garrigue) is the most varied formation of the Mediterranean region. Low shrubs and subshrubs occur in a multitude of species, forming a locally thriving plant community. Especially impressive is the 'mixed garigue', in which numerous shrubs combine to form a riot of colour, as can be seen in the photograph opposite, taken on the island of Rhodes: the pink is the flowers of *Cistus parviflorus*; the red, the tiny, massed flowers of the Thorny Burnet (*Sarcopoterium spinosum*) and the Mastic Tree (*Pistacia lentiscus*); the yellow, the thorny cushions of *Genista acanthoclada* and *Euphorbia acanthothamnos*; the blue, *Lithodora hispidula*; and the white, the Sage-leaved Cistus (*Cistus salviifolius*), and two species of juniper, *Juniperus phoenicea* and *J. oxycedrus*.

The distance between individual shrubs is governed mainly by the intensity of grazing and the form that it takes. Here there are herbaceous plants in great numbers, especially bulbous and tuberous plants, including an abundance of orchids, and also many annuals. Open stony and grassy pastures often create a mosaic-like effect on the surface of the ground. Of course the major part of the garigue is dominated by just one or two species of shrubs which more or less successfully avoid being eaten by grazing animals, mainly sheep and goats, by being thorny or poisonous or merely by having a 'nasty' taste caused by ethereal oils. Only a few of the many types of garigue are found throughout the larger part of the Mediterranean region, such as that consisting primarily of the Phoenician Juniper (*Juniperus phoenicea*) or *Thymelaea hirsuta*. Even the garigue composed of *Globularia alypum*, which extends far to the east, is absent from some areas. The extensive occurrence of Thyme (*Thymus vulgaris*) is characteristic of the interior of Spain and is known here as 'Tomillares', while the palmetto formation, composed of the Dwarf Fan Palm (*Chamaerops humilis*), is typical of the south-west Mediterranean coasts. Probably the most widespread form is the rockrose garigue, which is frequently helped by fire. Here the dominant plant over large areas is the Narrow-leaved Cistus (*Cistus monspeliensis*), but the Sage-leaved Cistus (*Cistus salviifolius*), and also the white-flowered, and pink-flowered species *C. albidus*, *C. incanus* and *C. parviflorus* play an important part, the last two species being especially prominent in the east. The chief plants in the Mint family that occur here and there are Rosemary (*Rosmarinus officinalis*), mainly on limestone, various species of lavender such as *Lavandula stoechas*, *L. dentata* and *L. latifolia* and also species of sage, chiefly *Salvia officinalis*, which forms large communities in parts of the Yugoslavian karst region.

Fig. 9 Garigue with Rockroses, *Genista acanthoclada*, *Lithodora hispidula* and Asphodels at Kattavia (Rhodes).

In the eastern Mediterranean region, where the garigue is also known as 'phrygana', the Thorny Burnet (*Sarcopoterium spinosum*) covers wide areas together with, for example, the dome-shaped bushes of *Euphorbia acantho-thamnos*, (which in this part replaces the central Mediterranean *E. spinosa*,) or the low-growing clumps of *Thymus capitatus*. In its undergrowth, too, the garigue of the eastern Mediterranean has only a few species in common with those of the central and western Mediterranean, though its composition in terms of life-forms is similar.

The streams and rivers, which to a great extent dry out in summer, are bordered by meadow shrubs including the Oleander (*Nerium oleander*), a common water-side plant. In this type of habitat it produces single, pink flowers during the hottest time of the year, while double-flowered forms are often planted as street-trees and in gardens. There are also clumps of various kinds of tamarisk (*Tamarix* spp.) and the Chaste Tree (*Vitex agnus-castus*), with its decorative blue inflores-cences. A particular shrub formation is occasionally found in the submediterra-nean zone of deciduous forests, mainly in the Balkan peninsula, which consists primarily of deciduous shrubs, and this is known as 'šibljak'. Species characteris-tic of this formation include Christ's Thorn (*Paliurus spina-christi*), *Pyrus* amygdaliformis, the Wig Tree (*Cotinus coggygria*), Pomegranate (*Punica granatum*), Judas Tree (*Cercis siliquastrum*), and the evergreen Firethorn (*Pyracantha coccinea*).

Grassy and stony pastures

Degeneration often does not end with maquis and garigue, but may lead on to the almost complete disappearance of shrubs and the formation of grassland, and from this stage on to stony pastures, especially in limestone regions if the fine soil is washed away. In summer these plant communities become yellow and brown as they wither, so that it is only in spring that one can see the variety of colour produced by the association of different species. Some of the dominant plants are grasses such as *Brachypodium ramosum*, *Hyparrhenia hirta*, species of *Aegilops*, Large Quaking-grass (*Briza maxima*) and *Stipa capensis*. There are also many annuals, especially members of the Pea family such as species of Bird's-Foot Trefoil, *Lotus edulis* and *L. ornithopodioides*, Disk Trefoil (*Hymenocarpos circinnatus*), species of clover (*Trifolium angustifolium* and *T. stellatum*), Annual Scorpion Vetch (*Coronilla scorpioides*) and *Neatostema apulum*. Where

Fig. 10 Esparto Grass steppe south of Almeria (S. Spain).

there is intensive grazing, prickly or poisonous weeds take over the pasture, producing areas covered with, for example, thistles such as *Carlina corymbosa* or *C. racemosa*, asphodels (species of *Asphodelus*) which are decorative but poisonous, or Sea Squills (*Urginea maritima*). Even the expansion of Esparto Grass steppe, named after the robust, tuft-forming Esparto Grass (*Stipa tenacissima*) and composed also of Albardine (*Lygeum spartum*) and numerous small annuals, is looked upon favourably by man nowadays, although this partly replaces, in the dry regions of S. Spain for example, the southern Mediterranean dry shrub communities. Only on the dry southern boundary of the Mediterranean region does the purely natural vegetation continue to flourish.

While in general the same species thrive on the stony pastures as in the open parts of the garigue, true rock-plants only grow where the cliffs are so tall and steep that they are naturally free of trees and shrubs, with fine soil and water confined to the smallest crevices. Plants that belong to this particular habitat of sunny or shady rock-crevices include several ferns such as *Cheilanthes fragrans*, the Rusty-back Fern (*Ceterach officinarum*), and the Southern Polypody (*Polypodium australe*). Species of navelwort such as *Umbilicus rupestris* are also found here. The majority of plants growing in these situations have a distribution restricted to certain areas, such as *Cymbalaria microcalyx* from the eastern Mediterranean, a number of campanulas such as *Campanula hagielia* from the Sporades, and species of *Inula* such as *I. verbascifolia*.

Cultivated land

The tree most characteristic of the cultivated land in the Mediterranean, from its northern boundary (e.g. by Lake Garda or S. France), to its southern limit on the edge of the Sahara, is the Olive (*Olea europaea*). With its comparatively narrow, shiny evergreen leaves, silvery on the underside, it is admirably suited to the climate of the region, while at the same time, as a source of oil, it has been one of the basic elements in human nutrition in this region since ancient times. The fruits, which have an oil content of 40–50%, are crushed and then pressed, first without heat, to obtain the best edible oil – 'virgin oil'. Even the oil from the second, warm, pressing is still usable for culinary purposes, while that from the third, hot, pressing is only suitable as lamp-oil or as a lubricant, or in the making of soap. In addition a considerable amount of hand-picked fruits come into the trade as edible olives after the bitter substances have been removed.

Olive trees, sometimes several hundred years old, are usually cultivated in open groves, which in many areas replace the evergreen forests. On soils rich in nutrients and with a good water supply agriculture is also possible, and in exceptional cases even mixed farming with vines and vegetables. Of course the land in the Olive groves is frequently left fallow, and so in spring it can be a real El Dorado for the plant-lover. Then one can find various geophytes in flower such as anemones (*Anemone coronaria* or *A. hortensis*), Rose Garlic (*Allium roseum*), Italian Arum (*Arum italicum*), Friar's Cowl (*Arisarum vulgare*) and the orchid genera *Serapias*, *Ophrys* and *Orchis* in a multi-coloured exchange with annuals such as *Scorpiurus muricatus*, Furrowed Melilot (*Melilotus sulcata*), species of pimpernel (*Anagallis arvensis* and *A. foemina*), Red Horned-poppy (*Glaucium corniculatum*), Honeywort (*Cerinthe major*), Field Marigold (*Calendula arvensis*), Crown Daisy (*Chrysanthemum coronarium*), Star Hawkbit (*Rhagadiolus stellatus*), and many more. Annual ploughing or hoeing prevents perennial herbaceous plants and shrubs gaining a foothold here. Another cultivated tree worthy of mention is the Carob Tree (*Ceratonia siliqua*), the fruits of which are used primarily as cattle-feed, but increasingly for human consumption. It is highly sensitive to frost and occurs mainly in the east and south of the Mediterranean region.

Fig. 11 Olive grove with Poppies, Corn Marigolds, Red Horned-poppies and Field Marigolds at El Fahs (Tunisia).

The deciduous Fig Tree (*Ficus carica*) often shares a terrace with the Olive. Its large, palmately lobed leaves unfold only in late spring, but the Almond tree (*Prunus dulcis*) is often showing its delicate pink flowers by the end of January. The latter in particular is also found up in the submediterranean zone. Other crop-bearing trees are more intensively cultivated, preventing this profusion of wild plants. This is just as true of vine-growing, widespread throughout the whole Mediterranean region, as it is of the cultivation of *Citrus* fruits, which is only possible in the warmest areas provided there is sufficient water, or in those parts which are almost free of frost. However, occasionally even here individual species can appear in such large numbers that at flowering time they dominate the entire landscape, e.g. the Bermuda Buttercup (*Oxalis pes-caprae*).

Ploughed land, especially that used for growing wheat, is generally treated with herbicides just as much as in northern Europe, so that many wild field-plants have become much rarer in the Mediterranean region as well. But from time to time one comes upon brightly coloured cornfields in which the graceful plant *Gladiolus italicus* grows so abundantly that one has to look closely in order to see the corn. Many of the plants spread into central Europe, such as the red-flowered poppies *Papaver dubium*, *P. hybridum* and *P. rhoeas*, but some have now become very rare here, like the Corn Cockle (*Agrostemma githago*), Winged Vetchling (*Lathyrus ochrus*), or some members of the Carrot family, e.g. Thorow-wax (*Bupleurum rotundifolium*), *Bifora radians*, Small Bur Parsley (*Caucalis platycarpos*) and Shepherd's Needle (*Scandix pecten-veneris*).

A guide to botanical terms

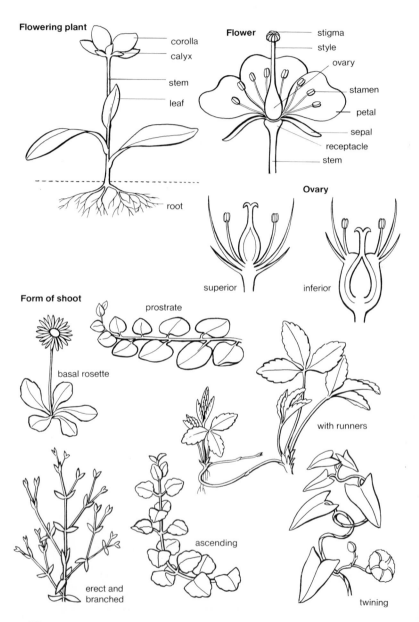

Flowering plant

corolla
calyx
stem
leaf
root

Flower

stigma
style
ovary
stamen
petal
sepal
receptacle
stem

Ovary

superior
inferior

Form of shoot

basal rosette
prostrate
with runners
ascending
erect and branched
twining

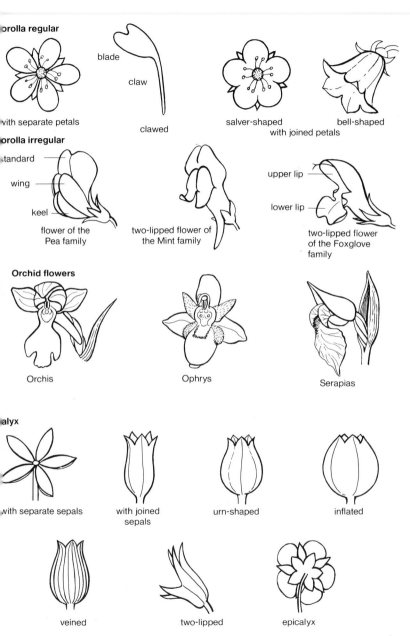

corolla regular

blade

claw

with separate petals

clawed

salver-shaped

bell-shaped

with joined petals

corolla irregular

standard

wing

keel

flower of the
Pea family

two-lipped flower of
the Mint family

upper lip

lower lip

two-lipped flower
of the Foxglove
family

Orchid flowers

Orchis

Ophrys

Serapias

calyx

with separate sepals

with joined
sepals

urn-shaped

inflated

veined

two-lipped

epicalyx

29

Inflorescences

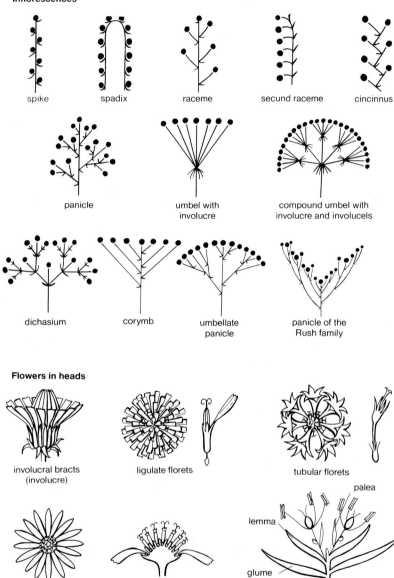

spike   spadix   raceme   secund raceme   cincinnus

panicle   umbel with involucre   compound umbel with involucre and involucels

dichasium   corymb   umbellate panicle   panicle of the Rush family

Flowers in heads

involucral bracts (involucre)

ligulate florets

tubular florets

ray florets (ligulate) disc florets (tubular)

receptacle with receptacular bracts

palea

lemma

glume

flowers in spikelets (grasses)

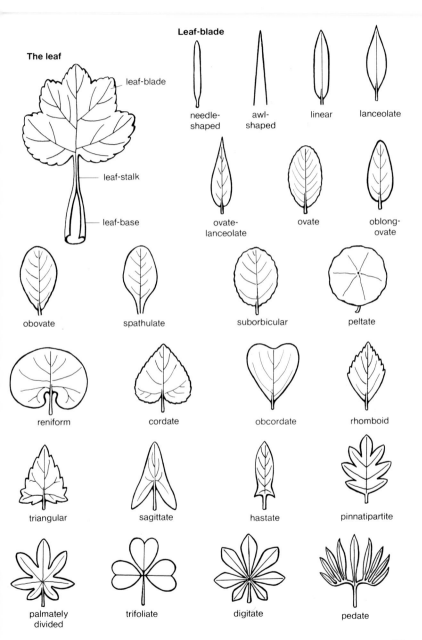

The leaf

leaf-blade

leaf-stalk

leaf-base

Leaf-blade

needle-shaped

awl-shaped

linear

lanceolate

ovate-lanceolate

ovate

oblong-ovate

obovate

spathulate

suborbicular

peltate

reniform

cordate

obcordate

rhomboid

triangular

sagittate

hastate

pinnatipartite

palmately divided

trifoliate

digitate

pedate

Leaf-blade

odd-pinnate

even-pinnate

bipinnate

with tendrils

Leaf-margin

entire

serrate

doubly serrate

toothed

prickly toothed

runcinate

crenate

sinuate

Venation

pinnately
veined

net-veined

parallel-
veined

Attachment of leaf

long-stalked

sessile

clasping

with
stipules

stipules united
into a sheath
(ochrea)

Leaf arrangement

alternate

opposite

whorled

decussate

Underground parts of plant

rhizome

stem-tuber

bulb

taproot

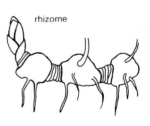

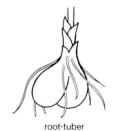

root-tuber

Key to the identification of plant families

This key is intended to help readers to assign easily a plant found in the Mediterranean region to a particular family, so that it can then be studied in the illustrated part of this book. We have tried to use, as far as possible, characters that can be clearly seen and understood by the non-botanist. Additional help is given by the line drawings (from Coste, Rechinger-Moser and Fiori-Paoletti), which however, especially in the larger families, can only show **one** example, and not always the particular genus and species concerned.

The key is divided first into the 4 main groups: spore-bearing plants, Gymnosperms, Dicotyledons (with 3 subsections) and Monocotyledons. The reader must first of all decide on one of these groups (A to F) and then turn to the corresponding key. It is then necessary to work through the key, starting with number 1 and choosing the most suitable alternative. In many cases this merely involves making a choice between 'a' and 'b', but there may be up to 5 alternatives, from 'a' to 'e'. This process will eventually lead to a description ending with the name of a family, and a reference to a page or pages where the appropriate illustrations and accompanying text may be found. In the larger groups there may be 4 or 5 stages or even more before one arrives at a suitable family description. In order to restrict the key to the most easily recognisable characters, it has sometimes been impossible to avoid keying out some genera separately from the rest, and these are given in brackets before the name of the family. Because some families are very varied in form, the key will often lead only to those species illustrated in this book.

The process of identification may be explained by using as an example the Oleander (*Nerium oleander*), which can be found as a wild plant with single flowers in August, for example in dried up stream beds. First look at the part of the key entitled 'Main Groups'. Sections 1 'Clubmosses, ferns' and 2 'Gymnosperms' do not apply, but section 3 'Dicotyledons' agrees with the plant in question. The leaves are net-veined, not parallel- or 1-veined, and the flower-parts are in fives, not threes or sixes. Now there is a choice to be made between 3a, 3b and 3c. The petals are clearly united below into a tube, and this leads to Group E, which begins on page 45. In the following extract from the key the alternative marked '+' is the correct one, that marked '−' is not true, and all irrelevant numbers have been omitted:

1a−
1b+Plants with green leaves
   3a−
   3b+Stem not twining or climbing
      8a−
      8b−
      8c+Flowers not in dense heads or not surrounded by a common involucre
         composed of many bracts
         10a−
         10b+Flowers regular
            19a−
            19b+Corolla 5-lobed, or rarely with up to 12 lobes

23a—
23b+Leaves opposite or whorled, but sometimes in a basal
　　rosette
　　29a—
　　29b+Leaves opposite or in whorls of 3 (4)
　　　　30a+Leaves evergreen
　　　　　31a—
　　　　　31b+Shrubs or prostrate subshrubs, flowers more
　　　　　　than 3cm across, twisted in bud
　　　　　　Periwinkle family *Apocynaceae* pp.180, 182

It is not difficult to decide that the plant must be Oleander from the illustration on page 181. Also, the text gives no reference to any similar species, so the identification as *Nerium oleander* L. is well-founded. In this example the process of identification took 8 stages to reach the correct result, but a glance at the keys to the groups shows that most families are arrived at much more quickly. In cases of doubt – for example, when it is not absolutely clear whether a leaf is evergreen or deciduous – it will be necessary to try both alternatives. By using this key frequently, the non-botanist will be gradually introduced to the underlying systematic arrangement of plants in this book. He or she will learn to recognise the characters of the more important families, and will finally be able to make use of one of the large national floras, or even *Flora Europaea*, which contains the complete flora of Europe.

The main groups

1. Clubmosses, ferns. Plants without flowers, reproducing by spores which are formed in special capsules called sporangia. — Group A　p.36
2. Gymnosperms. Trees or shrubs or Horsetail-like plants with needle-shaped or scale-like leaves, usually evergreen. Flowers unisexual, without involucre, later forming woody or berry-like cones. Seeds not enclosed in an ovary. — Group B　p.36
3. Dicotyledons. Leaves usually net-veined; if parallel- or 1-veined, then flower-parts not in threes or sixes, or involucre not composed of scales.
　3a Dicotyledons with inconspicuous flowers, involucral bracts absent or very small (up to 4mm long). — Group C　p.36
　3b Dicotyledons with conspicuous flowers, petals free to the base. — Group D　p.40
　3c Dicotyledons with conspicuous flowers, petals joined below into a long or short tube. — Group E　p.45
4. Monocotyledons. Leaves with parallel or curved veins, simple and undivided, sometimes cylindrical or needle-shaped, in the case of Palms fan-shaped or pinnate; if net-veined, then flower-parts in sixes or flowers in a spadix surrounded by a spathe. — Group F　p.51

Group A: Clubmosses, ferns

1a Plants moss-like, small, leaves in 4 rows (1)
                                            Clubmoss family   *Selaginellaceae*   p.54
1b Ferns, sporangia on underside of fronds forming groups (sori) of various shapes (2), partly covered by the recurved edge of the frond
                                                          Ferns   pp. 54, 56

Group B: Gymnosperms

1a Shrubs with male and female flowers on separate plants, plants Horsetail-like with long stem-joints, leaves opposite, reduced to small scales, fruits berry-like (3)
                                      Joint-pine family   *Ephedraceae*   p.60
1b Shrubs or trees, stem-joints short, leaves scale-like, appressed closely to the shoot (4) or needle-shaped and in whorls of 3 (5)
                                      Cypress family   *Cupressaceae*   p.60
1c Trees, leaves needle-shaped, spirally arranged, single, in pairs or in clusters on short shoots
                                      Pine family   *Pinaceae*   pp.56, 58

Group C: Dicotyledons with inconspicuous flowers, involucral bracts absent or very small (up to 4mm long)

1a Plants parasitic on species of Juniper (6)
                                      Mistletoe family   *Loranthaceae*   p.70
1b Trees or shrubs rooting in the ground (1c see page 39)
    2a Trees or shrubs, flowers in catkin-like inflorescences or in globular heads
        3a Inflorescence ovoid, later Blackberry-like, leaves undivided or lobed, plants with milky juice (7)
                                      Mulberry family   *Moraceae*   p.66

3b Inflorescence globular, pendent, greenish or reddish, leaves palmately lobed (8)
Plane family   Platanaceae   p.96

3c Inflorescence catkin-like or globular, bright yellow, leaves oblong and narrow or bipinnate
Acacia family   Mimosaceae   p.102

3d Inflorescence catkin-like, pink or whitish, leaves scale-like, lying close to the stems (9)
Tamarisk family   Tamaricaceae   p.158

3e Inflorescence elongated, whitish or yellowish

    4a Ripe fruits pendent, cone-like, styles 2, leaves without stipules (10)
Hazel family   Corylaceae   p.62

    4b Fruits completely or partially surrounded by a prickly or woody covering (cupula), styles 3, leaves with (often deciduous) stipules (11)
Beech family   Fagaceae   pp.62–66

    4c Fruits fleshy (12)
Pokeweed family   Phytolaccaceae   p.76

2b Trees or shrubs, flowers in other kinds of inflorescences or single

    5a Leaves pinnate

        6a Thorny shrubs
Rose family   Rosaceae   p.98

        6b Flowers arising directly from branches and trunk, fruit a pod (13)
Caesalpinia family   Caesalpiniaceae   p.100

        6c Fruit a 1-seeded pink or red, hairless or hairy drupe (14)
Cashew family   Anacardiaceae   pp.140, 142

    5b Leaves undivided or lobed

        7a Plants with milky juice

            8a Fruit a fig (15)
Mulberry family   Moraceae   p.66

            8b Fruit a capsule (16)
Spurge family   Euphorbiaceae   pp.132–136

        7b Evergreen shrubs or trees

        7c (see p.38)

9a Leaves on the upper part of the stems, spreading, obovate to oblong, silky hairy on both sides or only white-felted beneath, scale-like, appressed to the stems. Flower-parts in fours (17)
Daphne family *Thymelaeaceae* p.150

9b Leaves opposite

 10a Inflorescence consisting of a single 5- or 6-petalled female flower surrounded by 4-petalled male flowers
  Box family *Buxaceae* p.144

 10b Flowers bisexual, with 4 united sepals and 4 united petals (18)
  Olive family *Oleaceae* pp.178, 180

9c Leaves alternate

 11a Flowers with 3-lobed perianth, stems slender, erect (19)
  Sandalwood family *Santalaceae* p.68

 11b Flowers in racemes, calyx 5-lobed
  Buckthorn family *Rhamnaceae* p.144

 11c Flowers in compound umbels (20), flower-parts in fives, petals yellow
  Carrot family *Apiaceae* p.170

 11d Leaves smelling of eucalyptus when rubbed, young leaves decussate, flowers with numerous stamens (21)
  Myrtle family *Myrtaceae* p.162

7c Deciduous shrubs or trees

 12a Leaves opposite

  13a Fruit berry-like, leaves entire
   Coriaria family *Coriariaceae* p.140

  13b Fruit of 2 winged portions, leaves 3-lobed (22)
   Maple family *Aceraceae* p.142

 12b Leaves alternate

  14a Trees, fruits single and cherry-like, pendent, leaves in 2 ranks, obliquely ovate (*Celtis*, 23)
   Elm family *Ulmaceae* p.66

  14b Shrubs with silvery white leaves (*Atriplex*)
   Goosefoot family *Chenopodiaceae* p.74

  14c Shrubs, inflorescence at end of stems, flower-stalks at fruiting time with feathery hairs, leaves entire (*Cotinus*)
   Cashew family *Anacardiaceae* p.140

25   26   27   28

14d Shrubs with spiny stipules (24)
    Buckthorn family *Rhamnaceae* p.144
1c Herbaceous plants or subshrubs
 15a Plants fleshy, spadix-like, red-brown, without chlorophyll
    Balanophora family *Balanophoraceae* p.72
 15b Apparently leafless, jointed, fleshy plants (25) or leaves undivided, fleshy and sharp-pointed
    Goosefoot family *Chenopodiaceae* p.74
 15c Leaves present, not as above
  16a Plants with milky juice, inflorescence condensed, simulating a single flower, with one ovary and 5 groups of male flowers (cyathium) (16)
    Spurge family *Euphorbiaceae* pp.134, 136
  16b Flowers in heads, surrounded by a common involucre composed of numerous bracts (26); in *Xanthium*, 2 female flowers sunk in a prickly receptacle ending in 2 beaks (27) (Umbels resembling heads also found in some members of the Carrot family (28) *Eryngium*, p.164)
    Daisy family *Asteraceae* pp.226–252
  16c Flowers differently arranged
   17a Leaves only in a basal rosette (29)
    Plantain family *Plantaginaceae* p.220
   17b Leaves whorled (30)
    Bedstraw family *Rubiaceae* p.184
   17c Leaves opposite (at least the lower ones)
    18a Leaves with stinging hairs
     Nettle family *Urticaceae* p.68
    18b Leaves covered with grey-green meal (*Obione*)
     Goosefoot family *Chenopodiaceae* p.74
    18c Flowers in small sessile clusters with silvery bracts (*Paronychia*, 31)
     Pink family *Caryophyllaceae* p.78
    18d Flower-parts in fours, in erect, long-stalked, greenish, globular spikes (32)
     Plantain family *Plantaginaceae* p.220

29   30   31   32

33 34 35 36

17d Leaves alternate

    19a Flower-parts in fours, flowers forming dense, globular clusters in the leaf-axils (*Parietaria*, 33)
             Nettle family   *Urticaceae*   p.68

    19b Flower-parts in fives, flowers in compound umbels or globular heads, usually with involucre and involucels
             Carrot family   *Apiaceae*   pp.164–170

    19c Leaf-base with a tube clasping the stem (ochrea, 34; see also p.32)
             Dock family   *Polygonaceae*   p.72

    19d Tall, often red-tinged perennial with stalked ovate-lanceolate leaves 10–40cm long, flowers in long, stalked racemes (12)
             Pokeweed family   *Phytolaccaceae*   p.76

    19e Flowers unisexual, male above, female below, leaves grey-felted with star-shaped hairs, long-stalked (*Chrozophora*)
             Spurge family   *Euphorbiaceae*   p.132

Group D: Dicotyledons, petals free to the base

1a Flowers irregular (zygomorphic), sometimes only slightly

    2a Flowers spurred

        3a Petals 4 (*Fumaria*, 35)
             Poppy family   *Papaveraceae*   p.88

        3b Petals 5, surrounding petal-like honey-leaves (*Delphinium*, 36)
             Buttercup family   *Ranunculaceae*   p.82

    2b Flowers not spurred

        4a Flowers butterfly-like

            5a Petals 5, overlapping from the top downwards, the large petal pointing upwards called the standard, the 2 lateral petals called the wings, and the 2 lower petals joined to form the keel. All 10 stamens joined or the uppermost free (37, see also p. 29)
             Pea family   *Papilionaceae*   pp.104–128

            5b Similar, but petals overlapping from the base upwards, all stamens free. Tree or shrub with pink flowers (38)
             Caesalpinia family   *Caesalpiniaceae*   p.100

            5c The 2 lateral of the 5 sepals petal-like and simulating wings, the true petals united below, the lowest one keel-like with a fringed tip
             Milkwort family   *Polygalaceae*   p.140

        4b Flowers not butterfly-like

            6a Petals 4

                7a Petals yellow, the inner ones 3-lobed, stamens 4 (*Hypecoum*)
                Poppy family   *Papaveraceae*   p.88

37

38

39

40

7b Petals white, stamens numerous. Shrub, usually with spiny stipules (39)

Caper family *Capparidaceae* p.90

6b Petals 5 or 6

8a Flowers in compound umbels, marginal flowers often larger and irregular, inner flowers smaller and regular (40)

Carrot family *Apiaceae* pp.164–170

8b Flowers in racemes, petals 5 or 6, deeply cut at the end, stamens numerous (41)

Mignonette family *Resedaceae* p.94

1b Flowers regular

9a Sepals and petals up to 4 (or 5 in terminal flower)

10a Sepals and petals usually 3 (42)

Cneorum family *Cneoraceae* p.138

10b Sepals and petals usually 4

11a Perianth of one whorl, sepals absent (*Clematis*)

Buttercup family *Ranunculaceae* p.84

11b Perianth of 2 whorls, but sepals sometimes deciduous

12a Plants with yellow juice, flowers yellow or red (*Glaucium*, 43)

Poppy family *Papaveraceae* p.88

12b Plants without yellow juice

13a Prostrate or pendent shrubs usually with spiny stipules, flowers slightly irregular, white, with numerous stamens (39)

Caper family *Capparidaceae* p.90

13b Herbaceous plants or low subshrubs, flowers with 4 free sepals and 4 long-clawed petals, 2 outer short stamens and 4 inner longer stamens arranged in pairs. Fruit a capsule (siliqua, 44 or silicula) *Brassicaceae* pp.90–94

Mustard family *Brassicaceae* pp.90–94

41

42

43

44

46

47

45

48

13c Plant herbaceous, sometimes woody at the base, with strong aromatic scent, terminal flower with 5 sepals and petals (*Ruta*, 45)
        Rue family   *Rutaceae*   p.138

13d Tree, leaves opposite, pinnate, petals united in pairs at the base (*Fraxinus*, 46)
        Olive family   *Oleaceae*   p.178

9b Perianth usually of 5 sepals and petals, but sometimes of 6–10

  14a Stamens 5

    15a Ornamental shrub, leaves leathery, undivided, clustered at the ends of the stems, flowers with white petals about 1cm long (47)
        Pittosporum family   *Pittosporaceae* p.96

    15b Shrubs with smaller flowers or plants herbaceous

      16a Leaves opposite

        17a Leaves lanceolate to awl-shaped, stiff and spine-tipped, inflorescences resembling an umbel, flowers white or pink (*Drypis*, 48)
            Pink family   *Caryophyllaceae* p.78

        17b Leaves ovate, crenate-serrate to deeply lobed, inflorescence an umbel, fruits with a long beak (49)
            Geranium family   *Geraniaceae*   p.130

      16b At least the upper leaves alternate or leaves in a basal rosette

        18a Flowers in a loose panicle, yellow, sepals free (50)
            Flax family   *Linaceae*   p.132

        18b Flowers in compound umbels (20) or umbel-like heads, usually with involucre and/or involucels
            Carrot family   *Apiaceae*   pp.164–170

        18c Flowers in panicle-like inflorescences composed of small spikes all facing the same way. Sepals united below into a usually dry, membranous, coloured tube (*Limonium*, 51)
            Sea Lavender family   *Plumbaginaceae* p.176

  14b Stamens 6–10

    19a Leaves undivided

      20a Leaves opposite

        21a Herbaceous plants, petals clawed, notched to deeply 2-lobed, sepals joined into a 5-toothed tube (52)
            Pink family   *Caryophyllaceae* pp.78, 80

        21b Small subshrubs with needle-shaped leaves, flowers sessile in the leaf-axils on one side of the stem
            Sea Heath family   *Frankeniaceae*   p.160

49   50   51   52

20b Leaves alternate, flowers with 6 purple petals and 8 to 12-toothed hypanthium
            Loosestrife family   *Lythraceae*   p.162
19b Leaves pinnate or digitate
    22a Leaves of 3 leaflets, clover-like (53)
            Wood-sorrel family   *Oxalidaceae*   p.130
    22b Leaves pinnate (54), sometimes with only 1 pair of leaflets
            Caltrop family   *Zygophyllaceae*   pp.130, 132
14c Stamens numerous (usually more than 10)
    23a Leaves pinnate or digitate with 3–9 leaflets
        24a Plants woody (*Rosa*)
            Rose family   *Rosaceae*   p.98
        24b Plants herbaceous
            25a Flowers more than 8cm in diameter
                Paeony family   *Paeoniaceae*   p.86
            25b Flowers smaller
                26a Petals undivided (55)
                    Buttercup family   *Ranunculaceae*   pp.80–86
                26b Petals 3-lobed (41)
                    Mignonette family   *Resedaceae*   p.94
    23b Leaves undivided to deeply lobed
        27a Leaves fleshy, arranged spirally (*Sedum*, 56)
            Stonecrop family   *Crassulaceae*   p.96
        27b At least the lowest leaves opposite
            28a Petals after completely unfolding still crumpled

53   54   55   56

57

58

59

60

29a Petals 5, sepals 3 or 5, fruit a capsule (57)
    Rock-rose family   *Cistaceae*   pp.152–158
29b Petals often more than 5 and hypanthium often more than 5-toothed, bright red, fruit apple-shaped (58)
    Pomegranate family   *Punicaceae*   p.164
28b Petals smooth
    30a Petals yellow, stamens in bundles
    St John's Wort family   *Hypericaceae*   p.152
    30b Petals white (59)
        Myrtle family   *Myrtaceae*   p.162
27c Leaves alternate or usually in a basal rosette
    31a Flowers white, if pink then a cultivated tree
        32a Leaves with stipules (often deciduous), petals delicate
        Rose family   *Rosaceae*   pp.98, 100
        32b Leaves without stipules, petals fairly thick (4–)5(–8), citrus fruits (60)
          Rue family   *Rutaceae*   p.138
    31b Flowers coloured
        33a Stamens united into a tube (61)
        Mallow family   *Malvaceae*   pp.146, 148
        33b Stamens free
          34a Petals yellow, crumpled
          Rockrose family   *Cistaceae*   p.158
          34b Petals yellow or red, smooth (*Ranunculus*)
          Buttercup family   *Ranunculaceae*   pp.84, 86
9c Perianth of more than 10 sepals and petals
    35a Plants fleshy
        36a Plants without spines, but with fleshy leaves (62)
        Mesembryanthemum family   *Aizoaceae*   p.76
        36b Plants with fleshy, broadened stem-joints and cushion-like tufts of spines (63)
          Cactus family   *Cactaceae*   p.160

61

62

63

64

65

66

67

35b Plants not fleshy (64)
          Buttercup family   *Ranunculaceae*   pp.82–86

Group E: Dicotyledons, petals united below into a long or short tube

1a Plants without green leaves
  2a Corolla regularly 4-lobed (65)
          Rafflesia family   *Rafflesiaceae*   p.72
  2b Corolla 5-lobed, more or less 2-lipped (66)
          Broomrape family   *Orobanchaceae*   p.218
1b Plants with green leaves
  3a Stem twining or climbing
    4a Stem with spirally twisting tendrils (*Citrullus*, 67)
          Gourd family   *Cucurbitaceae*   p.160
    4b Stem without tendrils, the whole stem encircling the support
      5a Leaves whorled (*Rubia*)
          Bedstraw family   *Rubiaceae*   p.184
      5b Leaves opposite
        6a Even the uppermost leaves stalked, corolla regularly 5-lobed,
          with a small corona (*Cynanchum*, 68)
          Milkweed family   *Asclepiadaceae*   p.182
        6b Leaves below the inflorescence joined, corolla 2-lipped
          (*Lonicera*, 69)
          Honeysuckle family   *Caprifoliaceae*   p.222
      5c Leaves alternate
        7a Each group of 3 whitish, trumpet-shaped flowers surrounded by
          3 brightly coloured bracts
          Four o'clock family   *Nyctaginaceae*   p.76
        7b Plants with large funnel-shaped flowers (70)
          Convolvulus family   *Convolvulaceae*   pp.186, 188

68

69

70

71   72   73   74

3b Stem not twining or climbing
> **8a** Flowers in dense heads which are surrounded at the base by a common involucre composed of numerous bracts
>> **9a** Shrub up to 1m high, flowers 2-lipped, blue, ovary superior (71)
>>> **Globularia family**   *Globulariaceae*   p.218
>> **9b** Herbaceous plants, corolla distinctly 4-lobed, ovary inferior, with a cup-shaped epicalyx below the bristle-fringed calyx, leaves opposite (*Cephalaria*, 72)
>>> **Scabious family**   *Dipsacaceae*   p.222
>> **9c** Herbaceous plants or low shrubs. Corolla regular (5-lobed tubular flowers) or irregular (strap-shaped flowers). Flowers all tubular, or all strap-shaped, or the inner ones tubular and the marginal ones strap-shaped. Ovary inferior (73; see also p.30)
>>> **Daisy family**   *Asteraceae*   pp.226–252
> **8b** Flowers blue, clustered into a globular head, without an involucre of numerous bracts. Plants thistle-like (*Echinops*, 74)
>> **Daisy family**   *Asteraceae*   p.240
> **8c** Flowers not in dense heads or not surrounded by a common involucre composed of numerous bracts
>> **10a** Flowers irregular (zygomorphic), sometimes only slightly
>>> **11a** Perianth of a single whorl (75)
>>>> **Birthwort family**   *Aristolochiaceae* p.70

>>> **11b** Perianth divided into calyx and corolla
>>>> **12a** Leaves opposite (at least the lower ones) or whorled
>>>>> **13a** Flowers spurred, with 1 stamen (76)
>>>>>> **Valerian family**   *Valerianaceae*   p.222
>>>>> **13b** Flowers without a spur, stamens 2 or 4, flowers 2-lipped, sometimes the upper lip absent
>>>>>> **14a** Shrub, leaves long-stalked, digitate with 5–7 leaflets, flowers 8–10mm, blue or pink (*Vitex*, 77)
>>>>>> **Verbena family**   *Verbenaceae*   p.196
>>>>>> **14b** Robust, thistle-like perennial with large, pinnately divided basal leaves. Upper lip of calyx projecting beyond the corolla and simulating its upper lip. Corolla about 4cm long
>>>>>> **Acanthus family**   *Acanthaceae*   p.218

75

76

77

78

14c Shrubs or herbaceous plants with differently shaped leaves

    15a Ovary already at flowering time clearly in 4 parts, fruit falling in 4 separate portions (partial fruits). Flowers usually distinctly 2-lipped, sometimes lacking the upper lip, often grouped into false whorls of several flowers in the axils of leafy bracts and forming a spike-like inflorescence. Stem 4-angled (78)

        Mint family   *Lamiaceae*   pp.196–208

    15b Ovary not in 4 parts, stem usually round (79)

  Foxglove family   *Scrophulariaceae* pp.212–216

12b Leaves alternate or basal

    16a Flowers butterfly-like (see p. 29), leaves of 3 leaflets, stamens 10, 9 of which are joined into a tube surrounding the style (*Trifolium*)

        Pea family   *Papilionaceae*   p.118

    16b Flowers not butterfly-like, leaves not of 3 leaflets, stamens 2–5

        17a Ovary deeply divided into 4 parts, at maturity falling as 4 partial fruits, plants rough-hairy (*Echium*, 80)

      Borage family ' *Boraginaceae*   p.192

        17b Ovary not deeply divided into 4 parts

            18a Stamens 5, filaments at most hairy at the base (*Hyoscyamus*, 81)

Nightshade family   *Solanaceae*   p.210

79

80

81

82

83

84

85

18b Stamens 2 or 4 (if 5, then with purple or white woolly hairs) (82)

      Foxglove family   *Scrophulariaceae* pp.212–216

10b Flowers regular

    19a Sepals and/or petals 4

        20a Perianth of a single whorl, not divided into calyx and corolla (83)

            Daphne family   *Thymelaeaceae*   p.150

        20b Perianth of 2 whorls, calyx sometimes very small

            21a Leaves alternate (84)

                Laurel family   *Lauraceae*   p.86

            21b Leaves in whorls, needle-shaped (*Erica*, 85)

                Heath family   *Ericaceae*   p.172

            21c Leaves opposite

                22a Leaves without stipules, trees or shrubs (86)

                    Olive family   *Oleaceae*   pp.178, 180

                22b Leaves with stipules, low shrubs (*Putoria*, 87)

                    Bedstraw family   *Rubiaceae*   p.184

    19b Sepals and/or petals 5 or, rarely, up to 12

        23a Leaves alternate and/or in a basal rosette

            24a Basal leaves more or less circular, fleshy (*Umbilicus*, 88)

                Stonecrop family   *Crassulaceae*   p.96

            24b Basal leaves fairly thick and heart-shaped, arising from a solid corm, corolla-lobes bent back (*Cyclamen*, 89)

                Primrose family   *Primulaceae*   p.174

            24c Basal leaves differently shaped or absent

                25a Ovary deeply divided into 4 parts, fruit falling as 4 partial fruits, plants usually rough-hairy (90) (except for *Cerinthe*)

                    Borage family   *Boraginaceae*   pp.188–194

86

87

88

89

90

91

92

25b Ovary not deeply divided into 4 parts
    26a Flowers with 10–14 stamens
        27a Anthers with 2 long horns, flowers urn-shaped, shrubs or small trees with evergreen leaves (*Arbutus*, 91)
    Heath family   *Ericaceae*   p.172
        27b Corolla with a very short tube and 5–7 long lobes. Shrub with deciduous leaves (92)
    Storax family   *Styracaceae*   p.178
    26b Flowers with 5 stamens
        28a Stigma entire; if 2-lobed, then a spiny shrub (93)
    Nightshade family   *Solanaceae*   pp.210, 212
        28b Stigmas 2, flowers funnel-shaped (70)
    Convolvulus family   *Convolvulaceae*   pp.186, 188
        28c Stigmas 5, flowers with a long, narrow corolla-tube and widely spreading lobes (94), or flowers in panicle-like inflorescences composed of small spikes all facing the same way (51)
    Sea Lavender family   *Plumbaginaceae* p.176
        28d Stigmas 3(2) or 5, flowers bell-shaped or long funnel-shaped and in loose clusters (95)

93

94

95

96

97

98

Bellflower family   *Campanulaceae*   p.224
   26c Male flowers with 3 stamens (*Ecballium*, 96)
   Gourd family   *Cucurbitaceae*   p.160
23b Leaves opposite or whorled, sometimes also with a basal rosette
   29a Leaves in whorls of 4 (97) or more
      Bedstraw family   *Rubiaceae*   p.184
   29b Leaves opposite or in whorls of 3 (4)
      30a Leaves evergreen
         31a Shrubs or trees, flowers less than 1cm across (*Viburnum*, 98)
   Honeysuckle family   *Caprifoliaceae*   p.222
         31b Shrubs or prostrate subshrubs, flowers more than 3cm across, twisted in bud (99)
   Periwinkle family   *Apocynaceae*   pp.180, 182
      30b Shrubs with deciduous leaves, or herbaceous plants
         32a Shrubs or herbaceous plants, flowers with a small corona, seeds with a tuft of hairs (100)
   Milkweed family   *Asclepiadaceae*   p.182
         32b Herbaceous plants, stamens standing in front of the corolla-lobes (101)
   Primrose family   *Primulaceae*   p.174
         32c Herbaceous plants, stamens standing between the corrolla-lobes, corolla twisted in bud, with up to 12 lobes (102)
   Gentian family   *Gentianaceae*   p.180

99

100

101

102

103

104

105

Group F: Monocotyledons

1a Water plants living submerged in the sea (103)
      Posidonia family   *Posidoniaceae*   p.254
1b Land plants
  2a Plants shrub- or tree-like with large, fan-shaped or pinnate leaves
      Palm family   *Arecaceae*   p.286
  2b Plants twining or climbing, and/or spiny
    3a Plants shrubby, spiny, more or less climbing (104)
      Lily family   *Liliaceae*   pp.266, 268
    3b Plants herbaceous, twining, without spines, leaves deeply heart-shaped with curved veins, long-stalked (*Tamus*, 105)
      Yam family   *Dioscoreaceae*   p.270
  2c Plants not twining or climbing, without spines
    4a Perianth white or brightly coloured, usually more than 4mm long
      5a Flowers irregular (zygomorphic)
        6a Stamens 6 (*Asphodeline*)
          Lily family   *Liliaceae*   p.256
        6b Stamens 3, stigmas 3 (*Gladiolus*, 106)
          Iris family   *Iridaceae*   p.274
        6c Stamen 1, joined with the stigma to form a column, the lower, inner segment of the perianth variously modified into a lip (107; see also p. 29)
          Orchid family   *Orchidaceae*   pp.290–300
      5b Flowers regular
        7a Ovary superior, stamens 6 (108)
          Lily family   *Liliaceae*   pp.254–268
        7b Ovary inferior
          8a Stamens 6
            9a Leaves thick and fleshy, up to 2m long, spiny-toothed
              Agave family   *Agavaceae*   p.268
            9b Leaves differently formed, flowers often with a corona (109)
           Daffodil family   *Amaryllidaceae*   pp.268, 270

106

107

108

109

112

110   111

8b Stamens 3, style-branches often petal-like (110)
          Iris family   *Iridaceae*   pp.272, 274

4b Perianth absent or inconspicuous, less than 4mm long or only in the form of scale-like leaves (glumes)

    10a Flowers lacking a perianth, forming a spadix surrounded by a conspicuous spathe, leaves net-veined (111)
          Arum family   *Araceae*   p.288

    10b Perianth of 6 segments or composed of glumes

        11a Perianth or 6 segments

            12a Plants apparently with sharp, needle-shaped leaves (112) or pointed, flattened shoots bearing flowers (113)
               Lily family   *Liliaceae*   p.266

            12b Leaves cylindrical, stem-like, pointed, perianth membranous (114)
               Rush family   *Juncaceae*   p.274

        11b Perianth composed of glumes. Leaves linear, the lower part forming a sheath

            13a Inflorescence resembling an umbel or head, the uppermost stem-leaves surrounding the inflorescence, the leaf-sheath without a thickened node at the base. Flowers in spikelets, each flower arising in the axil of a single glume (115)
             Sedge family   *Cyperaceae*   p.284

            13b Inflorescence of finger-like spikes (116) or a panicle. Leaf-sheaths with a membrane or fringe of hairs at the top and with a thickened node at the base. Flowers usually enclosed by 1 lemma and 1 palea in 1 to many-flowered spikelets which usually have 2 glumes at the base (see p. 30)
             Grass family   *Poaceae*   pp.276–284

113   114   115   116

Abbreviations and symbols

⊙ annual
⊙ biennial
♃ perennial (herbaceous plant)
♄ perennial (tree, shrub or subshrub)
The black square in each group of 4 shows the position on the opposite page of the relevant photograph.

Clubmoss family *Selaginellaceae*
Fern families *Sinopteridaceae, Adiantaceae, Aspleniaceae*

■□ *Selaginella denticulata* (L.) Link *Selaginellaceae*
□□ 4–10cm; spores ripen March–August; ♃
Small, creeping, many-branched, moss-like plant with flattened leafy stems. Leaves in 4 rows, the pairs unequal: 2 rows of smaller leaves appressed to the stem, and on each side of them 1 row of larger, spreading, broadly ovate, pointed leaves, up to 2.5mm long, finely serrate (lens needed). Spore-cones sessile, not sharply differentiated.
Cool, shady places.
In the whole Mediterranean region, but on its northern edge restricted to the coastal strip and not common everywhere; also the Canary Islands.

□■ *Cheilanthes fragrans* (L.fil.) Swartz (*C. pteridioides* (Reichard) C. Chr., *C. odora* Swartz)
□□ *Sinopteridaceae*
Leaves (fronds) 5–15cm long; spores ripen February–September; ♃
Fronds in tufts, up to 15cm long, coumarin-scented. Leaf-stalk as long as or somewhat shorter than the blade, shiny red-brown, more or less covered with scales. Blade at least in mature plants hairless beneath, 1–3cm broad, ovate or oblong-lanceolate in outline, bipinnate, the lowest leaflets again pinnately divided, with oblong or almost circular, crenate terminal sections 1–3mm long. Sori partly hidden by the recurved leaf-margin.
Sunny, dry rock-crevices.
Mediterranean region.
The W. Mediterranean species *C. hispanica* Mett. is similar but is scentless, has a blackish leaf-stalk, and glandular hairs on the underside of the leaf. Nowadays 2 other species are also included in the same genus: *C. marantae* (L.) Domin (*Notholaena marantae* (L.) Desv.) which has leaves no more than bipinnate, is hairless above, but densely covered beneath with pale brown or colourless scales (Mediterranean region, particularly on serpentine rocks) and *C. catanensis* (Cosent.) H.P. Fuchs (*Notholaena vellea* (Ait.) Desv.) which has yellowish scales on both sides of the leaves (southern Mediterranean region, mainly on limestone).

□□ *Adiantum capillus-veneris* L. **Maidenhair Fern** *Adiantaceae*
■□ Fronds up to 60cm long; spores ripen June–September; ♃
Fronds overwintering, with a blackish brown stalk, scaly only at the base, up to 25cm long, and an ovate-oblong, 2–4-pinnate blade. Leaflets bright green, delicate, rhomboid or roundish, narrowing to an oblique, wedge-shaped base, irregularly cut along the upper margin, the terminal leaflet having a stalk as fine as a hair, hence its name. Sporangia without a covering on the underside of the recurved margins of the lobes. Formerly used medicinally for respiratory ailments.
Shady, damp, limestone rocks, often dripping with moisture.
Mediterranean region, on the Atlantic coast northwards to Ireland, Canary Islands, also throughout the world in tropical and subtropical regions, often as an ornamental plant.

□□ *Asplenium onopteris* L. **Acute-leaved Spleenwort** *Aspleniaceae*
□■ Fronds 10–50cm long; spores ripen March–June; ♃
Leaves overwintering, stalk about as long as the blade, red-brown, thickened at the base. Blade 2–3-pinnate, dark green, leathery, triangular-ovate in outline, tip and ends of leaflets elongated (tapered). Leaflets usually curving towards the tip of the blade. Terminal segments lanceolate to linear, wedge-shaped at the base, with pointed, almost bristle-like teeth. Sori close to the midrib.
Shady rocks, woods and undergrowth, usually on silicious rocks.
Mediterranean region, Canary Islands.
Closely related species are *A. adiantum-nigrum* L.: Leaf-tip and leaflets not tapering, terminal segments less pointed, often rounded at the base (W. Europe, more rarely in central and S. Europe) and *A. obovatum* Viv.: stalk not thickened at the base. Blade ovate-lanceolate, pointed, only bipinnate in the lower half. Segments with bluntly tipped teeth (S. Europe, N.W. Africa).

Fern families *Aspleniaceae, Polypodiaceae*
Pine family *Pinaceae*

■□ *Ceterach officinarum* DC. **Rusty-back Fern** *Aspleniaceae*
□□ Fronds up to 25cm long; spores ripen May–June, later in the north; ♃
Leaves overwintering, thick. Leaf-stalk short, with chaffy scales at least in the lower part,
blade oblong, pinnately divided, with 9–12 semicircular segments on each side, arranged
alternately, grey to dark green, dull and hairless above, densely covered beneath with shiny
golden-brown chaffy scales which form a fringe along the margin. Sori linear, running diago-
nally towards the midrib, at first hidden by the chaffy scales. During summer drought the
leaves roll round so that the protecting scales face outwards.
Sunny crevices in rocks and walls.
Mediterranean region, W. Europe, occasionally in warm areas of C. Europe.

□■ *Polypodium australe* Fée (*P. serratum* (Willd.) Saut., non Aub.) *Polypodiaceae*
□□ Fronds up to 50cm long or more; spores ripen in winter: ♃
Leaves overwintering. Blade ovate to triangular-ovate in outline, pinnately divided almost to
the midrib. Segments narrowly lanceolate, more or less deeply crenate-serrate, veins branch-
ing 3 or 4 times. Sori elliptical, in 2 rows on the underside of the segments. Rootstock creep-
ing horizontally in the ground or along its surface and covered with linear-lanceolate scales,
5–11mm long.
On damp, shady rocks.
Mediterranean region, Canary Islands.
P. vulgare L. is similar: new leaves in early summer, ovate to ovate-lanceolate, the segments
undulate or shallowly crenate-serrate on the margin. Scales 3–6mm (almost the whole of
Europe and in the Mediterranean region).

□□ *Abies cephalonica* Loud. **Greek Fir** *Pinaceae*
■□ Up to 30m; May–June; ♄
Needles stiff and sharply pointed, 15–35mm long, spreading outwards and upwards from the
twigs. Young shoots hairless, buds with abundant resin. Cones erect. Bracts protruding and
recurved at the tip.
Forms forests in the mountains between 750 and 1700m.
Greece, planted in Italy.
The following species of Fir also have a restricted distribution, entirely confined to the
mountains: *A. pinsapo* Boiss., **Spanish Fir**, with stiff, pointed needles, only 10–15mm long,
spreading out evenly all round the twigs. Bracts enclosed within the cones (S.W. Spain); *A.
nebrodensis* (Lojac.) Mattei, only a few specimens remaining in Sicily; *A. borisii-regis* Mattf.
in N. Greece with characteristics of *A. cephalonica* and *A. alba*, and other species in N.
Africa and Asia Minor. The C. European **Silver Fir**, *Abies alba* Mill., is distinguished by its
flexible needles, notched at the tip and 15–30mm long, which appear to be arranged in 2
ranks. Young shoots densely downy, buds not resinous. Scales protruding from the cones and
recurved at the tip. (In the Mediterranean region from N. Spain to N. Greece, Corsica).

□□ *Cedrus atlantica* (Endl.) Carrière **Atlas Cedar** *Pinaceae*
□■ Up to 40m; August–October; ♄
A stately tree with widely spreading branches. Leaves needle-shaped, evergreen, arranged
spirally on long shoots and in tufts on short shoots. Leading shoot stiffly upright, branches
slanting upwards, young shoots with downy hairs. Needles stiff, 1–3.5cm long, green or blue-
green. Male flowers in erect, cylindrical cones, 3–5cm long, female flowers ovoid, reddish.
Erect fruiting cones barrel-shaped, 5–8×3–5cm, flat or hollowed at the top, breaking up into
separate scales at maturity. Seeds with a large wing.
Forms forests in the Atlas mountains. In S. Europe the grey-blue form is quite commonly
planted as an ornamental tree or for its valuable timber.
Two other species cultivated are: *C. libani* A. Rich. with cones similar in shape but 7–12cm
long and with hairless young shoots (native in Turkey and Lebanon) and *C. deodara* (D. Don)
G. Don f. with cones rounded at the top and 8–12cm long. Needles soft, 2–5cm long, on
densely hairy twigs. (Native in the Himalaya).

Pine family *Pinaceae*

■☐ *Pinus pinaster* Ait. (*P. maritima* Lam.) **Maritime Pine**
☐☐ Up to 40m; April–May; ♄
Trunk with deeply fissured, reddish brown bark. Young shoots hairless, buds without resin. Needles in pairs on short shoots, green, stout and sharp, 10–25cm×2mm. The conical, shining, light brown cones are arranged in star-shaped clusters of 2–8, and with dimensions of 14–22×5–8cm are the largest borne by European pines. Cone-scales with a sharp ridge and a pronounced, pointed, straight or hooked boss. Seeds 7–8mm, with a wing up to 3cm long. This species, like several others, yields oil of turpentine which is used for medicinal purposes.
Forms forests on sandy soils and primitive rocks; also found up as high as the lower mountain zone.
S.W. Europe to central Italy, N.W. Africa, and occasionally planted to consolidate sand-dunes.

☐■ *Pinus nigra* Arnold **Black Pine**
☐☐ Up to 50m, but some subspecies considerably smaller; May–June; ♄
Trunk with dark grey, deeply fissured bark. Young shoots hairless and light brown, buds resinous. Needles in pairs on short shoots, dark green on both sides, more or less stiff and pointed, noticeably finely toothed, 4–19cm×1–2mm. Cones 3–8×2–4cm, broadly ovoid-conical in shape, shining, light brown, almost stalkless and spreading horizontally. Cone-scales more or less keeled, the boss usually bearing a small spine. Seeds 5–7mm, winged. Several subspecies, which are sometimes regarded as species, each having its own distribution.
Usually found in groups in the higher mountain zone, sometimes up to the timber-line.
Ssp. *nigra*: From Austria to Yugoslavia and Greece, central Italy; ssp. *pallasiana* (Lamb.) Holmboe: southern and eastern Balkans, Crimea, Near East; ssp. *dalmatica* (Vis.) Franco: N.W. Yugoslavia and islands; ssp. *laricio* (Poir.) Maire, see illustration: Corsica, Calabria, Sicily; ssp. *salzmannii* (Dun.) Franco: Cevennes, Pyrenees, central and E. Spain. In the northern Mediterranean region our native *P. sylvestris* L. is present: needles only 3–7cm long, at least the younger ones blue-green. Cones distinctly stalked, pendent, dull. Bark on the upper part of the trunk red-brown.

☐☐ *Pinus halepensis* Mill. **Aleppo Pine**
■☐ Up to 20m; March–May; ♄
The trunk and branches of this unassuming pine are often curved or twisted, giving the open crown its characteristic appearance. Bark at first silver-grey, later reddish brown and fissured. Young shoots hairless to finely hairy, remaining for a long time pale grey, buds not resinous. Needles in pairs on short shoots, soft and pliable, pale green, 6–15cm×0.7mm. Cones conical, shining red-brown, 5–12×4cm, on a stalk 1–2cm long which often curves downwards. Cone-scales flat with a slightly raised, spineless boss. Seeds 7mm with a wing 2–3cm long.
Often forming pure forests or mixed with other tree species, especially on limestone.
Mediterranean region, eastwards to Greece.
The closely related *P. brutia* Ten. is sometimes regarded as a subspecies: Young shoots reddish yellow or greenish, needles a darker green. Cones on horizontal or erect stalks (eastern Mediterranean region).

☐☐ *Pinus pinea* L. **Stone Pine**
☐■ Up to 30m; April–May; ♄
An easily recognisable species of pine because of its umbrella-shaped crown. Trunk with grey-brown bark, which leaves reddish patches where it peels off. Young shoots grey-green, later brown, buds without resin. Needles in pairs on short shoots, green, stiff and pointed, with very fine teeth directed forwards (lens needed), 10–20cm×1.5–2mm. Cones almost spherical when open, 8–14×10cm, shining red-brown. Cone-scales thick, with 5 or 6 radiating ridges and a large, flat, grey-white boss. Seeds 1.5–2cm long, barely winged, with a thick, hard shell (pine kernels, pinioli).
Forms fairly large, open woods in sandy regions near the coast, also frequently planted because of its tasty seeds or as a decorative tree.
S. Europe, Near East, sometimes cultivated in N. Africa and the Canary Islands.

Cypress family Cupressaceae
Joint-pine family Ephedraceae

■□ Cupressas sempervirens L. **Italian Cypress** Cupressaceae
□□ 20–30m or more; March–May; ♄
Tree with branches spreading horizontally (f. *horizontalis* (Mill.) Voss) or columnar in shape (f. *sempervirens*) with erect branches. Leaves dark green, 0.5–1mm, scale-like, closely overlapping. Cones 2.5–4cm, more or less spherical, hanging on short stalks, with 8–14 woody scales which have a pointed boss in the centre, yellowish grey at maturity. The ethereal oil is inhaled or rubbed in to alleviate breathing difficulties.
Mountains in the eastern Mediterranean region from Crete, Cyprus (hence its name), Asia Minor to Iran, sometimes forming forests (f. *horizontalis*), also occasionally grown as an ornamental tree. The columnar form is often planted throughout the whole Mediterranean region and in places becomes naturalised.

□■ Juniperus oxycedrus L. **Prickly Juniper** Cupressaceae
□□ 1–8(–14)m; April–May; ♄
Shrub or small tree with male and female flowers on separate plants. Leaves needle-shaped, pointed, up to 25mm long, with 2 whitish stripes on the upper side, spreading out from the twigs and always arranged in whorls of three. Flowers inconspicuous. Cones red-brown, berry-like, ripening in the second year. In ssp. *oxycedrus* (see illustration) the leaves are up to 2mm broad, and the ripe cones 8–10mm in diameter; in ssp. *macrocarpa* (Sibth. & Sm.) Ball, the leaves are up to 2.5mm broad and the cones 12–15mm in diameter. Oil of Cade, which is used medicinally, is obtained from the wood.
Ssp. *oxycedrus*: Common in the maquis and forests up to the mountain zone; ssp. *macrocarpa*: In coastal areas, especially on sand.
Both subspecies found throughout the Mediterranean region. Our native **Common Juniper**, *Juniperus communis* L., grows in the mountains in the south. This has only one whitish stripe on each needle, and the ripe cones ('Juniper berries') are blue-black and 6–9mm in diameter.

□□ Juniperus phoenicea L. **Phoenician Juniper** Cupressaceae
■□ 1–2(–8)m; February–April; ♄
Small tree or shrub with male and female flowers on the same plant. Leaves scale-like, closely appressed to the twigs, 1mm long, dark green, blunt, with a membranous margin and a glandular furrow on the back. By contrast, leaves of young plants are needle-shaped, spreading, and 5–14mm long. Flowers inconspicuous. The berry-like cones, 8–14mm in diameter, ripen in the second year, and eventually become a dark brown-red.
Forests, maquis and garigue, mainly near the coast.
Mediterranean region, Canary Islands.
The tree species *Juniperus thurifera* L. (Spain, W. Alps, Corsica, N. Africa), *J. excelsa* Bieb. and *J. foetidissima* Willd. (both Balkan peninsula, Near East) are restricted to smaller, mountain areas, and have leaves without a membranous margin.

□□ Ephedra distachya L. (*E. vulgaris* L.C.M. Rich.) Ephedraceae
□■ 0.2–1m; March–June; ♄
A low shrub with creeping, underground rhizomes and with male and female flowers on separate plants. Branches grey-green, finely grooved, slanting upwards like those of a Horse-tail. Leaves reduced to small scales up to 2mm long, green on the back, later grey-white. Male flowers in groups of 8–16, sessile or stalked, female flowers in pairs, usually stalked, surrounded by 3 pairs of bracts. Perianth inconspicuous. The seed protrudes from the ripe, red, berry-like fruit. Because of its ephedrine content the plant is sometimes still used medicinally.
Sandy coasts and river-banks.
S. Europe, Atlantic coast of France, eastwards to C. Asia.
E. fragilis Desf.: Branches easily breaking at the nodes. Male flowers in groups of 8–16, sessile; female flowers single or in pairs, sessile. Seeds entirely enclosed. Climbing or prostrate, up to 5m. *E. major* Host: Leaves almost completely membranous, later dark brown. Male flowers in groups of 4–8, sessile, female flowers single, stalked. Seeds protruding. Shrub up to 2m high (both species Mediterranean region, Canary Islands).

Hazel family *Corylaceae*
Beech family *Fagaceae*

■□ *Carpinus orientalis* Mill. **Oriental Hornbeam** *Corylaceae*
□□ 3–5(–15)m; March–May; ♄
Small deciduous tree or shrub with smooth grey bark. Leaves sharply doubly serrate, ovate or elliptic, wedge-shaped or rounded at the base, sparsely hairy on the veins beneath, 2.5–6cm long. Catkins appear with the leaves in spring, the female developing into a pendent, cone-like cluster of fruits, 3–6cm long, bracts of fruits triangular-ovate, serrate.
In deciduous mixed forest in the submediterranean Downy Oak zone.
S.E. Europe westwards to Sicily, S.W. Asia.
Our native Hornbeam *Carpinus betulus* L. has larger leaves, 4–10cm long, rounded to slightly heart-shaped at the base. Fruit-cluster 5–14cm long, bracts of fruits 3-lobed.

□■ *Ostrya carpinifolia* Scop. **Hop Hornbeam** *Corylaceae*
□□ 4–10(–20)m; April–May; ♄
Deciduous shrub or small tree, bark at first smooth and pale grey, later darker and fissured. Leaves ovate, pointed, almost heart-shaped at the base, sharply doubly serrate, hairy when young, later becoming hairless. Male catkins pendent, already appearing on the twigs in the autumn of the previous year and lengthening at flowering time to 12cm, female catkins at first erect, later pendent. Fruit-cluster to 6×3cm, ultimately reminiscent of the cone-like fruit of the Hop. Each nutlet enclosed by an ovate, bladder-like involucre with an entire margin.
In deciduous mixed forest in the submediterranean Downy Oak zone.
From the Riviera, Corsica and Sardinia eastwards to Asia Minor and the Caucasus.

□□ *Castanea sativa* Mill. (*C. vesca* Gaertn.) **Sweet Chestnut** *Fagaceae*
■□ 10–30m; June; ♄
Deciduous tree, trunk often twisted, with vertical cracks in the bark. Leaves 10–25cm, oblong-lanceolate, spiny-toothed, with prominent veins. Flowers appearing after the leaves with an inconspicuous, usually 6-lobed perianth, the male clustered together in erect catkins 10–20cm long, the female singly or up to 3 together at the base of the inflorescence with a common, scaly involucre. At maturity, the cupule (husk) is covered in long spines, and splits open in 4 portions revealing the 1–3 dark brown fruits. These fruits are rich in starch, and in former times they were of much greater importance as food than they are nowadays, being roasted, boiled, ground into flour or used as a coffee substitute. The leaves are used in cough medicines.
Usually on lime-free soils and often in cultivated parkland, also in mixed deciduous woods in the Downy Oak zone.
S. Europe westwards to Corsica and Italy, Asia Minor, frequently planted in W., central and N. Europe becoming naturalised in some places. Many groups of trees have fallen victim to ink disease which is caused by a fungus.

□□ *Quercus coccifera* L. **Kermes Oak** *Fagaceae*
□■ Up to 3(–12)m; March–May; ♄
An evergreen shrub with smooth, pale grey bark, also growing as a tree chiefly in the eastern Mediterranean region (then also known as *Q. calliprinos* Webb). Older leaves hairless, stiff, leathery, shining dark green above, paler beneath, 1.5–4cm long, broadly ovate to oblong with a heart-shaped or rounded base, veins prominent only on the upper side, margins sinuate-undulate with very prickly teeth. Leaf-stalks only 1–4mm long. Fruits very shortly stalked, the cupule with short, prickly scales spreading out all round. Formerly important as a host-plant for the Kermes insect, *Coccus ilicis* Planch., the females, when dried, producing a red dye.
Garigue, maquis, in the undergrowth of open woods, on chalk.
Mediterranean region but absent in central and N. Italy and Corsica.

Beech family *Fagaceae*

■□ *Quercus ilex* L. **Holm Oak**
□□ Up to 25m; April–May; ♄
Evergreen tree, with smooth, shining, pale grey bark, only becoming scaly with age. Leaves leathery, very variable in form, oblong-ovate to lanceolate, 3–7cm long, rounded or wedge-shaped at the base, entire to more or less prickly toothed (especially on long shoots), dark green and hairless above, densely grey-felted beneath with prominent veins, midrib straight, with 7–11 pairs of lateral veins. Leaf-stalk 6–15mm. Stipules narrow, densely hairy. Cupule with appressed, blunt-tipped, softly hairy scales. Acorns bitter.
Forms bushy, evergreen woods, nowadays often only in low-growing woods and maquis.
Mediterranean region, rarer in the east, Canary Islands.
Q. rotundifolia Lam., often considered as a subspecies of *Q. ilex*, occurs mainly in the south-western Mediterranean region: Leaves broadly ovate or almost circular, bluish grey-green above, with only 5–8 pairs of lateral veins. Stipules broader, membranous, becoming hairless. Acorns not bitter.

□■ *Quercus suber* L. **Cork Oak**
□□ Up to 20m; April–May and Autumn; ♄
Evergreen tree with exceptionally thick, corky bark. Freshly barked trunks light brown, later dark red-brown. Coarse, leathery leaves, ovate-oblong, 3–7cm long, shortly wedge-shaped at the base, shining dark green and hairless above, remaining thinly grey-felted beneath with prominent veins. Midrib usually rather crooked, leaf-margin with 4–5 short teeth on each side or almost entire. Leaf-stalk 8–15mm long. Cupule with grey-felted, loosely united scales. The first crop of cork can be taken after about 25 years, and subsequently a tree can be barked every 7–10 years.
Open, evergreen forest, rich in undergrowth, on primitive rocks.
Western Mediterranean region to Italy (especially on the west coast), Canary Islands.

□□ *Quercus macrolepis* Kotschy (*Q. aegilops* auct.) **Valonia Oak**
■□ Up to 15(–25)m; April; ♄
Semi-evergreen tree with dark brown, finely fissured bark. Leaves 6–12cm long, felted beneath, becoming hairless above, dull, oblong-ovate from a usually heart-shaped base, with 3–7 large teeth on each side ending in a sharp point. Leaf-stalk 1.5–4cm. Cupule large, with long, spreading to recurved scales. In earlier times an important source of a black dye and tannin.
Forms woods here and there.
Apulia, southern Balkan peninsula, Asia Minor.
Similar involucres occur in *Q. trojana* Webb (*Q. macedonica* DC.): Leaves almost hairless and shining, with 8–14 fairly small, pointed teeth on each side, leaf-stalk only 2.5mm long (S.E. Italy, Balkan peninsula, Asia Minor) and in *Q. cerris* L.: leaves deciduous, irregularly and deeply pinnately lobed with 4–9 divisions on each side, or the lobes shallow and merely toothed, stipules linear and persisting (eastern Mediterranean region, westwards to the Riviera).

□□ *Quercus pubescens* Willd. **Downy Oak**
□■ Up to 15(–25)m; April–May; ♄
A deciduous tree, very similar to our native **Sessile Oak** (*Q. petraea* (Matt.) Liebl.), but distin-. guished by densely grey-felted buds, young twigs, leaves and involucres. Older leaves becoming hairless above, 4–12cm long, obovate, with 4–7 sinuate lobes on each side and fewer than 8 pairs of lateral veins. Leaf-stalk 5–12mm long, not grooved. Fruits almost sessile or shortly stalked amongst the leaves on the current year's growth. Scales of the cupule closely appressed and felted.
The characteristic tree of the submediterranean, deciduous forest zone. Forms open, tall-growing forests with abundant undergrowth.
S. and central Europe, eastwards to the Crimea and the Caucasus, Asia Minor, only reaching central Europe in the extreme south-west and south-east.
Q. virgiliana (Ten.) Ten. is very similar but this has leaf-stalks 15–25mm Long (S. Europe from Corsica and Sardinia to the Black Sea).

Beech family *Fagaceae*
Elm family *Ulmaceae*
Mulberry family *Moraceae*

■□ *Quercus faginea* Lam. (*Q. lusitanica* auct.) **Portuguese Oak** *Fagaceae*
□□ Up to 20m; March–April; ♄
Semi-evergreen tree or shrub. Leaves with stalks 8–20mm long, ovate, elliptical, or some-times obovate, 4–10cm long, sinuately and bluntly toothed, with 5–12 pairs of veins, some-what shining above and becoming hairless, remaining felted beneath. Fruits almost sessile amongst the leaves, ripening in the first year. Cupule with broadly lanceolate or ovate scales.
Forests in hilly and mountainous country.
Iberian peninsula, Balearic Islands, N.W. Africa.

□■ *Celtis australis* L. **Nettle Tree** *Ulmaceae*
□□ Up to 25m: April–May; ♄
Deciduous tree or shrub with smooth grey bark. Leaves shortly stalked, obliquely ovate, long pointed, wedge-shaped to rounded at the base and 3-veined, sharply and usually simply serrate on the margin, rather rough on the upper side but softly hairy beneath, 4–15×1.5–6cm. In the lower leaf-axils male inflorescences appear at the same time as the leaves, in the upper ones are bisexual flowers whose stalks lengthen considerably and at maturity bear pleasant-tasting, fleshy, purple-brown fruits, 9–12mm long. Perianth 5-lobed, the segments free almost to the base, red-brown, deciduous.
In open forest and undergrowth, on verges and the edges of woods, frequently planted, especially in the Downy Oak zone.
Mediterranean region, Canary Islands, S.W. Asia.
C. tournefortii Lam.: shrub or small tree, 1–6m. Leaves pointed, ovate, crenate-serrate with broad, fairly blunt teeth, 5–7×2.5–4cm. Ripe fruit brown-yellow (Sicily, Balkan peninsula, S.W. Asia).

□□ *Morus alba* L. **White Mulberry** *Moraceae*
■□ Up to 15m; April–May; ♄
A cultivated, deciduous tree, leaves variously shaped, 6–18cm long, undivided, ovate and pointed, or divided by rounded sinuses into 3–5 lobes, base of blade rounded or obliquely heart-shaped, margin unequally and coarsely toothed, upper side usually smooth, hairless beneath or at most with hairs on the veins. Flowers inconspicuous, unisexual, male and female on the same or on separate plants, flower-parts in fours, inflorescence catkin-like. Fruits like a blackberry, fairly narrow, 1–2.5cm long with a stalk of about the same length, white, pink or purple-violet with an insipid taste when ripe. Leaves used as food for silk-worms.
Cultivated in the Mediterranean region since the 11th century, often becoming naturalised in S.E. Europe. Native in China.
M. nigra L.: larger and more robust than *M. alba* L. Leaves broadly ovate, rough above, hairy beneath. Fruits with a shorter stalk or almost sessile, broad, purple to blackish violet, with a pleasantly acid-sweet taste when ripe. Native in Asia, but cultivated since ancient times in the Mediterranean region for its fruits.

□□ *Ficus carica* L. **Fig** *Moraceae*
□■ 2–5m; June–September; ♄
Deciduous tree or shrub with smooth, silver-grey bark and thick twigs. Leaves appearing comparatively late in the year, up to 20cm long, with usually 3–5 palmate lobes, upper side rough, more or less softly hairy beneath. Numerous inconspicuous flowers are produced on the inner walls of fleshy, urn-shaped structures which develop into yellow or brown-purple, edible figs, 5–7cm long. In the case of the wild form there is a complex pollination process involving gall-wasps. The fruits are used fresh or dried as food, in making brandy or wine, or medicinally as a laxative.
Originally on rocks and in the garigue, widespread as a cultivated tree.
Mediterranean region to N.W. India, and in the Canary Islands, nowadays grown throughout the world in warm regions.

Nettle family Urticaceae
Sandalwood family Santalaceae

■□ *Urtica dubia* Forsk. (*U. caudata* Vahl non Burm. fil., *U. membranacea* Poir.) Urticaceae
□□ 15–80cm; January–December; ☉

Annual plant with stinging hairs. Leaves opposite, ovate, often slightly heart-shaped at the base, sharply serrate, 2–6cm long. Leaf-stalk almost as long as the blade, 2 small stipules at each node. Unisexual spike-like inflorescences in the leaf-axils; the upper male longer than the leaf-stalk, spreading out straight, the flowers mostly on one side of the enlarged axis; the lower female shorter than the leaf-stalk.
In moist, nitrogen-rich places, especially near settlements.
Mediterranean region, Canary Islands, S.W. Asia.
The perennial *U. atrovirens* Req. ex Lois. has 4 stipules at each node. Male and female flowers in the same inflorescence, without an enlarged axis (only Majorca, Corsica, Sardinia, Tuscany).

□■ *Urtica pilulifera* L. **Roman Nettle** Urticaceae
□□ 0.3–1m; April–October; ☉, ☉

Plant with stinging hairs. Leaves opposite, the blade ovate, pointed, truncate to heart-shaped at the base, sharply serrate on the margin, somewhat longer than the leaf-stalk, with 4 stipules at each node. Inflorescences unisexual, but at the same level in the leaf-axils, the male forming a branched panicle, the female in long-stalked, globular heads. Perianth of female flowers 4-lobed, inflated, with 2 short outer segments and 2 long inner ones which are densely covered with bristly hairs. Also cultivated in earlier times for its oily, mucilaginous seeds.
Damp, nitrogen-rich, weedy grasslands, waysides.
Mediterranean region, S.W. Asia.

□□ *Parietaria diffusa* Mert. & Koch (*P. officinalis* auct. non L., *P. judaica* L.) **Pellitory-of-the-**
■□ **wall** Urticaceae
Up to 40cm; April–October; ♃

Stem prostrate or more erect, much branched with short hairs. Leaves alternate, ovate or roundish, pointed, fringed with hairs on the margin, 2–5cm long. Stalk of the lower leaves shorter than the blade. Inflorescence globular, consisting of a few inconspicuous flowers in the leaf-axils. Flower-parts in fours. Bracts joined at the base, shorter than the perianth at fruiting time.
In usually damp, shady gaps in walls and at the foot of walls.
Throughout the Mediterranean region, W. Europe, S.W. to central Asia.
P. officinalis L. (*P. erecta* Mert. & Koch): stem 0.2–1m, erect, simple or only slightly branched. Leaves ovate-lanceolate, long-pointed, narrowed at the base, 3–12cm. Bracts free.
P. lusitanica L. with bracts that are as long as or longer than the perianth at fruiting-time. Leaves only up to 4cm long. A delicate annual, 5–30cm (both species distributed throughout the Mediterranean region and beyond).

□□ *Osyris alba* L. Santalaceae
□■ 0.4–1.5m; April–August; ♃

A usually low-growing shrub, parasitic on the roots of various trees and shrubs, with erect, rod-like stems, angular when young. Leaves evergreen, leathery, linear-lanceolate, only the midrib distinct, 1–2cm long. Male and female flowers on separate plants. Flowers inconspicuous, scented, with a yellowish, simple, 3-lobed perianth, the male in lateral clusters, the female standing singly at the ends of short shoots. Bracts leaf-like, persistent. Ripe fruits red, fleshy, 5–7mm in diameter.
In open maquis and forest.
Mediterranean region.
Osyris quadripartita Salzm. ex Decne.: leaves broader with pinnate veins, bracts small, deciduous. Shrub up to 2.40m high (S.W. Mediterranean region, eastwards to the Balearic Islands, Canary Islands).

Mistletoe family *Loranthaceae*
Birthwort family *Aristolochiaceae*

■□ *Arceuthobium oxycedri* (DC.) Bieb. *Loranthaceae*
□□ 3–20cm; July–September; ♄
A small, densely branched, yellow-green subshrub, parasitic on the branches of various species of Juniper, especially *Juniperus oxycedrus* L. Stems jointed, with small, opposite, scale-like leaves which are united in pairs and form a sheath round the stem. Flowers yellowish, inconspicuous, unisexual, the male solitary and sessile at the ends of short lateral branches, the female solitary or in pairs at the ends or in the axils, shortly stalked. Fruits green, about 2mm long, bursting open when ripe and projecting the sticky seeds a considerable distance.
N.W. Africa, Spain, only very local in S. France, absent in the central Mediterranean region, more frequent in the Balkan peninsula to S.W. Asia.

□■ *Aristolochia guichardii* Davis & Khan *Aristolochiaceae*
□□ 20–30cm; March–April; ♄
Plant with short rough hairs, stem simple or branched at the base, prostrate or ascending, not broader than 2mm. Leaves stalked, about as long as broad, heart-shaped or ovate, 3.5–5.5×3.5cm. Flowers modified so as to trap insects, and produced singly in the leaf-axils on hairy stalks up to 2cm long. Corolla-tube U-shaped and enlarged at the base, 2–3.5cm long, 1.2cm in diameter at the roundish or heart-shaped end, purple or dark brown, densely hairy within. Capsule 2–3cm.
Evergreen Oak and Pine woods.
Rhodes, S.W. Anatolia, typical of the many similar species of Birthwort which occur in small areas from Greece to the Near East.
U-shaped flowers are also found in *A. cretica* Lam.: flowers very large, 5–12cm, with long white hairs within. Leaf-margins undulate (Crete, Karpathos). *A. baetica* L.: flowers 2–5cm long, on hairless stalks. Plant woody, often climbing several metres, with evergreen, grey-green leaves (Iberian peninsula, N.W. Africa). *A. sempervirens* L. is similar but has hairy flower-stalks. Leaves dark green, leathery (southern Mediterranean region).

□□ *Aristolochia pistolochia* L. *Aristolochiaceae*
■□ 20–60cm; April–June; ♄
Erect, simple or branched, hairy plant with numerous oblong rhizomes. Characteristic, shining, dark green leaves, 1–3cm long, with a stalk only 1–5mm long, ovate-triangular, with fine, cartilaginous teeth or warts on the margin and the under side, deeply heart-shaped at the base. Flowers solitary in the leaf-axils, 2–5cm long, corolla-tube almost straight but enlarged at the base, brownish, the lip dark purple. Capsule spherical or pear-shaped, 2–3cm.
Dry places, also on cultivated land.
S.W. Europe, eastwards to Corsica.

□□ *Aristolochia rotunda* L. **Round-leaved Birthwort** *Aristolochiaceae*
□■ 15–60cm; April–June; ♄
Often branched, erect or prostrate plant, becoming hairless, with a spherical or ovoid rhizome. Leaves ovate-roundish, 2–7cm, almost sessile and clasping the stem. Flowers solitary in the leaf-axils, 3–5cm long, with a yellow-green, more or less straight tube, enlarged at the base, and a broad, dark brown-red lip, bluntly pointed or with a notched tip. Capsule spherical, 1–2cm.
Woods, wood-margins, hedges, also on cultivated land.
S. Europe.
The following two species have stalked leaves: *A. pallida* Willd. with a spherical rhizome, flowers green-yellow or brownish with darker stripes, their stalks shorter than the leaf-stalks (S. Europe westwards to France, Asia Minor), and *A. longa* L. with a cylindrical rhizome, flowers without dark stripes, their stalks about as long as the leaf-stalks (S. Europe, N.W. Africa, Canary Islands).

Rafflesia family *Rafflesiaceae (Cytinaceae)*
Balanophora family *Balanophoraceae*
Dock family *Polygonaceae*

■☐ *Cytinus hypocistis* (L.) L. *Rafflesiaceae*
☐☐ 4–10cm; April–June; ♄
A parasite with short, fleshy shoots which break out of the ground and form small clumps. Each stem has yellow, orange or scarlet scale-like leaves and 5–10 flowers, each surrounded by 2 bracts. Marginal flowers female, central flowers male, with a bright yellow, simple, 4-lobed perianth. The only representative of this tropical family in Europe. Several subspecies are parasitic on white-flowered Rockroses, on other members of the Cistaceae, and also on the pink-flowered *C. parviflorus* Lam. (see p. 152).
Mediterranean region, Canary Islands.
C. ruber (Fourr.) Komarov (*C. hypocistis* ssp. *kermesinus* Guss.) is very similar and is sometimes treated only as a subspecies. It has a whitish to pale pink perianth and is found on pink-flowered species of Rockroses (Mediterranean region, but in general less common).

☐■ *Cynomorium coccineum* L. *Balanophoraceae*
☐☐ 10–30cm; April–May; ♄
A curious, red-brown, fungus-like plant, without chlorophyll, parasitic on the roots of other species. Club-shaped, fleshy, straight or curved shoots arise from a branched, subterranean rhizome. At their base are triangular-lanceolate scale-leaves, and in the upper part, 10–20×3–8cm, there are closely packed male, female, and bisexual flowers, with the single stamen projecting, and deciduous, triangular bracts. This is the only representative of an otherwise tropical family. At the time of the crusades it was used to staunch wounds.
Sandy coasts, saltmarshes.
Mediterranean region, especially in the south, Canary Islands, S.W. Asia, generally rare.

☐☐ *Polygonum maritimum* L. **Sea Knotgrass** *Polygonaceae*
■☐ 10–50cm; April–October; ♄
Stems prostrate, branched, with evergreen, greyish, sessile, ovate to lanceolate leaves, up to 2.5cm long, and usually with the margin recurved. Stipular sheaths red-brown below, silvery and transparent above, deeply incised, with 8–12 prominent, branched veins, longer in the inflorescence than at the stem-joints. Flowers pink or whitish, 3–4mm long, singly or 2–4 together in the leaf-axils. Nuts triangular, shining brown, usually somewhat longer than the simple, 5-lobed perianth.
Dunes, shingly beaches, even at the tide-mark.
Coasts of the Mediterranean Sea, the Black Sea, and the Atlantic, northwards to the Channel Islands and southwards to the Canary Islands.
P. equisetiforme Sibth. & Sm. is found on waysides and waste ground. Plant Horsetail-like. Stipular sheaths membranous, brownish below, much shorter than the elongated sections of the stem. Leaves oblong or linear, 2–4cm, soon falling. Flowers in terminal, loose, spike-like inflorescences (Mediterranean region, sometimes absent in the north, Canary Islands, S.W. Asia).

☐☐ *Rumex bucephalophorus* L. **Horned Dock** *Polygonaceae*
☐■ Up to 40cm; March–September; ☉
A very variable species with several subspecies. Stems single, stout and erect, or several thin ones growing up at an angle. Leaves only 1–2cm long, stalked, spathulate or ovate-lanceolate. Flowers usually 2–3 together in the axils of the stipular sheaths, forming a spike. Stalks of fruit curving downwards, of 2 kinds: some slender, cylindrical and very short, others longer and club-shaped. At fruiting-time the inner 3 of the 6 perianth-segments are greatly enlarged and have 3 or 4 distinct teeth on each side; also a small callus.
Cultivated and fallow land on sandy soils, often forming large communities.
Mediterranean region, Canary Islands.

Goosefoot family *Chenopodiaceae*

■☐ *Atriplex halimus* L. **Shrubby Orache**
☐☐ 0.5–3m; June–October; ♄
One of the few shrubby representatives of the genus in the Mediterranean region, generally silvery-white and much-branched. Leaves shortly stalked, leathery, up to 6×4cm, ovate-rhombic or triangular-ovate, sometimes hastate, the upper ones narrower, lanceolate, flowers unisexual in small clusters, standing apart from each other forming a long, terminal, panicle-like inflorescence with leaves at its base. Male flowers with an inconspicuous, membranous perianth of 5 segments, female flowers with only 2 broadly ovate to almost circular, entire or toothed bracts, without appendages, which become enlarged at fruiting-time.
Sandy and rocky coasts, salty soils inland, also frequently cultivated.
Mediterranean region, Atlantic coast of S.W. Europe, Canary Islands.

☐■ *Halimione portulacoides* (L.) Aellen (*Obione portulacoides* (L.) Moq.) **Sea Purslane**
☐☐ 20–80cm; July–October; ♄
A grey-green, mealy subshrub with prostrate or ascending branches which often put out roots. Lower leaves opposite, in clusters, narrowly elliptic or obovate, narrowing gradually to a wedge-shaped base, usually entire, fleshy. Flowers unisexual, in very small clusters, forming yellowish, leafless spikes or panicles. Perianth of male flowers of 5 (or 4) membranous segments, female flowers with only 2 bracts, 2.5–5mm long, usually 3-lobed at their tips, which are almost completely joined and enclose the fruit.
Salt-marshes and meadows, sandy beaches, salty areas inland.
Coasts of the Mediterranean region, the Black Sea, the Atlantic and the North Sea northwards to Denmark, Canary Islands.

☐☐ *Arthrocnemum glaucum* (Delile) Ung.-Sternb. (*Salicornia macrostachya* Moric.)
■☐ 0.3–1m; May–September; ♄
Shrub with hairless, fleshy, jointed stems, grey-green at first, later yellowish green or reddish. The small scale-like leaves in opposite pairs clasp the stem to form a single joint, so that the stem appears leafless. Each fertile section produces 2 groups of 3 inconspicuous flowers of about the same size, slightly separated from each other, which leave behind a single hollow when they fall. Seeds black, warted.
Salt-marshes, mainly on the coasts, but also on salty soils inland.
Mediterranean region.
Two other species are also shrubby but the hollow left by the flowers is tripartite and the seeds are greenish brown or grey: *A. fruticosum* (L.) Moq. with seeds bearing short, conical hairs, and *A. perenne* (Mill.) Moss with seeds bearing curved or hooked hairs; plant with underground stems (both in the Mediterranean region). Species of *Salicornia*, which are distributed mainly along the coasts of the Atlantic, the North Sea and the Baltic, are annuals. The centre flower in the group of 3 stands higher than the lateral flowers, so that a triangle is formed.

☐☐ *Salsola kali* L. **Saltwort**
☐■ 0.1–1m; July–October; ☉
A very variable, fleshy plant, with numerous spreading or ascending branches, grey-green or yellowish, hairless or bristly. Only the lower leaves opposite, linear to awl-shaped, spine-tipped, broadened at the base and with a membranous margin, 1–4cm long. Flowers 1–3 in the leaf-axils, with 5 perianth-segments of varying widths, free to the base, having a tubercle or wing with a distinct midrib on the back. The 2 bracts longer than the flowers, stiff, ovate-triangular, with a long, light-coloured spine. Formerly used as a source of soda, and the young shoots eaten as a vegetable.
Sandy coasts, waste ground, also occasionally inland.
Europe, N. Africa, Canary Islands, Asia.
Salsola soda L.: plant hairless, often reddish. Leaves most of the way up opposite, semicircular in section and almost clasping the stem, with a short, soft tip. Bracts about as long as the perianth. (S. Europe, absent in the extreme south, Asia.)

Four o'clock family *Nyctaginaceae*
Pokeweed family *Phytolaccaceae*
Mesembryanthemum family *Aizoaceae*

■☐
☐☐ *Bougainvillea glabra* Choisy Nyctaginaceae
Up to 10m; flowering throughout almost the whole year; ♄
Woody, spiny climber, hairless or almost so, leaves alternate, with a stalk up to 12mm long, ovate or oblong, pointed, entire, up to 6×2.5cm. Flowers 14–24mm, tubular with a narrow, spreading rim, cream-coloured inside, olive-green outside, sometimes tinged purple, almost hairless. Each group of 3 flowers surrounded by 3 brightly coloured, broadly ovate, pointed bracts, pale or dark purple in colour and longer than the flowers, remaining on the plant after flowering-time and serving as a wing for the ripe fruit (rarely formed in the Mediterranean region).
Frequently cultivated in many forms as an ornamental plant, native in Brazil.
B. spectabilis Willd. is similar: leaves densely hairy beneath. Flowers 18–30mm, purple on the outside and densely hairy. Bracts often also scarlet, pink or orange, ovate, more or less hairy.

☐■
☐☐ *Phytolacca americana* L. (*P. decandra* L.) **Pokeweed** Phytolaccaceae
1–3.5m; July–October; ♃, ♄
A shrub, woody only at the base, with forked, hairless stems, frequently tinged red. Leaves ovate-lanceolate, entire, stalked 10–40cm long. Flowers in erect racemes, 10–15cm long, bending over at fruiting-time. Perianth of 5 segments, whitish, 2.5mm long. Fruits berry-like, usually 10-ribbed, purplish black, used for colouring wine. Root often used in homeopathy. Apart from the fleshy part of the fruit, all parts of the plant are poisonous, including the seeds.
Cultivated as a decorative plant, and also for its berries (in vine-growing districts), becoming naturalised. Native in N. America.
Phytolacca dioica L.: a tree, often planted in certain areas, with a noticeably broad base to the trunk. Flower-clusters pendent. Native in S. America.

☐☐ *Mesembryanthemum crystallinum* L. **Ice Plant** Aizoaceae
■☐ Creeping plant with stems up to 80cm long; March–July; ☉
A prostrate, branching plant, densely covered with sparkling, water-filled cells, which are reminiscent of ice crystals. Leaves spathulate or broadly ovate, flat or slightly undulate, fleshy, the longest 6–12cm. Flowers almost sessile, 2–3cm in diameter, the numerous, very narrow, whitish or pale pink petals longer than the sepals. Stigmas 5. Sometimes eaten as a salad, in earlier times used as a source of soda.
Sandy beaches, rocky coasts, salt-steppes.
Mediterranean region, Canary Islands, S. Africa.
M. nodiflorum L.: tinged red during dry periods. Leaves cylindrical, fleshy, 2–3cm long. Flowers to 1.5cm across, the whitish to yellowish petals shorter than the sepals (Mediterranean region, Canary Islands, S. Africa).

☐☐ *Carpobrotus acinaciformis* (L.) Bolus (*Mesembryanthemum acinaciforme* L.) **Red Hottentot**
☐■ **Fig** Aizoaceae
Up to 2m long; March–July; ♃
A prostrate plant forming dense mats. Leaves curved, fleshy, joined in pairs at the base, sharply triangular in cross-section, broadest at or above the middle, narrowing abruptly to a short point, smooth on the upper edge, 5–8cm long. Flowers 10–12cm in diameter with numerous, always bright carmine-purple petals and stamens.
Planted and becoming naturalised near coasts as an ornamental plant and to consolidate slopes and dunes. Native in S. Africa.
C. edulis (L.) N.E. Br. is similar: leaves regularly triangular in cross-section, gradually narrowing towards the tip and finely serrate along the upper edge, 8–12cm long. Flowers 6–9cm across, with pale yellow, yellowish pink or pale purple petals and yellow stamens.

Pink family *Caryophyllaceae*

■□ *Paronychia argentea* Lam.
□□ 5–30cm long; April–June; ⚇
Stems much-branched, prostrate, the sections of the stem usually as long as or longer than the opposite, ovate to lanceolate leaves, which are 4–8(–20)mm long and have the margin fringed with short hairs (lens needed). Stipules membranous. In the leaf-axils are well separated clusters of flowers, usually more than 8mm across, with ovate, pointed, silvery bracts, 4–6mm long. These bracts hide the inconspicuous perianth, which consists of 5 sepals of about equal length, each with a short bristle and a membranous margin.
Firm dunes and grassland, usually on sandy soils.
Mediterranean region, Canary Islands, absent in the north of the Balkan peninsula.
Some species are found only in the mountains, but another widely distributed species is *P. capitata* (L.) Lam. with grey-green, hairy leaves. The conspicuous clusters of flowers are about 10mm across, with bracts 6–10mm long. The green sepals, hidden by these bracts, are of unequal length and have no membranous margin.

□■ *Silene colorata* Poir.
□□ 10–50cm; April–June; ⚇
A finely hairy, branched, prostrate to erect plant, with sessile, opposite, spathulate leaves. Bracts of a pair uusually of unequal length. Flowers with deep pink to white, deeply divided petals, 1–2cm long. Styles 3. Calyx cylindrical, 11–17mm, longer than the flower-stalks, 10-veined, with blunt teeth densely fringed with hairs, broadly club-shaped at fruiting-time. Capsule 7–9mm, 6-toothed, on a 5–7mm long stalk. Seeds distinctly kidney-shaped, with a deep groove on the back between 2 undulate wings.
Sandy beaches, cultivated land.
Mediterranean region, Canary Islands, S.W. Asia, absent from France, Corsica and the Balearic Islands.
S. sericea All. is similar to and often confused with the previous species: flowers solitary, more rarely 2 or 3 at the ends of the stems. Calyx 12–20mm, with pointed teeth. Groove on the back of the seeds without undulate wings (western Mediterranean region).

□□ *Silene conica* L. **Sand Catchfly**
■□ 10–50cm; April–July; ⚇
Entire plant hairy, the ascending or erect stem with sessile, opposite, oblong to linear-lanceolate leaves. Flowers in groups of 5–30 with pink, more rarely white, petals, 13–20mm long, notched or 2-lobed. Styles 3. Calyx 8–18mm, distinctly 30-veined, the upper third or so divided into narrow, pointed teeth, conical to ovoid, later inflated and spherical. Capsule 6-toothed, 7–12mm. Several subspecies.
Sandy beaches, also inland often on sandy soils.
Mediterranean region, Canary Islands, S.E. Europe, S.W. Asia, uncommon in central Europe, and absent from the Balearic Islands, Corsica, Sardinia and W. Europe.
A variable genus, with numerous species sometimes restricted to certain areas. 166 species have been described for the flora of Europe alone, and few of these are absent from the Mediterranean region.

□□ *Drypis spinosa* L.
□■ 8–30cm; June–September; ⚇
A pale green, mat-forming plant with much-branched, square, brittle stems. Flowering shoots erect. Leaves opposite, sessile, lanceolate to awl-shaped, stiff and spine-tipped, grooved on the upper side. Inflorescences in the form of an umbel, surrounded by spiny-toothed bracts. Flowers small, with 5 white or pink, 2-lobed, long-clawed petals. Anthers bluish. In ssp. *spinosa* the petals are 2-lobed to the base and the spine-tipped bracts are much longer than the flowers. In ssp. *jacquiniana* Murb. & Wettst. ex Murb., the petals are 2-lobed to the middle, and the spine-tipped bracts are barely longer than the flowers.
Ssp. *spinosa*: mountains of central Italy and the Balkan peninsula; ssp. *jacquiniana*: sandy and rocky coasts of the northern Adriatic.

Pink family *Caryophyllaceae*
Buttercup family *Ranunculaceae*

■□ *Petrorhagia velutina* (Guss.) P.W. Ball & Heyw. (*Tunica velutina* (Guss.) Fisch. & Mey.
□□ *Caryophyllaceae*
10–50cm; March–April; ⊙
Stem erect, usually unbranched, glandular-hairy in the middle, with a basal rosette of a few
linear-lanceolate leaves, and with linear stem-leaves arranged in pairs and joined at the base,
their sheaths twice as long as the stem is broad. The terminal inflorescence is a head of flowers
surrounded by light brown, membranous, ovate, pointed bracts. Calyx cylindrical with 5
very short teeth. Petals deep pink, each with a long claw and with the expanded portion 2-
lobed and spreading horizontally. Seeds not larger than 1.3mm, with cylindrical warts.
Grassland and stony pastures.
Mediterranean region, Canary Islands.
In the following 2 species the stems and leaf-sheaths are without glands, and the sheaths are
about as long as the stem is broad: *P. prolifera* (L.) P.W. Ball & Heyw. (Mediterranean region,
central Europe) and *P. glumacea* (Chaub. & Bory) P.W. Ball & Heyw., the latter with bluntly
tipped bracts (Balkan peninsula, Crete).

□■ *Dianthus ciliatus* Guss. *Caryophyllaceae*
□□ 20–60cm; June–October; ♃
A cushion-forming plant, with basal leaves 1–2mm broad, pointed, fringed with hairs along
the margin, and only partially green at flowering-time. Flowering-stems more or less
branched, with 4–13 pairs of leaves, leaf-sheaths about as long as the stem is broad. The 5
pink petals each consist of a long claw and a spreading, toothed or entire expanded portion,
5–10mm long. Calyx 15–23×3mm, hairless, broadest below the middle, with usually 8
epicalyx-segments at its base, half as long as the calyx, ovate and pointed. 2 subspecies.
Stony and grassy pastures.
Countries bordering the Adriatic.
Very many species of Pinks, mostly restricted to small areas.

□□ *Helleborus lividus* Ait. *Ranunculaceae*
■□ 20–70cm; November–April; ♃
A robust, hairless perennial. All leaves on the stems, over-wintering, with 3 ovate-lanceolate
segments. Leaf-margins in ssp. *corsicus* (Willd.) Tutin (see illustration) prickly toothed, in
ssp. *lividus* distantly toothed or entire. Young leaves undivided. Flowers numerous, 5–6cm
across, all turning to one side, with lanceolate bracts. Perianth of 5 sepals, spreading, greenish white to pink. Fruit with a long, straight beak, splitting open along one side.
Woods and undergrowth in the mountain zone.
Ssp. *corsicus* on Corsica and Sardinia, ssp. *lividus* on the Balearic Islands.
Other species occur, especially in the eastern Mediterranean region, e.g. *H. cyclophyllus*
Boiss.: leaves not persisting, and the basal ones with 5–9 segments. Fruits not united at the
base, shortly stalked (Balkan peninsula).

□□ *Nigella damascena* L. **Love-in-a-mist** *Ranunculaceae*
□■ 10–50cm; May–July; ⊙
Leaves of this delicate, simple or branched plant 2 to 3-pinnate, with linear-lanceolate segments about 1mm broad. Flowers solitary, surrounded by a ring of pinnate bracts. Petals
bluish, oblong-ovate, 1.5–2cm long. Honey-leaves small, 2-lipped. Carpels joined together
along their whole length, forming a spherical, inflated fruit.
Cultivated land, fallow land, also grown as an ornamental plant, occasionally becoming
naturalised.
Mediterranean region, Canary Islands, S.W. Asia.
The weed of cornfields, *N. arvensis* L. is similar, but the ring of bracts is absent and the
carpels are only joined half-way (Mediterranean region, S.E. Europe, S.W. Asia). *N. sativa* L.
has whitish flowers, carpels joined right to the top, warted. Formerly much cultivated in S.E.
Europe and Asia Minor because of its use as a flavouring for bread, and becoming
naturalised there (native in W. Asia).

Buttercup family *Ranunculaceae*

■□ *Delphinium peregrinum* L. **Violet Larkspur**
□□ 30–80cm; May–August; ☉
Stem erect, finely hairy throughout or only at the base, branched. Leaves palmately lobed, the lobes pinnately divided into narrow segments, the uppermost leaves undivided, linear-lanceolate. Flowers in dense clusters, blue-violet, 1.5–2cm long. The outer perianth-segments are finely hairy on the outer surface, the uppermost having a spur, usually directed upwards, which is twice as long as the free part. The inner, lateral perianth-segments have an ovate lip, which is hairless and is narrowed gradually into a claw. The fruit consists of 3 separate follicles, hairy or hairless, which contain numerous seeds covered with scales.
Fallow land, cultivated land, stony pastures.
Eastern Mediterranean region, westwards to Italy and Sicily.
D. halteratum Sibth. & Sm. and *D. gracile* DC. are similar species native in the western Mediterranean region. In both species the lip of the lateral, inner perianth-segments is contracted abruptly into the claw. *D. staphisagria* L.: spur only 3–4mm long, sack-shaped. A few large seeds in inflated follicles (Mediterranean region). Other species are restricted to smaller areas.

□■ *Anemone apennina* L. **Blue Wood Anemone**
□□ 5–30cm; March–April; ⚄
Basal leaves divided into 3, like those of our native **Wood Anemone**, the segments stalked, deeply lobed and pointed. Stems 1-flowered, with a whorl of shortly stalked bracts, similar to the basal leaves. Perianth-segments 8–14, pale blue or white (var. *albiflora* Strobl), with downy hairs beneath. Anthers pale yellow or white. Fruit-cluster erect.
Mixed deciduous forests, especially Beech woods, confined to the mountain zone.
S. Europe, westwards to Corsica.
Anemone blanda Schott & Kotschy also has blue flowers: leaf-segments almost sessile, rounded, hairless on the underside. Perianth-segments more numerous, hairless. Fruit-cluster nodding (S.E. Europe, Asia Minor).

□□ *Anemone coronaria* L. **Crown Anemone, Poppy Anemone**
■■ 10–45cm; February–April; ⚄
Basal leaves divided into 3, the segments stalked, deeply lobed. Stems 1-flowered, with a whorl of 3 sessile, finely cut bracts. Flowers 3.5–6.5cm in diameter, with 5–8 elliptical perianth-segments, silky-hairy on the underside, bright red, blue, violet or white in colour. Anthers blue.
Cultivated land, also in open garigue.
Mediterranean region, often grown as an ornamental plant in numerous colour-forms, and sometimes with double flowers, and becoming naturalised. Frequently offered as a cut-flower in late winter in central Europe.
A. palmata L.: basal leaves roundish with 3–5 lobes, bracts joined at the base. Perianth-segments 10–15, yellow (S.W. Europe, N. Africa).

□□ *Anemone hortensis* L. (*A. stellata* Lam.)
□■ 20–40cm; February–April; ⚄
Basal leaves usually palmately divided into 3 wedge-shaped segments, with incisions along the front margin. Stems 1-flowered with a whorl of sessile, usually undivided, linear-lanceolate bracts. Perianth-segments 12–19 (usually 15), narrowly lanceolate, more or less purple. Anthers blue.
Cultivated land, garigue.
S. Europe from France to Yugoslavia and Albania.
A. pavonina Lam.: perianth-segments 7–12, broader, scarlet, pink or purple, often yellow at the base (found locally from S.W. France to Turkey).

Buttercup family Ranunculaceae

■☐ *Clematis flammula* L. **Fragrant Clematis**
☐☐ 3–5m; May–August; ♄
Stem climbing, more or less woody at the base. Leaves opposite, usually bipinnate, the leaflets long-stalked, narrowly oblong to almost circular, entire or with up to 3 lobes. Inflorescence a panicle, the sweetly scented flowers about 2cm in diameter, with 4 narrow, blunt-tipped, white perianth-segments, which are densely felted only on the margin. Fruits with a feathery plume up to 2cm long.
Maquis, hedges.
Mediterranean region.
Other white-flowered, climbing *Clematis* species in the Mediterranean region are our native *C. vitalba* L., which has simply pinnate leaves and perianth-segments white-felted on both sides, and the evergreen *C. cirrhosa* L.: flowers yellowish white, 4–7cm in diameter, single, bell-shaped, nodding, with a 2-lipped involucre below the flower. (Flowering-time December–April).

☐■ *Clematis viticella* L.
☐☐ 3–4m; June–August; ♄
A deciduous plant, woody at the base, with stems and leaves twining. Leaves opposite, long-stalked, odd-pinnate, the primary divisions with 3 ovate, often 3-lobed leaflets or undivided. The scented flowers, 4cm across, usually arise singly on long stalks in the leaf-axils, and the 4 spreading, blue-violet perianth-segments are broad at the top. Fruits without a plume of hairs, only the remains of the short, curved hairless style.
Thickets, hedges, damp deciduous woods, also as an ornamental plant.
Apennine peninsula, Balkan peninsula, S.W. Asia, elsewhere escaping from cultivation and becoming naturalised.
C. campaniflora Brot. is a similar species found in S. Spain and Portugal: Flowers pale violet, bell-shaped. Style hairy, lengthening in fruit.

☐☐ *Adonis annua* L. (*A. autumnalis* L.) **Pheasant's Eye**
■☐ 15–60cm: April–June; ☉
Stem erect, branched, bearing 3–4 times pinnately divided leaves, the lower ones stalked, the upper sessile, segments narrowly linear and pointed. Flowers solitary, 1.5–3cm across, with 6–10 blood-red petals, which are broadly ovate, entire or toothed at the tip, and have a dark blotch at the base. Sepals 5, somewhat shorter, spreading or recurved, deciduous. Fruits obliquely ovate, wrinkled, 3.5–5mm long, smooth along the upper edge, forming ovate-oblong clusters, 1.5–1.8cm long.
Cultivated and fallow land.
Mediterranean region, S.W. Asia, occasionally naturalised further north.
A. microcarpa DC.: Very similar, but flowers only 1cm across, petals red or yellow, twice as long as the sepals (Mediterranean region, Canary Islands). *A. flammea* Jacq., usually with hairy sepals, extends to central Europe.

☐☐ *Ranunculus asiaticus* L. **Turban Buttercup**
☐■ 10–30cm; February–May; ♃
A very attractive species of *Ranunculus* with an erect, hairy, simple or slightly branched stem. Basal leaves long-stalked, crenate-serrate, the outer ones undivided or 3-lobed, the inner divided into 3 wedge-shaped segments. Segments of stem-leaves linear. Flowers solitary, 3–6cm in diameter, with 5 spreading or recurved sepals (differing from *Anemone coronaria* L.) and 5 bright red, white, yellow or purple petals, receptacle hairless. Fruit-cluster cylindrical, 2–4cm. Fruits compressed, ovate to roundish in outline, 2–3mm long, with a long, hooked beak.
Stony pastures, cultivated land, maquis, open woods, grown as an ornamental plant in single and double forms.
Eastern Mediterranean region, westwards to Crete, S.W. Asia, N. Africa.

Buttercup family *Ranunculaceae*
Paeony family Paeoniaceae
Laurel family *Lauraceae*

■□ *Ranunculus muricatus* L. **Spiny-fruited Buttercup** *Ranunculaceae*
□□ 10–50cm; April–May; ⊙
A branched, almost hairless species. Lower leaves long-stalked, circular to kidney-shaped, deeply and coarsely crenate, often divided into 3 lobes, upper leaves shortly stalked, oblong. Flowers 1–1.5cm in diameter, the 5 yellow petals somewhat longer than the 5 recurved sepals. Fruit-clusters globular, falling in their entirety. Fruits 7–8mm, ovoid, compressed, with a beak 2–3mm long and a smooth, broad margin, the surfaces covered with spiny tubercles.
Damp localities: ditches, cultivated land, waysides.
Mediterranean region, Canary Islands, S.W. Asia.
R. parviflorus L.: plant hairy. Flowers 3–6mm across. Fruits 3mm with a short, curved beak (S. & W. Europe, N. Africa).

□■ *Ranunculus bullatus* L. *Ranunculaceae*
□□ 5–20cm; September–February; ♃
Leaves of this autumn-flowering plant all basal and spreading horizontally, broadly ovate, crenate, more or less convex, puckered, roughly hairy beneath. Flowers sweetly scented, fairly large, about 2.5cm in diameter, singly or in pairs on a leafless, hairy stem 5–20cm high. Petals 5–12, bright yellow, the 5 sepals greenish, hairy. Receptacle hairless, fruits ovoid, with a short, curved beak.
Stony pastures, maquis, tree-plantations.
Distributed locally in the Mediterranean region, eastwards to Cyprus.
Most of the other *Ranunculus* species are confined to smaller areas. One of several occurring in the eastern Mediterranean region is *R. millefoliatus* Vahl which has finely divided, Yarrow-like leaves.

□□ *Paeonia mascula* (L.) Mill. (*P. corallina* Retz.) **Paeony** *Paeoniaceae*
■□ 60–90cm; March–June; ♃
Stem erect, with very large, biternate leaves. Some segments occasionally further divided, making a total of 9–16 segments, oblong-lanceolate or ovate to broadly elliptic, 5–10cm broad, with entire margins, shining dark green above, pale green beneath. Flowers solitary, 8–14cm in diameter, with 5–8 red petals. Fruits usually 3–5, felted, 2.5–4cm long. 3 subspecies in S. Europe.
Deciduous woods, thickets, in the mountain zone.
S. Europe from France, Corsica and Sardinia eastwards to Israel, N.W. Africa.
P. officinalis L.: lower leaves with 17–30 narrowly elliptic to lanceolate segments, leaf-stalk deeply grooved on the upper side. Fruits 2 or 3, white-felted to almost hairless (S. Europe). *P. peregrina* Mill.: leaf-segments 17–30, with minute bristles along the main veins above, terminal segments short, broadly triangular, serrate, the incisions extending ⅕ or ⅙ into the blade (eastern Mediterranean region, westwards to Italy). Both the endemic species *P. rhodia* W.T. Stearn (Rhodes) and *P. clusii* F.C. Stern (Crete, Karpathos) have white flowers.

□□ *Laurus nobilis* L. **Laurel, Sweet Bay** *Lauraceae*
□■ 2–20m; March–April; ♄
Evergreen tree or shrub, the alternate, leathery and hairless leaves 5–10×2–4cm, oblong-lanceolate, pointed at both ends and slightly undulate along the margin. Male and female flowers on separate plants, arranged in groups of 4–6 to form panicle-like inflorescences arising from the leaf-axils. Perianth-segments 4, small, yellowish, united at the base. Fruit 1–1.5cm long, black when ripe (Laurel berry). Venerated since ancient times and used for making wreaths for heroes. Important nowadays primarily for its leaves which are of value as a flavouring. The sole European representative of the Laurel family, which is now almost entirely tropical, but which in the Tertiary period had a much wider distribution.
Shady and damp woods near the coast, also grown as an ornamental tree and for culinary purposes.
Mediterranean region, less common in the west.

Poppy family Papaveraceae

■□ *Glaucium flavum* Crantz **Yellow Horned-poppy**
□□ 20–90cm; April–September; G, ☉
Grey-green, sparsely hairy plant with yellow sap. Stem erect or ascending, much-branched. Basal leaves stalked, 15–35cm long, lyre-shaped and pinnately divided, with toothed or lobed segments, stem-leaves smaller, the upper ones ovate and lobed, clasping the stem. Flowers solitary at the end of the stems or in the leaf-axils, with 4 yellow petals 3–4cm long, the two sepals more or less hairy. Capsules 15–30cm long, often curved like a horn, smooth, or rough due to small tubercles.
Sandy and rocky coasts, waste ground, waysides.
Coasts of the Mediterranean, the Black Sea and the Atlantic, more rarely on the North Sea coast and the Canary Islands. Extending inland, even into central Europe.
G. leiocarpum Boiss. is similar: petals deep yellow. Pods not longer than 10cm and slightly constricted between the seeds (eastern Mediterranean region). *Argemone mexicana* L., a thistle-like plant introduced from America and now naturalised, is found occasionally on waste ground: Petals 2–3cm, pale yellow to orange. Fruit not a pod but a spiny, elliptical capsule (Mediterranean region, Canary Islands).

□■ *Glaucium corniculatum* (L.) Rudolph **Red Horned-poppy**
□□ 20–40cm; April–June; ☉, ☉
Plant with yellow sap. Stem erect or ascending, little branched, with spreading hairs. Leaves deeply pinnately divided with remotely toothed segments, the lower ones stalked, up to 25cm long, the upper sessile and smaller. Flowers solitary, more or less stalked if arising from the leaf-axils, or at the end of the stem, the 4 petals up to 3cm long, scarlet or orange-yellow, usually having a dark blotch with a pale margin at the base. Sepals 2, hairy, soon falling. Fruit a linear, almost straight capsule up to 20cm long, with appressed or spreading bristly hairs.
Cultivated and fallow land.
Mediterranean region, S.E. Europe, S.W. Asia, Canary Islands, sometimes naturalised in central Europe.

□□ *Hypecoum procumbens* L.
■□ 5–15cm; March–June; ☉
A grey-green, hairless plant with widely spreading, grooved stems. Leaves very fine, 2 to 3-pinnate, with linear to lanceolate segments. Flowers up to 1.5cm in diameter, forming a small cluster, with 4 yellow, 3-toothed petals, the lateral teeth of the 2 outer, larger petals shorter than the middle one. Fruit an erect, curved, jointed capsule, 4–6cm long.
Cultivated and fallow land, on sand, usually near the coast.
Mediterranean region.
Hypecoum imberbe Sibth. & Sm. is similar, but has an ascending to erect stem. Lateral teeth of the 2 outer, orange-yellow petals as long as or longer than the middle one (S. Europe, S.W. Asia). *H. pendulum* L. has a smooth stem. Petals pale yellow, the outer ones entire. Fruit pendent (Mediterranean region, S.W. Asia).

□□ *Fumaria capreolata* L. **Ramping Fumitory**
□■ 0.2–1m; May–September; ☉
A hairless, blue-green, delicate plant, with prostrate to erect, rather scrambling stems. Leaves stalked, bipinnate, the terminal segment oblong or ovate, usually irregularly crenate. Inflorescence a loose raceme of up to 20 flowers, shorter than its stalk. Petals 4, 10–14mm long, whitish or pink, dark purple-red at the tips, the upper one spurred. Sepals 2, soon falling, rather bluntly pointed, more or less toothed, 4–6×2–3mm. Fruits spherical, 2mm in diameter, smooth when dried, on recurved stalks.
Cultivated land, waste ground, walls.
Mediterranean region, W. Europe, uncommon and sporadic in central Europe.
F. flabellata Gaspar. is similar: raceme 10 to 30-flowered, longer than its stalk. Dry fruits densely warted (S. Europe from the Balearic Islands to Crete, N.W. Africa, Canary Islands).

Caper family *Capparidaceae*
Mustard family *Brassicaceae (Cruciferae)*

■☐ *Capparis ovata* Desf. **Caper** *Capparidaceae*
☐☐ 0.3–1m; April–September; ♄
A prostrate shrub with long stems which spread out on the ground or hang down from walls. Leaves alternate, rather fleshy, sometimes hairy, stalked, oblong to elliptic, abruptly pointed or tapering, usually tipped with a small but distinct spine, and with 2 spiny stipules at the base. Solitary, long-stalked flowers, 4–5cm across, arise from the leaf-axils. There are 4 sepals and 4 white petals, the lower ones longer than the upper, numerous purple or white stamens and a protruding, long-stalked ovary. Capers are the flower-buds, pickled in vinegar.
Rocks and walls, often also cultivated.
Mediterranean region, S.W. Asia.
C. spinosa L. is similar, but has hairless, more rounded leaves, usually notched at the end rather than spine-tipped. Flowers 5–7cm across, the petals almost equal in length (Mediterranean region).

☐■ *Bunias erucago* L. **Crested Bunias** *Brassicaceae*
☐☐ 30–60cm; May–July; ☉, ☉
Stem erect, branched, with glandular tubercles, roughly hairy below. Lower leaves lobed, the lobes pointing towards the base, the upper linear-lanceolate, entire or toothed. Flowers in well-spaced, few-flowered racemes, on a glandular stalk, with 4 yellow petals 8–13mm long. Fruits characteristic, 10–12mm long, glandular, beaked, and with 2 triangular, jagged wings on each of the 4 sides.
Cultivated land, waste ground, waysides.
S. Europe, N.W. Africa, W. Anatolia. Introduced into central Europe but uncommon.

☐☐ *Matthiola sinuata* (L.) R. Br. **Sea Stock** *Brassicaceae*
■☐ 8–60cm; May–September; usually ☉
A shore plant, covered with a dense, woolly felt, and woody at the base. Basal leaves sinuately toothed to pinnately divided, with oblong, rounded lobes, the upper stem-leaves entire. Flowers in loose racemes, the lower ones with a 4–15mm long stalk at fruiting time, the 4 petals up to 25mm long and 8mm broad, pale violet. Sepals erect, 8–12mm, the lateral ones enlarged and pouch-like. Capsules 5–15cm long, up to 5mm broad, erect or spreading, with large and conspicuous, stalked, yellow or black glands, without prominent horns at the end.
Sandy shores, also on rocky coasts.
S. and W. Europe, N.W. Africa.
The perennial *M. incana* (L.) R. Br. is similar, but flowers earlier in the year. It has white-felted to almost hairless, usually entire, narrowly lanceolate leaves. The capsules are also without prominent horns, but have no glands, and are covered with star-shaped hairs (Mediterranean region, W. Europe, also grown as an ornamental plant).

☐☐ *Matthiola fruticulosa* (L.) Maire (*M. tristis* R. Br.) **Sad Stock** *Brassicaceae*
☐■ 5–60cm; April–July; ♃, ♄
Grey-felted to sparsely hairy plant, woody at the base. Leaves linear, pinnately divided or undivided, usually forming a basal rosette. Flowers completely or almost sessile in lax racemes, the 4 petals oblong, undulate, 12–28mm long, purple, rust-coloured or yellowish. Sepals erect, 6–14mm long, the lateral ones enlarged and pouch-like. Capsules shortly stalked, 2.5–12cm long and 1–3mm broad, cylindrical, with or without glandular hairs, sometimes having straight 2–3mm long horns at the end. A very variable species with several subspecies.
Garigue, stony pastures, also on sandy soils.
Mediterranean region, Canary Islands.
M. longipetala (Vent.) DC.: Very similar, but usually an annual with numerous forms. At the end of the capsule are 2 horns 2–10mm long and another much shorter one (eastern Mediterranean region, N. Africa). *M. tricuspidata* (L.) R. Br. is also an annual, distinguished by having 3 horns of equal length, all more than 2mm (Mediterranean region).

Mustard family Brassicaceae (Cruciferae)

■☐ *Cheiranthus cheiri* L. **Wallflower**
☐☐ 20–80cm; March–June; ♃
An erect, branched subshrub. Leaves oblong-lanceolate, entire or slightly toothed, the lower ones gradually narrowing into a stalk and close together, the upper ones sessile, all with appressed, 2-branched hairs. Flowers in dense racemes, violet-scented, golden yellow, in cultivated varieties also orange to red or brown. The 4 petals are 1.5–2.5cm long, cut off squarely or notched at the end and narrowing abruptly into a long claw. Stigma deeply 2-lobed, spreading. Sepals erect, 9–11mm, the lateral ones enlarged and pouch-like. Capsules 2.5–7.5cm long and 2–4mm broad, compressed, on erect or spreading stalks 5–15mm long. In ancient times used for decorating altars and wine-barrels, and nowadays again employed as a medicinal plant and added to some medicines for the glycosides which have an effect on the heart.
Rock-crevices, old walls.
Originally native in S. Greece and the S. Aegean, in widespread cultivation in numerous varieties, escaping and becoming naturalised since olden times.

☐■ *Arabis verna* (L.) R. Br.
☐☐ 5–40cm; March–May; ☉
A small plant with a basal rosette of ovate, coarsely toothed leaves narrowing into a short stalk. Stems one or more, mostly unbranched, and usually bearing only 1 or 2 leaves, heart-shaped at the base. Flowers few (1–10) with 4 purple petals, yellowish or white at the base and 5–8mm long. Flower-stalk shorter than the calyx, which has spreading hairs. Capsules erect or spreading, 4.5–6cm long and up to 2mm broad.
Shady, stony pastures, fallow land, grassy pastures, extending into the mountain zone.
Mediterranean region.

☐☐ *Aubrieta columnae* Guss.
■☐ 5–20cm; April–June; ♃
A slender-stemmed, delicate plant, forming carpets to dense cushions. Leaves broadly obovate or spathulate according to subspecies, entire or with 2(–4) teeth, only slightly exceeded by the racemes of flowers. Flowers with 4 red-purple, long-clawed petals, 11–18mm long, the sepals erect, appressed, the lateral ones pouched. Fruits with only star-shaped hairs, usually net-veined, 5–16×2–4.5mm, 4 times as long as broad, style 3–10mm. There are 3 subspecies, the one illustrated being ssp. *italica* (Boiss.) Mattf. from Monte Gargano.
Rock-crevices, walls.
Central and S. Italy, Croatia to Montenegro, S. Carpathians.
A. deltoidea (L.) DC.: leaves far exceeded by the racemes of flowers. Petals 12–28mm long. Fruits with star-shaped hairs and long, unbranched hairs (Sicily to W. Anatolia, naturalised in S. and W. Europe). Garden forms have a mixture of the characters of both species.

☐☐ *Lobularia maritima* (L.) Desv. **Sweet Alison**
☐■ 10–40cm; April–September, also in winter; ♃
A very common species with ascending or erect stems, often branched at the base. Leaves narrow, linear-lanceolate, 2–3mm broad, pointed or blunt, more or less grey-green because of the appressed, forked hairs. The white or slightly pink, honey-scented flowers are clustered in racemes which lengthen considerably in fruit. Petals 4, about 3mm long, rounded, sepals spreading. Capsule 2–3.5mm long, ovate, pointed, each of the 2 compartments containing a sharp-tasting seed.
Rocky and sandy coasts, waysides, fields, walls.
Mediterranean region, Canary Islands, also cultivated in colder parts of Europe as an annual bedding plant and sometimes escaping and becoming naturalised.
L. libyca (Viv.) Webb & Berth.: similar, but an annual. Capsule 3–7mm, each compartment with 4–5 seeds (southern Mediterranean region, Canary Islands).

Mustard family *Brassicaceae (Cruciferae)*
Mignonette family *Resedaceae*

■☐
☐☐ *Biscutella didyma* L. (*B. apula* L.) *Brassicaceae*
10–60cm; February–May; ☉

Stem simple or branched, with spreading hairs, leafy, usually having a basal rosette of obovate or wedge-shaped, toothed leaves up to 2.5cm long. Racemes of flowers dense, the 4-petalled flowers on erect or spreading stalks, with petals 4mm long, narrowing gradually to the base and without auricles, and with sepals 2mm long. Capsules hairy on the margin, 4.5–7×9–12.5mm, falling when ripe in 2 separate, almost circular portions.
Stony, and open grassy pastures, garigue.
Mediterranean region, eastwards to Iran, absent in Spain, France and the Balearic Islands. Other annual species are *B. eriocarpa* DC., which is only 15–30cm high, with capsules 4×6–8mm, and *B. lyrata* L. which has a dense basal rosette consisting of lyre-shaped, pinnately divided leaves with a broadly ovate terminal segment. Plant 10–60cm high (both species in the central Mediterranean region). In addition there are a number of perennial species, mainly in higher places in the western Mediterranean region.

☐■
☐☐ *Moricandia arvensis* (L.) DC. **Violet Cabbage** *Brassicaceae*
20–60cm; March–June; ☉ to ♃

A hairless, erect and branched plant, variable in form with blue-green rather fleshy leaves, the lower ones obovate, with curved teeth, the upper ones entire, with a broad, heart-shaped base clasping the stem. Flowers 10–20(–25) in a long raceme, the 4 petals about 2cm long, violet. Capsule 3–8cm long and 2–3mm broad, compressed, 4-angled, each of the 2 valves of the fruit with a prominent vein. Seeds about 1mm, arranged in 2 rows.
Fallow land, waysides, rocks, mainly on chalk.
S. Europe, N.W. Africa, Canary Islands.
M. moricandioides (Boiss.) Heyw. has more flowers in the racemes and *M. foetida* Bourgeau ex Cosson is abundantly branched from the base (both from S. Spain).

☐☐
■☐ *Cakile maritima* Scop. **Sea Rocket** *Brassicaceae*
15–60cm; May–October; ☉

Stem strongly branched, prostrate or ascending. Leaves hairless and grey-green, fleshy, very variable, undivided to pinnately divided. Flowers scented, with 4 lilac, more rarely white, clawed petals, arranged in racemes, without bracts, and lengthening in fruit. Fruits standing out almost horizontally, 1–2.5cm long, on short, thick stalks, with one seed in each of the 2 sections. The lower section has 2 prominent, lateral projections at its end, giving the fruit a spear-shaped appearance. There are 4 subspecies in Europe, ssp. *aegyptiaca* (Willd.) Nym. occurring throughout almost the whole of the Mediterranean region.
Splash-zone of beaches.
Coasts of the Mediterranean region, W. and N. Europe, Canary Islands, S.W. Asia.

☐☐
☐■ *Reseda alba* L. **White Mignonette, Upright Mignonette** *Resedaceae*
30–90cm; April–September; ☉, ☉ or ♃

Stem erect, often branched in the upper part, leafy up to flowering-time. Leaves slightly grey-green, pinnately cut and comb-like, with 5–15 lobes on each side, rough on the margins. Racemes dense, many-flowered. Flowers with 5(6) white petals, up to 6mm long, exceeding the lanceolate sepals, with 3 narrow teeth at the end, the lateral ones often further divided. Stamens persisting until the fruit is ripe, carpels 4. Capsule 8–15mm, oblong-elliptic, 4-angled, erect.
Waysides, waste ground, ruins.
Mediterranean region, S.W. Asia, sometimes grown in central and N. Europe as an ornamental plant, occasionally escaping and becoming naturalised. There are other species, mostly found only in certain areas, especially in the western Mediterranean region.

Stonecrop family _Crassulaceae_
Pittosporum family _Pittosporaceae_
Plane family _Platanaceae_

■□
□□
Umbilicus rupestris (Salisb.) Dandy (_U. pendulinus_ DC.) **Wall Pennywort, Navelwort**
Crassulaceae
10–50cm; May–July; ♃
Basal leaves fleshy, shield-shaped, with a navel-like depression where the stalk is attached, crenate. Stem-leaves becoming smaller towards the top, kidney-shaped to linear. The single, erect stem is densely covered with flowers for more than half its length, sometimes branched at the base. Flowers with 3–9mm long stalks, pendent, petals 6–10mm, greenish white, yellow or pink, or even spotted, joined, the tube about 4 times as long as the ovate, sharply pointed lobes.
Shady rock-crevices, walls.
Mediterranean region, W. Europe.
U. horizontalis (Guss.) DC.: Stems bearing flowers for not more than half their length. Flowers horizontal, almost sessile, rather narrower and shorter. Corolla-lobes lanceolate, pointed (Mediterranean region, Canary Islands, absent from France and Corsica).

□■
□□
Sedum sediforme (Jacq.) Pau (_S. nicaeense_ All.) _Crassulaceae_
15–60cm; May–August; ♃
A robust species, woody at the base. Leaves fleshy, oblong, flattened on the upper side, about 4mm broad and 1–2cm long, with a fine point and shortly spurred, closely overlapping on non-flowering shoots. Flowering stem erect, with remote leaves, the inflorescence erect, almost spherical at first, concave in fruit. Flowers numerous, very shortly stalked, with 5–8 spreading, greenish white or straw-coloured petals, 4–7mm long. Sepals 2.5mm, hairless. Fruits erect.
Stony pastures, garigue.
Mediterranean region.
S. ochroleucum Chaix: Similar, but only 15–30cm high. Leaves distinctly spurred. Sepals 5–7mm, glandular hairy (S. Europe, Asia Minor).

□□
■□
Pittosporum tobira (Thunb.) Ait. f. **Japanese Pittosporum** _Pittosporaceae_
2–3m; March–August; ♄
Evergreen shrub, the leathery, shining, dark green leaves obovate, narrowing into the stalk, about 5×3cm, hairless, somewhat recurved at the margin, clustered at the ends of the twigs. Flowers strongly scented, in terminal, umbel-like clusters, the 5 rather blunt petals at first white, later yellowish, about 1cm long. Fruit a leathery, yellowish brown capsule, the seeds embedded in a sticky liquid.
Frequently planted in the Mediterranean region as an ornamental shrub, native in China and Japan.
P. undulatum Vent. is also cultivated, a tree with lanceolate, hairless, wavy-edged leaves and with pointed petals (native in Australia).

□□
□■
Platanus orientalis L. **Oriental Plane** _Platanaceae_
Up to 30m; April–May; ♄
A deciduous tree with the bark coming off in flakes, and with male and female flowers on the same tree. Leaves long-stalked, usually wedge-shaped at the base, palmately lobed to over halfway with 5–7 segments, the middle one much longer than its basal breadth, generally sinuately toothed, more rarely entire. Flowers with 4 perianth-segments, the female purplish red, in dense, globular heads, 3–6 on each hanging stalk.
Wet woods, river-banks, planted as a decorative tree or as a shade-tree.
Eastern Mediterranean region as far as the Himalaya, westwards to Yugoslavia.
Platanus hybrida Brot.: leaves cut off squarely at the base or slightly heart-shaped, divided no more than halfway to the middle into 3–5 lobes, the middle lobe only a little longer than its basal breadth. Heads of flowers mostly in pairs. Origin unknown, regarded either as a hybrid between _P. orientalis_ and the formerly more frequently cultivated _P. occidentalis_ L. from N. America, or as a cultivated form of _P. orientalis_. More resistant to frost and therefore preferred for planting in central and N. Europe.

Rose family *Rosaceae*

■□ *Rosa sempervirens* L. Rosaceae
□□ 5–10m; May–June; ♄
A climbing, evergreen rose. Prickles sparse, slightly curved and prolonged at the base. Leaves hairless, leathery and shining, usually 5-pinnate, the leaflets sharply serrate, ovate-lanceolate, the terminal one especially tapering gradually to a point. Inflorescence of 3–7 flowers, each with 5 white petals, 1–2cm long, the styles united into a usually hairy column. Sepals ovate, abruptly long-pointed, usually entire, and, like the long flower-stalks, covered with stalked glands. Fruit ovoid or spherical, red, about 1cm.
Maquis, open woods, hedges.
Mediterranean region, the only widely distributed species.

□■ *Sarcopoterium spinosum* (L.) Spach (*Poterium spinosum* L.) **Thorny Burnet**
□□ 30–60cm; March–May; ♄
A low, much-branched, rounded shrub, the young stems densely grey-felted, and leafless, thorny lateral shoots branching off at an angle. Leaves odd-pinnate, with 9–15 narrow, often finely serrate leaflets, densely hairy beneath, which soon fall. Flowers without petals, clustered into spherical or elongated heads up to 3cm, the upper flowers usually female with conspicuous, red, feathery stigmas, the lower ones male with 10–30 long, yellow stamens. Fruits reddish, berry-like.
Garigue, often in large patches.
Eastern Mediterranean region, westwards to Sardinia.

□□ *Pyrus amygdaliformis* Vill.
■□ 1–6m; April–May; ♄
Deciduous shrub or small tree, much-branched and frequently thorny, young growth hairy. Leaves with stalks 2–5cm long, 2.5–8×1–3cm, narrowly lanceolate to obovate, entire or indistinctly toothed towards the tip, hairy when young, later becoming hairless and finely warted on the underside. Flowers in umbel-like clusters of 8–12 on felted stalks, with 5 elliptical petals, 7–8mm long, usually notched at the tip. Fruits globular, 1.5–3cm, yellow-brown, on equally long, stout stalks, with persistent calyces.
Open woods, undergrowth, stony pastures.
S. Europe, Asia Minor.

□□ *Eriobotrya japonica* (Thunb.) Lindley **Loquat**
□■ 2–10m; October–February: ♄
A small, evergreen tree. Leaves shortly stalked, oblong-lanceolate with a coarsely toothed margin and strongly marked veins, dark green and shining above, brownish or yellow-felted beneath, 12–25cm long. Flowers about 1cm in diameter, yellowish white, 5-petalled, scented, in dense, panicle-like inflorescences covered in brown hairs, sepals persistent. The pear-shaped, golden yellow fruits (loquats) are 3–6cm long and ripen in the spring. Flesh of the fruit refreshingly acid, with 2–3 large, inedible, dark brown seeds. Only keeping for a short while, and therefore mainly found in local markets. Native in S.E. Asia, cultivated in the Mediterranean region and areas with a similar climate for its fruit or as an ornamental tree, occasionally becoming naturalised. During the autumn in southern markets, one sometimes finds fruits of the Medlar, *Mespilus germanica* L., which are brownish when ripe, and only become soft and palatable when they begin to decay. The leaves of this deciduous shrub or small tree are lanceolate, 5–12cm long, and entire or finely serrate. Flowers solitary, 3–4cm across. Fruits 2–3cm (eastern Mediterranean region, elsewhere cultivated and occasionally becoming naturalised).

Rose family Rosaceae
Caesalpinia family Caesalpiniaceae

■☐ *Pyracantha coccinea* M.J. Roem. **Firethorn** *Rosaceae*
☐☐ 1–2m (in cultivation up to 6m); May–June; ♄
An evergreen, much-branched, thorny shrub with leathery leaves, dark green and shining above, paler beneath, elliptic to ovate-elliptic, pointed, finely crenate-serrate, 2–6cm long. Young shoots, leaves and leaf-stalks somewhat hairy. Flowers in erect, umbel-like clusters, 0.5–1cm across, with 5 white or yellowish white petals. Fruits as big as a pea, bright red, more rarely orange or yellow, often remaining on the plant throughout the winter.
Hedges, thickets, also grown as an ornamental plant, sometimes escaping and becoming naturalised.
S. Europe, Asia Minor, eastwards to Iran.

☐■ *Prunus dulcis* (Mill.) D.A. Webb (*P. amygdalus* Batsch) **Almond** *Rosaceae*
☐☐ Up to 8m; February–April; ♄
A small tree or shrub, with thorny twigs in the case of wild plants. Leaves hairless, narrowly lanceolate, 4–12cm long and up to 3cm broad, glandular serrate along the margin, with a stalk 1.2–2.5cm long. Flowers usually in pairs, almost sessile, appearing before the leaves, with 5 pink petals, about 2cm long, which become paler during the flowering period. Fruit 3.5–6cm, the leathery, felted, outer layer splitting open at maturity. Almonds are used mainly in cooking and in the production of the expensive almond oil for medicinal, cosmetic and technical purposes. Bitter Almonds contain the poisonous glycoside amygdalin.
Native in S.W. Asia, cultivated in the Mediterranean region since ancient times for its fruit and as a decorative tree, sometimes escaping and becoming naturalised.
Also common are *P. persica* (L.) Batsch, **Peach:** Leaves lanceolate, leaf-stalk only 1–1.5cm long. Flowers usually solitary, remaining bright pink (native in China) and *P. armeniaca* L., **Apricot:** leaves broadly ovate, often somewhat heart-shaped at the base. Flowers mostly solitary, white or only pale pink (native in S.E. Asia).

☐☐ *Cercis siliquastrum* L. **Judas Tree** *Caesalpiniaceae*
■☐ Up to 10m; March–April; ♄
Deciduous tree or shrub. Leaves appearing as a rule after the flowers, long-stalked, almost circular, blunt or notched at the tip, with a heart-shaped base, 7–12cm, quite hairless. Flowers very numerous, rose-red, up to 2cm, arising in short racemes directly from the older branches, similar to the Papilionaceae, but the 3 upper petals smaller than the 2 lower ones, and with the upper petals of the 2 lateral pairs enclosing the uppermost one. Stamens 10, free. Pods 6–15cm long, compressed, red-brown and hairless. According to tradition Judas is supposed to have hanged himself on this tree.
Wet woods, maquis, and stony slopes, also grown as an ornamental tree.
Originally in the eastern Mediterranean region and S.W. Asia, nowadays cultivated throughout the whole Mediterranean region, occasionally escaping and becoming naturalised.

☐☐ *Ceratonia siliqua* L. **Carob Tree, Locust Tree** *Caesalpiniaceae*
☐■ 4–10m; mainly August–October; ♄
An evergreen, slow-growing tree with spreading, densely leafy branches and with male and female flowers on different trees. Leaves even-pinnate, with 4–10 shortly stalked, obovate leaflets, blunt or notched at the end, shining dark green, leathery and slightly undulate. The inconspicuous, greenish flowers, which have no petals, arise directly from the trunk and branches. Pods 10–30cm long, compressed flat, brown-purple, leathery. The sugary fruits (carobs) are nowadays mainly used as cattle-feed, but are also enjoyed by human beings. In addition, they are also used in the production of fruit-juices and fermented drinks, in the treatment of digestive upsets in children, and roasted as a coffee-substitute. Because of their uniform weight, the dried seeds were formerly used to weigh jewels and gold (carat).
On rocky places near the coast, also in the maquis, planted for its fruit and as a shade-tree.
Mediterranean region, especially in the south, its original distribution uncertain.

Acacia family *Mimosaceae*

■□ *Acacia karoo* Hayne (*A. horrida* auct. non Willd.)
□□ 1–4m; August–September; ♄
A shrub immediately recognisable, even before the leaves appear, by its stout, white, spiny stipules, 5–10cm long. Leaves bipinnate, green on both sides, consisting of 2–7 pairs of primary leaflets and 5–14 pairs of secondary leaflets, 6–10×2–4mm. Flowers slightly scented, forming globular heads 1cm in diameter, which arise in groups of 4–6 in the axils of the upper leaves. Heads of flowers on hairless stalks, up to 2.5cm long. Fruits flat, 8–13cm long and 6–8mm broad, sickle-shaped, slightly constricted between the seeds.
Cultivated for ornament and as a hedge-plant in the south-western Mediterranean region, occasionally escaping and becoming naturalised, native in S. Africa.
A. farnesiana (L.) Willd.: also shrubby and deciduous, but with spiny stipules 2.5cm long. Leaflets 10–25 pairs, very small, 3–5×1–1.5mm. Heads of scented flowers with hairy stalks, 1–2cm long. Fruits cylindrical, 50–90×10–15mm. Cultivated in S.W. Europe as an ornamental shrub and as a source of perfume (native in Central America).

□■ *Acacia dealbata* Link **Silver Wattle, Mimosa**
□□ Up to 30m; February–April; ♄
A tree with white-felted young stems and leaves, the latter evergreen, somewhat bluish, bipinnate, with glands at the point of attachment of the 8–20 pairs of primary leaflets. Secondary leaflets 30–50 pairs, 3–4mm long. Spiny stipules absent. Heads of flowers globular, 5–6mm in diameter, forming dense panicle-like clusters which are longer than the leaves. Pods 4–10cm long, 1–1.2cm broad, compressed, barely constricted between the seeds. Sprays offered by our florists as 'Mimosa'.
Frequently planted in the Mediterranean region as a decorative tree, also to consolidate ground and as a source of wood, sometimes escaping and becoming naturalised, native in Australia.
A. mearnsii De Wild.: stems and young leaves with yellowish hairs, pods distinct, constricted between the seeds (planted especially in the western Mediterranean region, native in Australia).

□□ *Acacia longifolia* (Andrews) Willd. **Sydney Golden Wattle**
■□ Up to 8m; February–April; ♄
Shrub or small tree with hairless stems. Leaves reduced to broadened leaf-stalks (phyllodes), 7–15cm long, up to 3cm broad, lanceolate, 2 to 4-veined. Inflorescences pale yellow, catkin-like, 2–6cm long, composed of small heads of flowers and arising in the leaf-axils. Pods 7–15cm long, up to 5mm broad, cylindrical, constricted between the seeds. Sprays offered by our florists as 'Mimosa'.
Planted as a decorative tree and to consolidate dunes, especially in the western Mediterranean region, sometimes escaping and becoming naturalised, native in Australia.

□□ *Acacia retinodes* Schlecht. (*A. floribunda* auct. non Willd.)
□■ Up to 10m; can flower at any time of the year; ♄
A small tree, the slender stems usually brown, not pendent. The leaf-like, broadened leaf-stalks (phyllodes) lanceolate, fairly straight, with only one middle vein, 6–15×0.4–1.8cm, green. The pale yellow heads of flowers, 4–6mm in diameter, are in groups of 5–10 and form lax racemes in the leaf-axils. Pods flat, at most only slightly constricted between the seeds. Seeds encircled by their red stalks.
Planted as an ornamental tree on Mediterranean coasts, sometimes becoming naturalised, native in Australia.
Other similar Australian species include *A. cyanophylla* Lindley: Stems pendent, phyllodes blue-green and rather larger. Heads of flowers fairly large, 10–15mm in diameter, in groups of 2–6. Pods distinctly constricted between the seeds. Stalk of seed short, whitish. *A. pycnantha* Bentham: phyllodes distinctly sickle-shaped. Heads of flowers deep yellow, 8–10mm in diameter, in groups of 10–20 forming long, dense racemes.

Pea family *Papilionaceae*

■□ *Calicotome villosa* (Poir.) Link **Spiny Broom**
□□ 0.5–2m; January–June; ♄
    Much-branched, spiny shrub. Young stems, under side of leaves and calyx more or less densely covered with silky or woolly hairs. Leaves stalked, composed of 3 leaflets, usually falling by the summer. Flowers golden yellow, 12–18mm, usually in clusters of 2–15, or in leafless racemes. As the flower opens, the upper part of the calyx breaks away from the lower part, hence the botanical name for the genus. Pod densely covered with coarse or silky hairs, 2–4cm long, with a distinctly thickened line where it opens.
    Maquis, prevalent in areas where woods have been cleared.
    Mediterranean region, absent from France and the Balearic Islands.
    C. spinosa (L.) Link is very similar: spines stouter, hairs generally less dense. Flowers usually solitary, sometimes in clusters. Pods hairless or almost so, line of opening hardly thickened (western Mediterranean region, eastwards to Italy).

□■ *Cytisus sessilifolius* L.
□□ 0.5–2m; April–June; ♄
    A spineless, much-branched, hairless shrub, with bright green leaves composed of 3 leaflets, more or less sessile on flowering stems, but elsewhere sometimes stalked. Leaflets broadly ovate to almost circular, shortly pointed, the middle one larger. Flowers in groups of 3–12 in short, leafless, terminal racemes. Corolla golden yellow with an almost circular standard petal 11mm long and beaked keel curving sharply upwards. Calyx shortly bell-shaped, 2-lipped. Pod 2.5–4cm long and up to 1cm broad, curved above the strongly narrowed base.
    Deciduous woods and undergrowth up to the mountain zone, occasionally cultivated.
    S.W. Europe, eastwards to Italy, absent from the islands.

□□ *Cytisus villosus* Pourr. (*C. triflorus* L'Hér.)
■□ 1–2m; March–May; ♄
    A spineless, erect shrub. Young stems 5-angled, hairy at the end. Leaves with stalks 2–10mm long and composed of 3 oblong-elliptical, entire leaflets, 1–3cm long, hairless above and with appressed hairs beneath, the middle leaflet longer than the 2 lateral ones. Flowers solitary or in groups of 2 or 3 with hairy stalks 5–10mm long, arising in the upper leaf-axils and forming a long, leafy raceme-like inflorescence. Petals yellow, the standard 15–18mm long, striped red-brown at the base, and shorter than the keel. Calyx shortly bell-shaped, hairy, 2-lipped, the teeth shorter than the tube. Pod 2–4.5cm long and up to 7mm broad, with long hairs at first but becoming hairless later.
    Maquis, woods, especially on acid rocks.
    S. Europe, N.W. Africa.
    There are numerous other yellow-flowered species, usually restricted to small areas in the western Mediterranean region. The only white-flowered species is *C. multiflorus* (L'Hér.) Sweet (northern Iberian peninsula).

□□ *Genista corsica* (Lois.) DC.
□■ 20–60cm; March–June; ♄
    An erect, spiny shrub, with alternately branching stems. Lower leaves of 3 leaflets, the upper ones simple, almost sessile, narrowly obovate or oblong, 3–11×1.5–2mm, sparsely hairy, soon falling. Stout spines, curving slightly backwards and sometimes branched, arise in the leaf-axils. Flowers with small bracts and with stalks 2–5mm long, singly or in small groups of 2–6. Petals yellow, hairless, 7–12mm, all the same length. Calyx as in all species of *Genista* 2-lipped, the upper lip deeply divided into 2 parts, the lower lip 3-toothed, in this species the lips as long as the tube. Pod oblong, 12–20mm, hairless, seeds 2–8.
    Garigue, maquis.
    Corsica, Sardinia.
    G. scorpius (L.) DC.: flowers on the lateral spines. Lips of calyx shorter than the tube. Pod 15–40mm (western Mediterranean region). In the western Mediterranean region particularly, there are numerous other species of *Genista* of widely differing habit, also many mountain plants.

Pea family *Papilionaceae*

■□
□□ *Genista acanthoclada* DC.
0.3–1m; March–June; ♄
A low shrub with dense, opposite branched stems ending in spines, the older stems with conspicuously thickened leaf-bases. Leaves of 3 narrowly lanceolate leaflets, 5–10×1–3mm. Flowers solitary in the axils of 3-lobed or simple bracts at the ends of the stems. Petals yellow, the standard with silky hairs, 7–14mm long, shorter than the keel. The 2-lipped calyx 2.5–5mm long, hairy, with the lower lip 3-toothed and the upper one deeply divided into 2 parts, the lips almost as long as the tube. Pod about 9mm, ovoid, pointed, silky-hairy, with 1 seed.
Garigue, maquis, Pine woods.
Eastern Mediterranean region.

□■
□□ *Lygos sphaerocarpa* (L.) Heyw. (*Retama sphaerocarpa* (L.) Boiss.)
1–2(–3.5)m; May–June; ♄
A switch-shrub, the young stems erect, later arching over, grooved, appearing silvery from a distance. Leaves linear to lanceolate, with silky hairs, soon falling. Flowers in small, lateral racemes with a yellow corolla 5–8mm long. Calyx 3mm, with a 2-toothed upper lip and 3-toothed lower lip. Fruit a smooth, ovoid, usually 1-seeded pod, 7–13mm long, which remains closed.
Pasture-land.
Central and southern Iberian peninsula, N.W. Africa.
There are 2 white-flowered species with overhanging stems which occur on sand: *L. monosperma* (L.) Heyw., corolla 10–12mm, pod 12–16mm, with a short point (south-western Mediterranean region, Canary Islands) and *L. raetam* (Forsk.) Heyw., corolla 15–17mm, pod 10–20mm, with a long beak (Sicily, N. Africa, Canary Islands, S.W. Asia).

□□
■□ *Spartium junceum* L. **Spanish Broom**
1–3(–5)m; April–July; ♄
A tall switch-shrub with grey-green, hairless, erect stems and undivided, linear-lanceolate leaflets, 1–3cm long, with silky hairs beneath, individual leaflets soon falling. Flowers usually arising singly but forming erect, terminal racemes, bright yellow, 2–2.5cm long, scented. Wing-petals shorter than the almost circular standard petal and the keel. Calyx membranous, split above, with 5 short teeth. Pods flat, 4–8cm long, with silky hairs, later becoming hairless and dark brown, with 10–18 shining reddish yellow seeds. Poisonous because of the alkaloid spartein. Formerly used as a medicinal plant, and the stems for basket-weaving.
Garigue, maquis, mainly on chalk, frequently cultivated as an ornamental shrub, sometimes with double flowers.
Mediterranean region, Canary Islands.

□□
□■ *Ulex parviflorus* Pourr.
0.4–1.5m; April–May; ♄
A densely branched shrub, with all leaves, bracts, as well as the short and long shoots, which are more or less covered with curly hairs, modified into spines. Yellow flowers in the axils of the spines at the ends of the stems, 6–12mm, standard and keel about as long as the yellowish calyx which is 2-lipped like other species of Gorse, wing-petals shorter. Bracts as narrow as the flower-stalk. Pod ovoid, 10–15mm long, brown or blackish, seeds 1–3. A variable species with several subspecies.
Garigue, open woods, particularly on acid rocks.
Iberian peninsula, France, N.W. Africa.
Several species are native in the W. European–Atlantic region, especially in Portugal, but only *U. europaeus* L. has a wider distribution: flowers 15–20mm, the calyx with more or less spreading hairs only ²/₃ as long. Bracts much broader than the flower-stalks (W. Europe eastwards to Italy, Canary Islands, also cultivated, sometimes escaping and becoming naturalised).

Pea family *Papilionaceae*

■☐ *Lupinus angustifolius* L. **Narrow-leaved Lupin**
☐☐ 20–80cm; April–July; ☉
Leaves digitate with 5–9 linear leaflets, up to 5cm long and 2–5mm broad, rounded at the tips, hairless above, somewhat hairy beneath. Flowers blue, 11–13mm long, arranged alternately and forming racemes 10–20cm long. Fruits shortly hairy, with 4–7 seeds. Poisonous.
Cultivated and fallow land, garigue, on acid, often sandy soils.
Mediterranean region, Canary Islands, sometimes escaping and becoming naturalised in central Europe.
Species with whorls of flowers and leaves hairy on both sides are *L. micranthus* Guss. with leaflets 5–15mm broad and *L. varius* L. with leaflets 6–9mm broad and larger flowers, 15–17mm long (both species native in the Mediterranean region).

☐■ *Argyrolobium zanonii* (Turra) Ball (*A. linnaeanum* Walp., *Cytisus argenteus* L.)
☐☐ 10–30cm; April–July; ♄
A small subshrub, woody at the base, with ascending, silky-hairy stems. Leaves stalked, with 3 almost sessile, elliptical leaflets, lanceolate further up, almost hairless and dark green above, with appressed, densely silky hairs on the under side. Stipules 2, small, lanceolate and free. Flowers golden yellow, 9–12mm long, in 1 to 4-flowered racemes at the ends of the stems, standard hairy on the outside, and, like the wings, longer than the keel. Calyx with silky hairs, more than half as long as the corolla, 2-lipped, the 5 teeth longer than the tube. Pod 1.5–3.5cm long, flat, somewhat curved, densely silky-hairy.
Stony and grassy pastures, Pine woods, especially on limestone.
Western Mediterranean region, eastwards to Albania.

☐☐ *Colutea arborescens* L. **Bladder Senna**
■☐ 1–6m; May–August; ♄
Deciduous shrub, stems appressed hairy at first, later becoming hairless. Leaves odd-pinnate, with 7–11 shortly stalked leaflets, up to 3×2cm, broadly elliptic, obovate or ovate. Erect, stalked racemes, shorter than the accompanying leaf, arise from leaf-axils. Flowers 2–8, nodding, 16–20mm long, standard almost circular, frequently striped reddish brown, about as long as the blunt-ended keel. Calyx widely bell-shaped, slightly 2-lipped. Pod strongly inflated, with light brown, parchment-like walls at maturity, 5–7×3cm, seeds up to 4×3.5mm.
Submediterranean deciduous woods, undergrowth, pine woods, mainly on chalk.
Mediterranean region northwards to the Upper Rhine, cultivated even further north as an ornamental shrub, sometimes escaping and becoming naturalised.
C. orientalis Mill.: flowers 11–13mm, orange-red, the keel with a small beak. Pod 4×2cm, split at the end, seeds up to 2.5mm (often planted as a decorative shrub, sometimes escaping and becoming naturalised, native in the Caucasus region). The hybrid between the 2 species (*C.× media* Willd.) is also cultivated, occasionally escaping and becoming naturalised.

☐☐ *Astragalus massiliensis* (Mill.) Lam. (*A. tragacantha* L.p.p.)
☐■ 10–30cm; April–June; ♄
A shiny, cushion-forming shrub. Leaves 2–7cm long, with 6–12 pairs of leaflets, the leaf-stalk stout and ending in a spine. Leaflets soon falling, narrow, 4–6mm long, densely hairy beneath, the hairs attached at the centre (lens needed). Racemes of 3–8 white flowers, with the standard 13–17mm long. Calyx with appressed hairs, the teeth ⅕–¼ as long as the tube. Pod 9–10mm, oblong, pointed, densely appressed, hairy, scarcely beaked.
Coastal garigue.
S.W. Europe, eastwards to Corsica and Sardinia.
A. balearicus Chat.: Leaves with 3–5 pairs of leaflets. Flowers white to pink, 11–12mm long (Balearic Islands). *A. sirinicus* Ten.: flowers yellowish, tinged violet, 14–19mm long. Hairs on calyx and pod spreading (central Mediterranean region). Members of a large genus, which is represented in the Mediterranean region by numerous annual and perennial herbaceous plants and by bushy, cushion-forming shrubs. Centre of distribution in S.W. to central Asia, 372 species in Asia Minor.

Pea family *Papilionaceae*

■□ *Psoralea bituminosa* L. **Pitch Trefoil**
□□ 0.2–1m; April–August; ♄
A variable species with more or less hairy stems smelling strongly of tar. Leaves long-stalked, with 3 linear-lanceolate to broadly ovate leaflets, entire, dotted with glands, 1–6×0.3–2cm. Flower-heads with a stalk up to 30cm long, composed of 7–30 dingy lilac, sometimes white flowers 15–20mm long, surrounded at the base by 2 or 3-toothed bracts. Fruit with a sword-shaped beak, 6–10mm long.
Waysides, weedy ground, fallow land.
Mediterranean region, Canary Islands.
Psoralea americana L. has toothed leaflets and racemes of whitish-violet flowers (south-western Mediterranean region, Canary Islands).

□■ *Vicia hybrida* L. **Hairy Yellow Vetchling**
□□ 20–60cm; April–June; ☉
A softly hairy or almost hairless, prostrate, ascending or climbing plant. Leaves with 3–8 pairs of leaflets and a tendril at the end, leaflets obovate-elliptic, notched or blunt-ended with an abrupt point. Flowers solitary on short stalks in the upper leaf-axils, with a pale yellow, sometimes purple-veined corolla, 18–30mm long, the standard with silky hairs on the back and the calyx-teeth of different lengths. Pod flat, 2.5–4cm long, brownish, hairy.
Cultivated land, waysides, grassy pastures.
Mediterranean region, S.W. Asia.
V. lutea L.: Flowers 1–3, 20–35mm long, pale yellow, often purple-veined, the standard hairless (Mediterranean region, W. Europe, Canary Islands). *V. melanops* Sibth. & Sm.: Flowers 1–4, 15–22mm long, the standard greenish yellow, hairless, the wings with blackish tips, and the keel purple (S. Europe, westwards to S. France, Asia Minor). Numerous other species with yellow, lilac or blue flowers.

□□ *Lathyrus latifolius* L. **Everlasting Pea**
■□ 0.6–3m; June–August; ⅄
A conspicuous and robust species with prostrate, ascending or climbing, broadly-winged stems. All leaves with only 2 5-veined, ovate to linear-lanceolate leaflets, 4–15cm long, and a winged stalk. Stipules 3–6cm long, half spear-shaped, more than half as broad as the stem. Racemes of flowers longer than the bracts, with 5–15 carmine red flowers, 2–3cm long. Calyx-teeth very unequal, the lowest tooth at least twice as long as the 2 upper ones. Pods 5–11cm long and up to 1cm broad, brown, hairless.
Undergrowth, waysides, grassy pastures, also grown as an ornamental plant.
S. and central Europe, N.W. Africa, occasionally escaping and becoming naturalised.
The closely related species *L. sylvestris* L., which is found throughout almost the whole of Europe, has stipules less than half as broad as the stem. Leaflets 3-veined.

□□ *Lathyrus clymenum* L.
□■ 0.3–1m; March–June; ☉
A hairless, climbing plant with a winged stem. Lower leaves consisting only of a broadened leaf-stalk, the upper ones with 2–4 pairs of linear to lanceolate or elliptical leaflets, 3–11mm broad and 2–6cm long, which are broader than the winged axis of the leaf. Flowers up to 2cm, with violet wings and a purple-red, notched standard, in groups of 1–5 on a long stalk. Calyx-teeth the same length, shorter than the tube. Pod 3–7cm long, brown, with a groove along the back edge.
Cultivated and fallow land, waysides, formerly grown as fodder.
Mediterranean region, Canary Islands.
Lathyrus articulatus L. is very similar and not easily distinguished. It has narrower leaflets, and flowers with white or pink wings and a pointed standard. Back edge of pod not grooved (Mediterranean region, Canary Islands).

Pea family *Papilionaceae*

■☐
☐☐ *Lathyrus cicera* L. **Red Vetchling**
10–60cm; March–June; ☉
A delicate plant with narrowly winged stems. Leaves with usually only 1 pair of linear to lanceolate leaflets, up to 9cm long and 1–6mm broad, the lower ones with a bristle, the upper ones with a simple or branched tendril. Stipules half spear-shaped, 1–2cm, about as long as or somewhat longer than the narrowly winged leaf-stalk. Flowers solitary on 1–3cm long stalks, with a purple-red corolla 10–14mm long. Calyx-teeth almost equal, 2–3 times as long as the tube. Pod 20–40×5–10mm, hairless, doubly keeled along the back edge. Seeds 2–6, angular.
Cultivated and fallow land, grassy pastures.
Mediterranean region, Canary Islands, S.W. Asia.
Of the species occurring in the Mediterranean region, the following are similar: *L. inconspicuus* L., stems not winged, leaves usually without tendrils, leaflets 25–40×1–4mm. Flowers 4–9mm, pale purple, with a stalk 2–5mm long. Young pods densely hairy, later becoming hairless, 30–60×2–5mm, with 5–14 smooth seeds. *L. setifolius* L.: Stems narrowly winged, leaflets 20–90×0.5–3mm. Flowers 8–11mm, orange-red, with a stalk 1–4cm long. Pod becoming hairless but remaining hairy along the back edge, 15–30×7–11mm, with 2–3 finely warted seeds. *L. sativus* L., **Chickling Pea**, is generally stouter, and is cultivated as a fodder-plant, sometimes escaping and becoming naturalised: Stems broadly winged, leaflets 2.5–15cm×2–7(–9)mm. Flowers 12–24mm, white, pink or bluish, with a 3–6cm long stalk. Pods 10–18mm broad, hairless, with 2 wings along the back edge, 2 to 4-seeded.

☐■
☐☐ *Lathyrus annuus* L. **Annual Yellow Vetchling**
0.4–1.5m; April–June; ☉
Stems stout, hairless, winged above. Leaves with 1 pair of linear-lanceolate leaflets, 5–15cm long and 4–18mm broad, with an often much-branched tendril. Stipules less than 1mm broad, half spear-shaped. Flowers 1–3, long-stalked, with a yellow corolla 12–18mm long. Calyx-teeth equal, as long as or rather longer than the tube. Fruit straight, 3–8cm long and 7–12mm broad, hairless, with 7–8 warted seeds.
Cultivated and fallow land.
Mediterranean region, Canary Islands, S.W. Asia.
Similar species are *L. hierosolymitanus* Boiss.: corolla only 7–12mm long, pinkish yellow, pod 5–7mm broad, and *L. gorgoni* Parl.: Corolla 18–25mm long, reddish yellow, calyx-teeth 2–3 times as long as the tube (both species in the eastern Mediterranean region).

☐☐ *Lathyrus ochrus* (L.) DC. **Winged Vetchling**
■☐ 20–60cm; March–June; ☉
A hairless, climbing, blue-green plant with winged stems and leaves which consist of the leaf-like, broadened, ovate-oblong leaf-stalk, the lower ones only with tendrils, the upper ones also having 1–2 pairs of ovate leaflets. Flowers pale yellow, 16–18mm long, solitary or in pairs, their stalks shorter than the leaves. Calyx-teeth unequal, about as long as the tube. Pod 4–6cm long and about 1cm broad, with 2 wings along the back edge.
Cultivated land, especially in cornfields.
Mediterranean region, Canary Islands, earlier cultivated locally as a fodder-plant.

☐☐ *Lathyrus aphaca* L. **Yellow Vetchling**
☐■ 30–80cm; April–July; ☉
Stems slender, ascending or climbing, 4-angled but without wings, and completely hairless. Leaves only consisting of a simple or branched tendril, rarely the lower ones with a single, elliptic-lanceolate leaflet. Stipules in pairs, facing each other, large, up to 5×4cm, broadly ovate, with 2 spreading lobes at the base, flowers usually solitary, rarely in pairs, long-stalked, with a pale yellow corolla, 6–18mm long. Calyx-teeth 2–3 times as long as the tube, almost equal. Pod pointing upwards, 2–3.5cm long and 3–8mm broad, flat, with 4–8 conspicuous seeds.
Cultivated land, especially in cornfields, waysides.
Mediterranean region, Canary Islands, S.W. Asia, rarely introduced north of the Alps.

112

Pea family *Papilionaceae*

■□ *Ononis natrix* L. **Large Yellow Restharrow**
□□ 0.2–1m; April–July; ♃
A much-branched plant, erect or ascending, densely glandular-hairy in all parts and there-fore sticky, more or less woody in the lower part. Leaves of 3 leaflets apart from the upper-most ones, the leaflets up to 2cm long, ovate-lanceolate, usually toothed. Flowers solitary on jointed stalks in loose, leafy racemes. Corolla yellow with red or violet veins, 6–20mm long. Pods cylindrical, 10–25mm long, hairy, pendent. A very variable species with several subspecies.
Fallow land, waysides, weedy ground, garigue, especially on chalk.
Mediterranean region, Canary Islands.
Numerous yellow or red-flowered, perennial or annual species, especially in the western Mediterranean region.

□■ *Ononis variegata* L.
□□ 10–30cm; April–June; ☉
Stems branched from the base, prostrate or ascending, with simple and glandular hairs. Leaves very shortly stalked, almost all consisting of 1 leaflet, folded, obovate, sharply toothed and with very prominent veins, 5–10mm long. Stipules large, ovate. Flowers solitary on short, unjointed stalks in the upper leaf-axils, with a yellow corolla, 12–14mm long, which protrudes far beyond the bell-shaped calyx, standard hairy on the outer side. Pod pointing upwards, about 8mm long, hairy. Seeds 10–14, reddish brown, smooth.
Sandy beaches.
Scattered throughout the whole Mediterranean region, Canary Islands.
On sandy or rocky coasts of the Mediterranean region there are also 2 pink-flowered, annual species: *O. diffusa* Ten., stems glandular-hairy, leaves of 3 leaflets, the uppermost bracts usually simple. Flowers solitary, almost sessile in the leaf-axils, forming a dense, spike-like inflorescence, corolla 9–11mm, and *O. mitissima* L., similar, but with the stem felted or almost hairless. Calyx of flower with very prominent, white veins.

□□ *Melilotus sulcata* Desf. **Furrowed Melilot**
■□ 10–40cm; April–June; ☉
Stem branched or simple, erect, with long-stalked leaves composed of 3 leaflets. Leaflets stalked, oblong to wedge-shaped, toothed. Stipules of the middle leaves distinctly toothed. Flowers 3–4mm long, in 8 to 25-flowered racemes, which at fruiting time are as long as or longer than the leaves. Standard shorter than the keel. The almost circular, concentrically ribbed pods, 3–4mm across, are characteristic of this species.
Cultivated and fallow land, waysides.
Mediterranean region, Canary Islands.
Several other yellow-flowered species of *Melilotus* occur in the Mediterranean region, including *M. indica* (L.) All.: stipules almost entire. Corolla pale yellow, only 2–3mm long. Pod 1.5–3mm, almost circular, distinctly net-veined, and *M. messanensis* (L.) All.: racemes of flowers much shorter than the leaves, 3 to 10-flowered, corolla 4–5mm. Pod 5–8mm, obliquely ovate, pointed, concentrically ribbed.

□□ *Medicago arborea* L. **Tree Medick**
□■ 1–4m; March–August; ♄
A densely leafy shrub, the young stems white with silky hairs. Leaves of 3 obovate leaflets, wedge-shaped at the base, entire or toothed at the end, the young leaves in particular silky-hairy on the underside. Flowers 4–10 in more or less spherical racemes, corolla 12–15mm long, golden yellow. Fruits twisted spirally 1–1½ times, leaving a hole in the middle, com-pressed flat, net-veined on the surface, 12–15mm in diameter. The genus *Medicago* is centred in the Mediterranean region, but this is the only shrubby representative.
Rocky coasts, also frequently grown as an ornamental plant.
Southern Mediterranean region, sometimes introduced further north and becoming naturalised.

Pea family *Papilionaceae*

■□ *Medicago orbicularis* (L.) Bartal. **Large Disk Medick**
□□ 10–80cm; April–June; ⊙
A prostrate species, hairless or sparsely hairy, which is easily recognisable by its fruits. Leaves stalked, consisting of 3 obovate to wedge-shaped leaflets, minutely toothed in the upper part. Flowers 1–5 in small, stalked racemes, at first shorter than the leaves, with a yellow corolla, 2–5mm long. Pod a flat, pale green, later light brown disk, in a spiral of 4–6 turns, slightly convex, hairless or somewhat glandular-hairy, and without spines, 10–17mm in diameter, the veins indistinct.
Cultivated and fallow land, waysides.
Mediterranean region, Canary Islands, S.W. Asia.
M. scutellata (L.) Mill.: plant more or less glandular-hairy. Corolla 6–7mm long. Fruit cup-shaped, in a spiral of 4–8 turns (Mediterranean region). There are over 30 other perennial and annual species with interesting types of fruit, not always very easy to distinguish.

□■ *Medicago rugosa* Desr. (*M. elegans* Jacq. ex Willd.)
□□ 10–50cm; March–June; ⊙
A prostrate plant with simple and glandular hairs. Leaves stalked, with 3 obovate to oblanceolate leaflets, toothed in the upper part. Racemes with stalks shorter than the leaves, 1 to 5-flowered, corolla 2–4mm, yellow. Fruit shaped like a snail, without spines and becoming hairless, 6–10mm in diameter, the 2–3 turns with 15–30 thickened, radial veins.
Cultivated and fallow land.
Mediterranean region, only introduced into S.W. Europe.

□□ *Medicago marina* L. **Sea Medick**
■□ 20–50cm; April–June; ♃
A creeping or ascending plant growing in sandy places, and easily recognised by the dense silvery white hairs which cover it. Leaves stalked, with 3 obovate to wedge-shaped leaflets, toothed towards the end, stipules almost entire. Flowers pale to orange-yellow, 7–10mm long, in 5 to 12-flowered heads, which have stalks about as long as the leaves. Fruits 5–7mm in diameter, snail-shaped, in a spiral of 2–3 turns, with a small hole in the middle and with usually 2 rows of spines up to 2mm long on the back and projecting out of the dense hairy covering.
Sandy beaches, dunes.
Coasts of the Mediterranean, Black Sea, and the Atlantic as far north as Brittany, also the Canary Islands.

□□ *Medicago polymorpha* L. (*M. hispida* Gaertn., *M. polycarpa* Willd.) **Hairy Medick**
□■ 10–60cm; April–June; ⊙
A prostrate plant, hairless or sparsely hairy. Leaves stalked, with 3 obcordate to obovate leaflets with a wedge-shaped base and small teeth at the end. Flowers 1–5(–8) in small, stalked racemes, corolla yellow, 3–4.5mm long. Fruit snail-shaped, in a spiral of 1½–6 turns, usually hairless, finally dark brown, 4–10mm in diameter. Near to the line of opening and parallel to it are veins bearing 2 rows of spines, often hooked, and with a groove running between them. Spines sometimes absent. Radial veins joined, forming a network.
Cultivated and fallow land, grassy pastures.
Mediterranean region, W. Europe, Canary Islands, S.W. Asia, introduced into other areas with wool etc.
Many similar species occur in the Mediterranean region, e.g. *M. arabica* (L.) Huds.: leaflets almost always with a dark patch. *M. coronata* (L.) Bartal.: fruit 2–4mm, hairy, in a spiral of 2 turns, border broad and flat, with one row of spines pointing upwards and one row downwards.

Pea family *Papilionaceae*

■□ *Trifolium tomentosum* L. **Woolly Trefoil**
□□ 5–15cm; March–June; ☉
A very variable species, low-growing and branched at the base. Leaves stalked, with 3 obovate leaflets, wedge-shaped at the base and sharply toothed. Flowers pink, twisted, so that the standard points downwards and the keel upwards, arranged in spherical heads in the leaf-axils, enlarging to 7–14mm in diameter at fruiting time and becoming almost sessile. Calyx white-felted, the upper lip soon becoming inflated and spherical, its teeth generally hidden.
Grassy pastures, waysides.
Mediterranean region, Canary Islands, S.W. Asia.

□■ *Trifolium stellatum* L. **Star Clover**
□□ 5–25cm; March–July; ☉
Stem simple or branched from the base, with soft spreading hairs. Leaves long-stalked with 3 obcordate leaflets, toothed towards the end, and large, ovate, toothed stipules which are membranous and green-veined. Flowers in spherical to ovoid heads, 15–25mm, on stalks 3–10cm long, arising singly. The long-pointed, 3-veined calyx-teeth, twice as long as the tube, erect at first, but spreading out like a star and conspicuously red-brown on the inner surface at fruiting time, are characteristic of the species. The 10-veined calyx-tube is silky-hairy on the outer surface, and as the normally pink flowers, 8–12mm long, are hardly longer than the tube, they appear inconspicuous.
Cultivated land, waysides, open places in the garigue.
Mediterranean region, Canary Islands, S.W. Asia.
T. dasyurum Presl, in the eastern Mediterranean region, is similar: uppermost leaves almost opposite, entire. Flower-heads 20–35mm, often in pairs. Calyx-teeth 2–4 times as long as the tube.

□□ *Trifolium cherleri* L.
■□ 5–25cm; April–June; ☉
Stems prostrate or ascending, fairly thick and hairy, bearing stalked leaves composed of 3 slightly toothed, obcordate leaflets with a wedge-shaped base. Stipules oblong-ovate, shortly pointed. Flower-heads sessile, spherical, surrounded by leaves with large, roundish, leaf-like stipules. Flowes 6–8mm, white or pink, at least as long as the hairy calyx. Calyx-teeth equal, bristle-like, erect at fruiting time. Fruiting head falling in one piece.
Grassy pastures, established dunes, stony pastures.
Mediterranean region, Canary Islands, S.W. Asia.
Trifolium hirtum All. is similar: stipules lanceolate, narrowing to a long, straight point. Corolla red, longer than the calyx. Fruiting head not falling in one piece. (Mediterranean region, Canary Islands).

□□ *Trifolium angustifolium* L. **Narrow-leaved Crimson Clover**
□■ 10–60cm; April–July; ☉
Stem with appressed hairs, erect, branched at the base, the lateral shoots ascending and shorter. Leaves stalked, with 3 pointed, entire leaflets, 2–8cm long and only 2–4mm broad. Flower-heads 2–8cm long, narrowly ovoid to cylindrical arising singly on stalks 2–4cm long. Flowers all opening at the same time, pink, 10–12mm long, not or barely exceeding the calyx. Calyx-teeth bristle-like or awl-shaped, fringed with hairs, spreading out like a star at fruiting time.
Cultivated and fallow land, waysides, garigue, not found on chalky soils.
Mediterranean region, Canary Islands, S.W. Asia.
Trifolium purpureum Loisel.: Similar, but flowers opening from the bottom upwards. Corolla 16–25mm long, bright red, far exceeding the very unequal calyx-teeth (mainly in the eastern Mediterranean region). There are numerous other endemic species, some widespread, others with only a local distribution. An easily recognisable species amongst others is *Trifolium uniflorum* L. which has heads of only 1–3 flowers, corolla 15–20mm, white, purple or bicoloured (eastern Mediterranean region, westwards to Sicily and S. Italy).

Pea family *Papilionaceae*

■□
□□ *Dorycnium hirsutum* (L.) Ser.
20–50cm; April–July; ♄

A subshrub, woody at the base, usually with dense, spreading hairs. Leaves sessile, pinnate, the leaf-axis very short or absent, leaflets obovate-oblong, up to 2.5cm long. Flowers 4–10 in shortly stalked heads, corolla 1–2cm long, the standard and wings white to pink, the keel with a blunt, dark red or black tip. Wings folded lengthwise, pocket-like. Pods small, 6–12mm, hardly longer than the calyx.
Garigue, maquis, open woods.
Mediterranean region.
D. rectum (L.) Ser. has appressed hairs: Leaf-axis 5–10mm long. Flowers 5–6mm, in heads of 20–40 (Mediterranean region). The variable species *D. pentaphyllum* Scop. has very narrow leaflets and flowers 3–6mm long in heads of 5–25. Calyx-teeth unequal (Mediterranean region, also in central Europe).

□■
□□ *Lotus edulis* L.
10–40cm; February–June; ☉

A prostrate to ascending, slightly hairy plant with leaves of 5 leaflets. As in the other species of this genus, the 2 lowest leaflets are attached like stipules to the stem and are separated from the other 3, which in this species are smaller and pointed. Flowers singly or in pairs, corolla yellow, 10–16mm long, with a 3-foliate, sessile bract at the base, and with the stalk 2–3 times longer than the accompanying leaf. Calyx with 5 equal, linear-lanceolate teeth, longer than the tube. Pod conspicuous, 2–4cm long and 4–8mm broad, fleshy when young, curved slightly upwards and grooved along the back.
Cultivated and fallow land, grassy pastures.
Mediterranean region.

□□
■□ *Lotus cytisoides* L.
20–30cm; March–June; ♃

A prostrate to ascending species, frequently found in large patches. Leaves more or less hairy, often fleshy, with 5 lanceolate to ovate leaflets, the lowest pair much smaller, about as long as the leaf-axis. Flowers in 2 to 6-flowered heads, the stalks of which are 2–4 times as long as the accompanying leaves. Corolla yellow, 8–14mm, the standard notched, the keel shorter than the wings and with a shortly curved, sometimes purple beak. Calyx 2-lipped, the 2 upper teeth curving upwards, the 2 lateral ones blunt and shorter than the rest. Pod cylindrical, straight or slightly curved, 2–5cm long.
Mostly on rocky coasts.
Mediterranean region.
L. creticus L. is similar: leaves densely silvery-hairy, leaf-axis only ¼ to ½ as long as the lowest leaflets. Flowers 12–18mm long, the standard entire, the keel with a long, straight, purple beak, the lateral calyx-teeth more pointed. Mainly on sandy beaches (Mediterranean region, Canary Islands, absent in places).

□□
□■ *Lotus ornithopodioides* L.
10–50cm; April–June; ☉

An erect or ascending, branched, hairy plant. Leaves with 5 leaflets, the upper ones obovate to rhombic, the lower usually much smaller, triangular or rhombic-circular. Heads 2 to 5-flowered, surrounded by 3 sessile bracts, and usually with longer stalks than the leaves when in fruit. Corolla yellow, 7–10mm. Calyx distinctly 2-lipped, the lateral teeth much shorter than the others and rounded. Pods pendent, linear, slightly curved, 2–5cm long and 2–3mm broad, flat, and constricted between the seeds.
Grassy and stony pastures, waysides.
Mediterranean region, Canary Islands.
L. peregrinus L. is similar: inflorescence 2 to 3-flowered, its stalk thick and shorter than the accompanying leaf. Pod cylindrical, straight, barely constricted (eastern Mediterranean region). Other species are usually restricted to smaller areas.

Pea family *Papilionaceae*

■□
□□ *Tetragonolobus purpureus* Moench (*Lotus tetragonolobus* L.) **Winged Pea, Asparagus Pea**
10–40cm; March–June; ☉

An ascending to erect plant with soft, spreading hairs. Leaves as in species of *Lotus* with 5 leaflets, the terminal leaflet broadly obovate to rhombic, the 2 lowest ones smaller, pointed, ovate, and resembling stipules. Flowers singly or in pairs, 15–22mm long, scarlet, with a 3-foliate, sessile bract at the base, and the stalk shorter to about as long as the accompanying leaf. Calyx-teeth 1–2 times as long as the tube. Pod 3–9cm×6–8mm, hairless, with 4 wings, at least 2mm broad.
Cultivated land, waysides, grassy pastures, formerly occasionally grown for its edible fruits or as green fodder.
Mediterranean region, Canary Islands.
In *T. requienii* (Mauri ex Sanguin.) Sanguin. also, the stalk of the inflorescence is shorter than, to as long as, the leaves: Plant annual, flowers 1–2, corolla 13–15mm long, red, yellow or bicoloured. Pod with only 2 wings on the upper side (southern Mediterranean region). In the following 2 species the stalk of the flower or the inflorescence is at least twice as long as the leaves: *T. maritimus* (L.) Roth, plant perennial, flowers solitary with a pale yellow corolla, 25–30mm long. Calyx-teeth shorter than the tube. Pod almost hairless, with 4 wings (in damp places, Mediterranean region, uncommon in the south, northwards to S. Sweden) and *T. biflorus* (Desr.) Ser., plant annual, flowers 1–4, with an orange-yellow corolla, 17–25mm long. Pod hairy, with 4 wings (southern Mediterranean region).

□■
□□ *Hymenocarpos circinnatus* (L.) Savi **Disk Trefoil**
10–50cm; March–May; ☉

Stem with soft, spreading hairs, prostrate or ascending to erect. Lower leaves undivided, obovate-oblong, the upper ones with 2–4 pairs of leaflets and a larger terminal leaflet. Flowers 2–8 in stalked heads, yellow, 5–7mm long, with a leaf at the base. Calyx 5–6mm, the teeth narrowly linear, much longer than the tube. Plant easily recognisable by the flat, kidney-shaped pods, 1–2cm in diameter, with a winged, often toothed margin.
Fallow land, grassy pastures.
Mediterranean region, absent from the Iberian peninsula and the Balearic Islands.

□□
■□ *Anthyllis cytisoides* L.
30–80cm; April–June; ♄

A spineless subshrub with erect, almost rod-like, white or grey-felted stems. Lower leaves simple, the upper ones of 3 leaflets, the terminal leaflet narrowly elliptic, very much larger than the 2 lateral ones. Flowers solitary, in pairs or in groups of 3 in the axils of simple, broadly ovate, pointed bracts, forming a long, spike-like inflorescence. Petals pale yellow 5–8mm long. Calyx with woolly hairs, 4.5–7mm long with 5 equal teeth, which are shorter than the tube. Pod hairless, 1-seeded.
Garigue, especially near the coast.
Spain, Balearic Islands, S. France, N.W. Africa.
A. terniflora (Lag.) Pau is similar: all leaves undivided, oblong or narrowly elliptic. Calyx only 3–4.5mm long. Plant generally less robust, with fine silky hairs (Spain, Morocco).

□□
□■ *Anthyllis hermanniae* L.
10–50cm; April–July; ♄

A low, much-branched, spiny shrub with twisted, woody stems, the older ones ending in a spine, hairy at first, later more or less hairless. Leaves simple or with 3 narrowly oblong leaflets, often folded, silky-hairy especially beneath, and 1–2cm long. Flowers 2–5, more rarely solitary, with curved yellow corollas 6–9mm long arising from the leaf-axils and forming a long, interrupted inflorescence. Calyx 3–5mm, with 5 teeth of about the same length that are shorter than the silky-hairy tube. Fruit ovoid, 2–3mm, 1-seeded, hairless.
Garigue.
S. Europe, Asia Minor, absent from the Iberian peninsula and France.

Pea family *Papilionaceae*

■□ *Anthyllis barba-jovis* L. **Jupiter's Beard**
□□ 0.5–1.5(–2)m; April–June; ♄
A beautiful shrub, noticeable because of its silky hairs, with odd-pinnate leaves, the 13–19 narrowly elliptic to obovate leaflets almost equal, green and silky on the upper side, and with a silvery sheen beneath. Groups of 10 or more pale yellow flowers, 9–10mm long, from terminal heads, with a bract divided into finger-like segments at its base. Calyx hairy, 4–6mm long, with 5 more or less equal teeth that are shorter than the tube. Pod 1-seeded.
Rocks by the sea, also in gardens as a cultivated plant.
From E. Spain to the Balkan peninsula, N.W. Africa.
A. aegaea Turrill is closely related: Leaves narrowly elliptic to linear. Heads with only 5–9 flowers, calyx 6–9mm (Crete, Cyclades).

□■ *Anthyllis vulneraria* L. ssp. *praepropera* (A. Kerner) Bornm. (*A. spruneri* (Boiss.) G. Beck)
□□ 10–40cm; March–July; ☉, ♃
An ascending to erect, herbaceous plant with appressed silky hairs. Lowest leaves often consisting only of 1 ovate leaflet, the uppermost ones with 7–13 equal, narrow leaflets. Flowers red, in 1–2 dense terminal heads that are enclosed at the base by 2 palmately divided bracts. Calyx 12–13.5mm long, with 5 unequal teeth, oblique at the mouth, the tips purple, inflated at flowering time. Pod 1(2)-seeded.
Grassy and stony pastures, garigue.
S. Europe, absent in Spain and parts of Italy, Asia Minor.
In the Mediterranean region, the subspecies illustrated is one of the most widely distributed of the 30 subspecies of our native **Kidney Vetch**, the flowers ranging from yellow to whitish, orange, red or multicoloured. Some red-flowered forms, difficult to identify, are restricted to the Iberian peninsula.

□□ *Anthyllis tetraphylla* L. (*Physanthyllis tetraphylla* (L.) Boiss.) **Bladder Vetch**
■□ Creeping up to 50cm long; March–June; ☉
A prostrate plant with hairy stems and leaves, the latter odd-pinnate with at most 5 leaflets, the terminal leaflet more or less obovate and considerably larger than the lateral ones. Flowers up to 7 in a cluster in the leaf-axils, corolla pale yellow, the keel often tipped red. Characteristic of the species is the inflated, densely silky-hairy calyx, 12–15mm long, only slightly shorter than the flower and up to 12mm broad in fruit, straight at the mouth and with 5 almost equal, pointed teeth. Pod usually 2-seeded, constricted between the seeds.
Waysides, cultivated and fallow land, garigue.
Mediterranean region.

□□ *Ornithopus compressus* L.
□■ 10–50cm; February–May; ☉
A prostrate to ascending, hairy plant, branched from the base. Leaves odd-pinnate, with 15–37 elliptical or oblong-lanceolate, finely pointed leaflets. Flowers yellow, 5–8mm long, 2–5 clustered in heads on long stalks in the leaf-axils, with a bract pinnately divided into 7–9 leaflets. Calyx-teeth finally about half as long as the tube. Pod 2–5cm long, curved, and more or less compressed at the sides, not or only slightly constricted between the 5–8 segments, and with a hooked beak, 7mm long or longer, at the end.
Cultivated land, pastures, open woods.
Mediterranean region, Canary Islands.
O. pinnatus (Mill.) Druce: plant hairless or sparsely hairy. Leaflets only 7–15, linear to lanceolate. Heads of flowers without a pinnately divided bract. Pod 2–3.5cm long, curved, cylindrical, with 8–12 segments. Beak not longer than 5mm (Mediterranean region, W. Europe, Canary Islands).

Pea family *Papilionaceae*

■□
□□ *Coronilla emerus* L. **Scorpion Senna**
1–2m; April–June; ♄

A deciduous shrub with angular, green stems and green, pinnate leaves, hairless, only the young shoots, flower-stalks and calyces with scattered hairs. Leaflets 5–9, about the same size, obovate, 1–2cm long, not fleshy. Flowers mostly several together, nodding, the standard 14–22mm long, and the claws of the petals 2–3 times as long as the calyx, a distinguishing character of this species. Pods pendent, straight, and more or less cylindrical, 5–11cm long, only slightly constricted, with 3–12 segments. In ssp. *emerus* the heads are 1 to 5-flowered, and the inflorescence-stalk is about as long as the leaves; in ssp. *emeroides* (Boiss. & Sprun.) Hay. the heads have up to 8 flowers, and the inflorescence-stalk is longer than the leaves. Undergrowth, wood-margins, open woods, also cultivated.
S. Europe, northwards in places to Norway and Sweden; ssp. *emeroides* occurs in S. Italy, the Balkan peninsula, and S.W. Asia, and intermediate forms are found where the 2 subspecies meet.

□■
□□ *Coronilla juncea* L. **Rush-like Scorpion Vetch**
Up to 1m; April–June; ♄

A subshrub with furrowed, green, rush-like stems. Stem-joints long, leaves deciduous, odd-pinnate, with 3–7, almost equal, narrow, fleshy leaflets, 5–25mm long. Flowers in groups of 5–12 in crown-shaped heads on a long stalk. Petals yellow, 6–12mm long. Pods pendent, 1–5cm long, only slightly curved, 4-angled, jointed, with 2–11 segments.
Coastal garigue, cliffs.
Western Mediterranean region, eastwards to W. Yugoslavia.
C. valentina L.: plant blue-green, leaves not fleshy, evergreen, with 5–15 elliptical to obovate leaflets, notched at the tip. Flowers in groups of 4–12 with the corolla 7–12mm long. Fruits somewhat compressed, bluntly 4-angled (S. Europe, N.W. Africa).

□□
■□ *Coronilla scorpioides* (L.) Koch **Annual Scorpion Vetch**
10–40cm; March–June; ☉

A hairless, ascending to erect, blue-green annual. Leaves sessile, slightly fleshy, only the lower ones simple, the upper ones with 3 leaflets, the terminal leaflet 1–4cm long, elliptical or almost circular, much larger than the 2 lateral, circular leaflets. Stipules small, membranous, and united. Flowers 2–5 in crown-shaped heads on a stalk, about as long as the leaf, arising in the leaf-axils, corolla pale yellow, 4–8mm long. Pods 2–6cm, thin, strongly curved, the 2–11 segments straight with 4–6 blunt angles.
Cultivated and fallow land, garigue.
Mediterranean region, S.W. Asia.
C. repanda (Poir.) Guss. is similar but the upper leaves are odd-pinnate with 5–7 oblong leaflets, all about the same size, and with a blunt or notched tip. Sections of the pod distinctly curved (southern Mediterranean region).

□□
□■ *Hippocrepis unisiliquosa* L.
5–40cm; March–June; ☉

A small, prostrate to ascending plant. Leaves with 7–15 linear to obovate leaflets, 2–12mm long. The yellow flowers, 4–7mm long, are usually solitary, more rarely in pairs or groups of 3, very shortly stalked (less than 5mm) in the upper leaf-axils. Fruit laterally compressed, only slightly curved, 1.5–4cm long, with horseshoe-shaped segments, hairless or sparsely warted.
Cultivated land, pastures, garigue.
Mediterranean region, S.W. Asia.
Two other annual species occur in the Mediterranean region: *H. multisiliquosa* L., flowers 5–8mm long, in 2 to 6-flowered heads with stalks about as long as the leaves. Fruits curved, 2–4cm long, hairless or with a few small tubercles. *H. ciliata* Willd., heads also of 2–6 flowers and stalked. Corolla only 3–5mm long. Fruits curved, 1.5–2.5cm long, warted round the edge of the horseshoe-shaped segments.

Pea family *Papilionaceae*

■☐ *Scorpiurus muricatus* L.
☐☐ 5–60cm; April–June; ☉
Stems prostrate to ascending, more or less hairy. Leaves simple, spathulate, narrowed gradu-ally into the stalk, with 3–5 parallel veins, 3–10cm long. Flowers usually 2–5 in long-stalked heads, corolla yellow, 5–10mm long. The genus received its name because of the very vari-able, characteristic, spirally twisted pods, often with tubercles or spines on the outer ribs. Seeds semicircular. A variable species.
Cultivated and fallow land, waysides.
Mediterranean region, Canary Islands, S.W. Asia.
S. vermiculatus L. is similar, with usually solitary, rarely pairs of flowers, 10–20mm long. Outer ribs of the pods with short, flattened swellings. Seeds elliptical (western Mediterra-nean region, Canary Islands).

☐■ *Hedysarum coronarium* L. **Italian Sainfoin, French Honeysuckle**
☐☐ 0.3–1m; April–June; ☉, ☉, ♃
A robust, herbaceous, ascending to erect plant with scattered, appressed hairs. Leaves with 5–11 broadly ovate leaflets, 1.5–3.5cm long, almost hairless on the upper side, and with appressed hairs beneath, stipules free. The bright carmine-red flowers, 12–15mm long, are in groups of 10–35 and form a conspicuous, erect, dense, long-shaped inflorescence on a long stalk. Calyx sparsely to densely hairy, the 5 teeth about as long as the tube. Pod flat, con-stricted between the 2–4 seeds, with or without small spines.
Cultivated and fallow land, waysides, also grown as fodder or as an ornamental plant, some-times escaping and becoming naturalised.
Mediterranean region, in places only introduced.

☐☐ *Hedysarum spinosissimum* L.
■☐ 10–40cm; April–May; ☉
A delicate, prostrate plant with appressed hairs. Leaves with (5–)9–17 narrow, almost hair-less or hairy leaflets, 5–12mm long. Flowers 2–10 in long-stalked, head-like racemes. Corolla white to pale pink, 8–11mm long, 1½–2 times as long as the calyx. Calyx 4–6mm, the teeth as long as or longer than the tube. Pod flat, constricted between the 2–4 seeds, with woolly hairs and hooked spines.
Garigue, steppes.
Mediterranean region.
H. glomeratum Dietr. (*H. capitatum* Desf.) is similar, also an annual, leaflets 17–21, elliptic to obovate. Inflorescence a head of flowers up to 3cm across. Flowers with a rose-red corolla, 14–20mm long, 2½ to 5 times as long as the calyx. Pod usually with 2 seeds (S. Europe, N.W. Africa).

☐☐ *Onobrychis caput-galli* (L.) Lam. **Cockscomb Sainfoin**
☐■ 10–90cm; April–July; ☉
A slender, hairless or sparsely hairy, prostrate to erect plant. Leaves odd-pinnate, the 9–17 leaflets narrowly oblong, 4–20×2–6mm. Flowers 2–5, in small racemes with stalks about as long as the leaves at flowering time. Corolla purple, 5–8mm, only slightly longer than the calyx, calyx-teeth 2–4 times as long as the tube. Fruit a flat, hairy, semicircular pod, 6–10mm, with a fringe of numerous, awl-shaped teeth, 2–5mm long, on the margin, and a network of veins on the 2 sides bearing teeth similar to those on the margin, 1-seeded.
Cultivated and fallow land, waysides.
Mediterranean region, absent from the Balearic Islands, Corsica and Sardinia.
O. aequidentata (Sibth. & Sm.) D'Urv. is similar but the inflorescence-stalks are much longer than the leaves. Corolla larger, 10–14mm. Pod with 4–7 broadly triangular teeth on the mar-gin, much larger than those on the sides (S. Europe, Near East).

Wood-sorrel family *Oxalidaceae*
Geranium family *Geraniaceae*
Caltrop family *Zygophyllaceae*

■□ *Oxalis pes-caprae* L. (*O. cernua* Thunb.) **Bermuda Buttercup, Cape Sorrel** *Oxalidaceae*
□□ 10–50cm; December–May; ♃
A subterranean stem, which breaks up into bulbils, gives rise to a rosette of long-stalked, clover-like leaves up to 20cm long, leaflets deeply obcordate. The long-stalked inflorescence consists of 6–12 funnel-shaped flowers, nodding in bud, and arranged like an umbel. Petals 5, lemon-yellow, 2–2.5cm long. Fruiting capsules are rarely formed, since, of the 3 possible forms of the flower with styles and stamens of varying lengths, only one occurs in the Mediterranean region, and so pollination is not possible. In this area reproduction is exclusively by means of the bulbils.
On cultivated land, mainly amongst trees, in places dominating the landscape at flowering time; the double form is also occasionally grown, sometimes escaping and growing wild.
Native in S. Africa, introduced into the Mediterranean region and elsewhere in the 19th century and becoming naturalised.

□■ *Erodium malacoides* (L.) L'Hér. **Soft Storksbill** *Geraniaceae*
□□ 10–60cm; February–June; ☉, ○
Stems spreading to erect, with recurved, often glandular hairs. Leaves stalked, ovate to oblong with a heart-shaped base, crenate-serrate or shallowly lobed, 2–10×1–5cm. Flowers 3–10, forming an umbel-like inflorescence, on long glandular hairy stalks, with several ovate to circular, whitish bracts at the base. Petals 5, pink, not notched, 5–9mm long. Sepals 5, glandular-hairy, 5–7mm long. Partial fruits 5mm, with white or brownish hairs; at the base of the beak is a groove, and below that a ring-like constriction, both covered with minute glands. Beak only 2–3cm long, twisting corkscrew-like after separating from the axis.
Fallow land, waysides, grassy pastures.
Mediterranean region, Canary Islands, S.W. Asia.
E. chium (L.) Willd.: very similar, but the bracts brown, ovate and pointed. Partial fruits 3.5–4.5mm, without a ring-like construction below the groove at the end, beak 3–4cm (Mediterranean region, Canary Islands).

□□ *Fagonia cretica* L. *Zygophyllaceae*
■□ 10–40cm; April–June; ♃
A prostrate plant with stiff, spreading branches, and opposite, stalked leaves with 3 leaflets. Leaflets 5–15mm long, leathery, lanceolate, spine-tipped and asymmetrical. Stipules spiny, shorter than the leaf-stalks. The attractive, stalked flowers, produced singly in the leaf-axils, are 1–2cm across with 5 clawed, red-purple petals and 5 deciduous sepals. Fruits with persistent style about 1cm long, composed of 5 sharply angled cells with fringed margins.
Garigue, stony pastures.
S. Europe, N. Africa, Canary Islands.

□□ *Zygophyllum fabago* L. **Syrian Bean-caper** *Zygophyllaceae*
□■ 0.3–1m; May–August; ♃
An erect, hairless plant. Leaves opposite, each with a pair of obovate to elliptic, asymmetrical, fleshy leaflets, between which there is often a small extension of the leaf-axis. Flowers solitary in the leaf-axils, with 5 white-edged sepals and 5 oblong-ovate petals, whitish above and red-orange beneath. Stamens 10, orange, much longer than the petals. Fruit a pendent, cylindrical and angled capsule, 2–3.5cm long. In former times the flower-buds, pickled in vinegar, were used as capers.
Waste ground, waysides.
Eastern Mediterranean region, northwards to Romania, S. Russia, S.W. Asia to Egypt, occasionally naturalised in the west.

Caltrop family *Zygophyllaceae*
Flax family *Linaceae*
Spurge family *Euphorbiaceae*

■□ *Tribulus terrestris* L. **Maltese Cross, Small Caltrops** *Zygophyllaceae*
□□ 10–60cm; May–September; ☉
A prostrate, more or less densely hairy plant. Leaves opposite, often of unequal size, with 5–8
pairs of obliquely ovate-oblong leaflets, 0.6–1.2cm long. Flowers with 5 yellow petals, 4–
5mm, produced singly in the leaf-axils on stalks 2–4mm long. Fruit composed of 5 triangular
partial fruits, arranged like a star, that have tubercles ending in a bristle on the back, and usually 2 stout, spiny outgrowths on each side.
Several subspecies.
Cultivated and fallow land, waysides, often on sandy soils.
Mediterranean region, Canary Islands, S.E. Europe, introduced into other warm regions
throughout the world.

□■ *Linum maritimum* L. *Linaceae*
□□ 20–80cm; May–September; ♄
A tall, usually hairless plant, with several erect to ascending, slender, finely grooved stems.
Leaves sessile, narrowly elliptic to lanceolate, 2–4mm broad, the lower ones opposite and 3-
veined at the base, the middle and upper ones alternate and 1-veined. Flowers with their parts
in fives in a loose, panicle-like inflorescence. Petals yellow, 8–15mm long, sepals ovate,
pointed, 3mm long, indistinctly fringed at the margin. Stigma club-shaped. Capsule about as
long as the sepals.
Saltmarshes, coastal areas.
Mediterranean region, absent from some places in the east. Two other species also have yellow flowers, but these are annuals, less tall, and usually flower earlier in the year: *L. strictum*
L., all leaves alternate, finely serrate on the margin, often recurved. Petals 6–12mm, sepals 4–
6mm, stigma spherical, and *L. trigynum* L. (*L. gallicum* L.), all leaves alternate, with smooth
margins. Petals 4–6mm, sepals 3–4mm, stigma linear (both species in almost the whole of the
Mediterranean region).

□□ *Chrozophora tinctoria* (L.) A. Juss. (*Croton tinctorium* L.) **Turn-sole** *Euphorbiaceae*
■□ 10–50cm; May–October; ☉
A branched, grey-green plant with star-shaped hairs but without milky juice. Leaves stalked,
2–9cm long, ovate to rhombic, wedge-shaped at the base, entire or sinuately toothed. Male
and female flowers separate on the same plant, inconspicuous, the male grouped in small,
erect racemes, the female solitary or up to 4 together, on long stalks at the base of the inflorescence. Formerly used as a source of a dye.
Cultivated and fallow land, often near the coast.
Mediterranean region, S.W. Asia.
C. obliqua (Vahl) A. Juss. ex Spreng.: Plant densely white-felted with star-shaped hairs.
Leaves cut off squarely or almost heart-shaped at the base. Stamens 4–5 (southern Mediterranean region, S.W. Asia).

□□ *Ricinus communis* L. **Castor Oil Plant** *Euphorbiaceae*
□■ 0.5–4m; February–October; ☉ to ♄
A quick-growing plant, sometimes as big as a tree, with male and female flowers separate.
Leaves palmately divided into 5–9 lobes. Flowers in erect panicles, the male with branched
yellow stamens, the female with bright red stigmas, petals inconspicuous. Fruit a 3-celled
capsule, up to 2cm long, usually spiny, with 3 shining, mottled, bean-like seeds. The fatty oil
obtained from the seeds is of great technical importance as a lubricant, and with the poisonous proteins removed, is used also for medicinal (as a laxative) and cosmetic purposes. 5–20
seeds are fatal to human beings.
An ornamental plant, growing wild on roadsides and waste ground.
Naturalised in the Mediterranean region, much cultivated in the subtropics and tropics,
native in tropical Africa.

Spurge family *Euphorbiaceae*

■□ *Euphorbia peplis* L. **Purple Spurge**
□□ Spreading 5–40cm long; May–October; ☉
A slightly fleshy, hairless plant with usually 4 prostrate branches. Leaves opposite, blue-green, characteristically asymmetrical, ovate to oblong or sickle-shaped, rounded or notched at the end, 0.5–1.5cm long, with stalks 2–3mm long. Stipules inconspicuous, awl-shaped. Flower-heads solitary in the leaf-axils. Glands semicircular, reddish brown, with small, paler appendages. Capsule hairless, 3–5mm, seeds about 3mm, ovoid, smooth.
Sandy beaches, uncommon inland.
Coasts of the Mediterranean region, W. Europe, Canary Islands, Black Sea and Caspian Sea.
E. chamaesyce L.: A dwarf species, with very small, roundish, slightly asymmetrical, opposite leaves. Capsule hairless or with dense, spreading hairs, 2mm. Seeds wrinkled, 1.2mm, 4-angled (Mediterranean region, S. and central Russia, S.W. Asia).

□■ *Euphorbia dendroides* L. **Tree Spurge**
□□ 0.5–2(–3)m; April–June; ♄
A tall, hairless, rounded shrub, often with a trunk as thick as the arm and regular, forked branches. Leaves at the ends of the stems from autumn until about May, falling with the onset of the dry period, oblong-lanceolate, rounded at the end but with a short point, 25–65×3–8mm. Inflorescence an umbel, with 5–8(–10) rays. Ray-leaves at the base somewhat broader and shorter than the leaves. Nectar-glands roundish, irregularly lobed. Fruit-capsule 5–6mm, 3-angled, seeds 3mm, laterally compressed, smooth, grey.
On rocks near the coast, often forming colonies, mainly on chalk.
Local throughout the Mediterranean region.
Similar tree-species of spurge occur only in the Canary Islands and in Africa.

□□ *Euphorbia acanthothamnos* Heldr. & Sart. ex Boiss. **Greek Spiny Spurge**
■□ 10–35cm; March–May; ♄
A low, hairless, much-branched shrub forming rounded cushions, very spiny because of the previous year's umbel-rays that harden as they wither and become sharply pointed. Leaves bright green, elliptical, 0.5–2cm long and 2–5mm broad, ray-leaves at the base of the inflorescence like the stem-leaves. Umbels usually 3-rayed, the rays often forked 2 or 3 times. Raylet-leaves obovate, yellowish. Capsule 3–4mm, with short, cylindrical tubercles. Seeds 2mm, brown, smooth.
Garigue.
Greece and islands, W. Anatolia.
E. spinosa L. adjoins the distribution area of *E. acanthothamnos* on its western side: Withered rays of the umbel persistent, but not sharply pointed. Leaves blue-green, lanceolate, 5–15mm long. Ray-leaves obovate, much broader than the stem-leaves and about as long as the 1–5 rays, each of which bears one flower-head. Capsule 3–4mm, often with long, conical tubercles. Seeds 2–3mm, smooth (mainly in the montane and subalpine zone, S. Europe from S. France to Albania).

□□ *Euphorbia myrsinites* L. **Broad-leaved Glaucous Spurge**
□■ Up to 40cm; March–August; ♃
A stout, hairless, blue-green, fleshy plant with simple, prostrate or ascending, very densely leaved stems. Leaves obovate to spathulate, pointed. Inflorescence an umbel with 5–12 rays, ray-leaves broadly ovate to circular with an abrupt point. Nectar-glands with short, broad horns. Capsule hairless, smooth or with minute tubercles, seeds usually rough. A variable species.
Stony pastures, garigue, waysides, open woods, also grown as an ornamental plant.
S. Europe from the Balearic Islands to the Crimea, Asia Minor and to the Persian Gulf.
Euphorbia rigida Bieb. (*E. biglandulosa* Desf.): stem woody at the base, ascending to erect, with paler grey-green, lanceolate, pointed leaves. Seeds smooth (southern and eastern Mediterranean region).

Spurge family *Euphorbiaceae*

■☐ *Euphorbia biumbellata* Poir. **Whorled Spurge**
☐☐ 30–80cm; April–June; ⌘
An erect, hairless species, occasionally branched at the base and striking because of the 2, rarely 3 umbels, standing above each other, each with 8–21 rays, separated by leafless portions of the stem. Leaves numerous, linear to linear-lanceolate with a short, abrupt point, ray-leaves at the base of the inflorescence lanceolate to ovate-triangular. Raylet-leaves kidney-shaped. Nectar-glands with long horns, broadened and club-shaped. Capsule 3–4mm, finely warted, seeds finely wrinkled.
Rocky and sandy places near the coast, also open woods and thickets.
Western Mediterranean region to Italy and Sicily.

☐■ *Euphorbia pithyusa* L.
☐☐ 20–70cm; May–September; ⌘, ♄
A blue-green plant, branched at the base and often woody, finely warted (lens needed), with ascending or erect stems bearing up to 20 lateral branches in the leaf-axils, that occasionally form a whorl. Leaves very numerous and overlapping, 5–28mm long, linear-lanceolate, pointed, curved in the lower part of the stem. Ray-leaves at the base of the 5 to 8-rayed umbel ovate with an abrupt point, entire or irregularly serrate. Raylet-leaves obliquely ovate to almost circular. Nectar-glands sometimes with horns. Capsule finely warted.
Ssp. *pithyusa*: sandy beaches and coastal rocks in the western Mediterranean region from the Balearic Islands to Italy, and ssp. *cupanii* (Guss. ex Bertol.) A.R. Sm.: shrubby and stony places inland. Islands of the western Mediterranean region to Sicily.

☐☐ *Euphorbia paralias* L. **Sea Spurge**
■☐ 20–70cm; May–September; ⌘
A stiffly erect, blue-green, hairless plant, somewhat fleshy, and branched at the base. Leaves very numerous, overlapping, 0.3–3cm long, oblong-elliptic, the upper ones ovate like the ray-leaves of the umbel. The latter with 3–6 rays, branched in the axils of leaves with up to 9 lateral branches. Raylet-leaves kidney-shaped. Nectar-glands notched with short horns. Capsule 4.5–6mm broad, hairless, finely warted. Seeds 2.5–3.5mm, smooth.
Sandy and shingly beaches.
Coasts of the Mediterranean region, Black Sea, W. Europe and the Canary Islands.

☐☐ *Euphorbia characias* L. **Large Mediterranean Spurge**
☐■ 0.3–0.8(–1.8)m; February–July; ⌘, ♄
A stately, usually hairy species, woody at the base and with stout, erect, unbranched stems. Leaves in the upper part of the stem densely clustered, some bending downwards, up to 13cm long and 1cm broad, linear to lanceolate, entire. The long inflorescence is composed of a terminal umbel with 10–20(–40) rays and 13–40 rays arising from the leaf-axils. Ray-leaves at the base of the umbel like the upper stem-leaves, raylet-leaves circular-triangular, joined in pairs to form a dish-shaped structure. Fruit-capsule 5–7mm, smooth, softly hairy, seeds 2.5–3.8mm, ovoid, silver-grey. The plant illustrated is ssp. *characias*, with dark red-brown nectar-glands and short horns, plant about 80cm high; ssp. *wulfenii* (Hoppe ex Koch) A.R. Sm. has yellowish nectar-glands and usually long horns. Plant generally taller, up to 1.8m.
Maquis, open woods, pastures, waysides.
Ssp. *characias*: from Portugal to Yugoslavia, Morocco, Cyrenaica; ssp. *wulfenii*: from Italy to Asia Minor.

Rue family *Rutaceae*
Cneorum family *Cneoraceae*

■□ *Ruta chalepensis* L. (*R. bracteosa* DC.) **Fringed Rue** *Rutaceae*
□□ 20–60cm; April–July; ♃, ♄
A strongly aromatic, usually hairless plant, branched at the base. Leaves bipinnate, with bluntly pointed, oblong or obovate segments. Bracts broader than the stems to which they are attached. Inflorescence almost always without glands, cymose, usually with a central, 5-petalled flower surrounded by 4-petalled ones. Petals yellow-green, fringed at the margin.
Garigue, stony pastures, waysides, also grown as an ornamental plant.
Mediterranean region, Canary Islands, eastwards to Arabia.
R. angustifolia Pers.: petals fringed, inflorescence glandular. Bracts hardly broader than the stems to which they are attached (Mediterranean region, eastwards to N.W. Yugoslavia). *R. montana* (L.) L.: petals entire, undulate, inflorescence glandular. Leaf-segments linear (Mediterranean region, local. Flowering in summer).

□■ *Citrus limon* (L.) Burm. f. **Lemon** *Rutaceae*
□□ 2–7m; January–December; ♄
A low-growing, evergreen tree, with stout spines in the axils of the young shoots. Leaves broadly elliptic, pointed, irregularly crenate-serrate. Leaf-stalk only slightly winged, distinctly separated from the blade. Flowers solitary or in few-flowered racemes, with usually 5 white petals, tinged reddish on the outer side, and 25–40 stamens. Ripe fruits nipple-shaped at the end, with a relatively thin rind, and acid pulp.
Cultivated in the Mediterranean region and other areas with a similar climate, native in S.E. Asia.
C. medica L., **Citron**: leaf-stalk not winged, not clearly separated from the blade. Fruits larger, with a very thick, wrinkled rind.

□□ *Citrus sinensis* (L.) Osb. **Sweet Orange** *Rutaceae*
■□ 2–5m; April–October; ♄
A small, evergreen tree with a rounded crown, and with thin spines produced singly in the axils of the young shoots. Leaves dark green, broadly elliptic, pointed, rounded at the base, indistinctly crenate. Stalk narrowly winged, lateral veins barely visible, oblanceolate in outline. Flowers solitary or in small clusters, with usually 5 thickish, white, strongly scented petals and about 20 stamens.
Cultivated in the Mediterranean region since the 16th century, native in China.
The following species also originate in S.E. Asia: *C. aurantium* L., **Seville Orange**, leaf-stalk more broadly winged, the wings often with lateral veins. Fruit like the Sweet Orange, but with thicker, rougher, more bitter rind, pulp sour; used for making orangeade and orange marmalade. The ethereal oil of the flowers and the rind is used by the pharmaceutical industry and in the manufacture of perfume. *C. deliciosa* Ten., **Tangerine, Mandarin**: leaves narrowly elliptic, only 4–5×1–2cm. Rind thin, loosely attached to the pulp. *C. bergamia* Risso & Poit., **Bergamot Orange**: fruits smooth, pale yellow, pear-shaped, and inedible, cultivated in Sicily and Calabria for its sweet-smelling ethereal oil. *C. paradisi* Macf., **Grapefruit**, and *C. grandis* (L.) Osb., **Pomelo** or **Shaddock**, have very broad, obcordately winged leaf-stalks.

□□ *Cneorum tricoccon* L. *Cneoraceae*
□■ 0.3–1.3m; March–June; ♄
A small, hairless, evergreen shrub with thick, sessile leaves, 1–3cm long and 3–7mm broad, rounded at the end and narrowed at the base, with indistinct lateral veins. Flowers shortly stalked, solitary or 2–3 together in the upper leaf-axils, with 3, sometimes 4, yellowish petals, 5mm long. A striking feature of the plant is the red, later black, fruits, that split into 3(4) spherical portions, each about 5mm across.
Maquis, evergreen woods, often on chalky soils.
S. Europe from Spain to central Italy, absent from Corsica.

Milkwort family *Polygalaceae*
Coriaria family *Coriariaceae*
Cashew family *Anacardiaceae*

Polygala nicaeensis Risso ex Koch *Polygalaceae*
15–40cm; April–July; ⚃

Stems mostly ascending, woody at the base. Lower leaves obovate-lanceolate, middle and upper ones linear-lanceolate, longer than the lower. Flowers 8–40, pink, more rarely blue or white, in loose, terminal racemes 3–15cm long. Bracts slightly exceeding the flower-buds, deciduous. Two of the 5 sepals petal-like (wings), large, 8–11mm, 3 to 5-veined. Corolla-tube about half as long as the wings, shorter than the free part of the petals. Fruit-capsule shorter than the wings. A very variable species with numerous subspecies.
Garigue, maquis, open woods.
S. and S.E. Europe, N.W. Africa, but absent from the Balearic Islands, Sardinia, Sicily and Crete.

Coriaria myrtifolia L. **Mediterranean Coriaria** *Coriariaceae*
1–3m; April–July; ♄

A hairless shrub with erect, 4-angled stems. Leaves opposite, more rarely in whorls of 3 or 4, almost sessile, leathery, ovate-lanceolate, pointed, 3–6cm long, with 3 main veins (*Myrtus communis* L., see p. 162, has 1 main vein and is dotted with pale glands). Flowers 5-petalled, in short racemes. Petals greenish, shorter than the sepals, both enlarged at fruiting-time, dark red-brown and fleshy, compressed between the ring of carpels. Fruit berry-like, ribbed, finally becoming black and shining, very poisonous. Leaves used in former times for tanning and dyeing.
Open woods, thickets, hedges.
Western Mediterranean region to N. Italy, not on Corsica or Sardinia.

Rhus coriaria L. **Sumach** *Anacardiaceae*
1–3m; May–August; ♄

Shrub or small tree with milky sap. Stems with fine hairs. Leaves pinnate, 10–20cm long, with 7–21 sessile leaflets 1–5cm long, ovate-lanceolate, coarsely crenate-serrate, softly hairy. Leaf-axis winged at least at the upper end. Flowers in dense, erect, hairy panicles, 10–20cm long. Petals 5, whitish, about twice as long as the calyx. Fruits brown-red, hairy, poisonous in the raw state. Formerly used for tanning and dyeing.
In the undergrowth of open woods and thickets, mainly on chalk, also cultivated, sometimes escaping and growing wild.
Mediterranean region, S.W. Asia, Canary Islands, not on the Balearic Islands, Corsica or Sardinia.
Two species with digitate leaves extend from N. Africa to Sicily: *R. pentaphylla* (Jacq.) Desf., leaflets 3–5 and *R. tripartita* (Ucria) Grande, leaflets always 3. The **Stag's-horn Sumach**, *R. typhina* L., that is also frequently planted in our gardens, is naturalised here and there in S. Europe (native in N. America).

Cotinus coggygria Scop. (*Rhus cotinus* L.) **Wig Tree, Smoke Tree, Venetian Sumach**
Anacardiaceae
1–3(–5)m; May–July; ♄

An aromatic, hairless shrub. The long-stalked, ovate-circular, entire leaves, 3–8cm long, and bluish green beneath, become a handsome dark red colour in autumn. Small, 5-petalled, yellow-green flowers form much-branched, erect, terminal panicles, 15–20cm long. The inflorescences contain numerous flower-stalks lacking fertile flowers. At fruiting-time the stalks lengthen, and, being covered with feathery, purple hairs, give the fruit-cluster the appearance of a wig. The plant is very rich in tannin, and was used in former times for tanning and dyeing, and medicinally for gargling and to staunch the blood.
Open woods and thickets, mainly on chalk, frequently grown as an ornamental plant.
S. Europe, from S.E. France to S.W. Asia.

Cashew family *Anacardiaceae*
Maple family *Aceraceae*

■□
□□ *Pistacia terebinthus* L. **Turpentine Tree, Terebinth** *Anacardiaceae*
2–5m; April–July; ♄
A deciduous, aromatic shrub or small tree with odd-pinnate leaves, the 3–9 leaflets ovate, 2–8.5cm long, with a short, abrupt point. Leaf-axis not winged. Male and female flowers on separate plants, in long panicles, brownish. Fruits 5–7mm, red at first, brownish later.
Open woods, maquis, growing up into the mountain zone, mostly on chalk.
Mediterranean region, in the eastern part ssp. *palaestina* (Boiss.) Engl.
The following 2 species are deciduous trees: *P. vera* L., with leaves of 1–3 leaflets, leaf-stalk hairy. Native in Asia, but cultivated elsewhere for its edible seeds up to 25mm long, known as pistachio nuts. *P. atlantica* Desf.: leaves with 5–11 oblong leaflets, without a short, abrupt point. Leaf-stalk hairy, leaf-axis narrowly winged (N. Africa, eastern Mediterranean region to Pakistan, Canary Islands).

□■
□□ *Pistacia lentiscus* L. **Mastic Tree, Lentisc** *Anacardiaceae*
1–3(–8)m; March–June; ♄
Evergreen shrub or more rarely a small tree, remaining dark green even during the most severe summer drought. Leaves even-pinnate, of 8–12 elliptic-lanceolate, blunt leaflets, up to 5cm long, with a short, abrupt point. Leaf-axis broadly winged. Male and female flowers on separate plants, in short, dense inflorescences in the leaf-axils, the male flowers conspicuous with their dark red anthers, the female greenish. Fruits about 4mm, red, later black. The resin mastic, obtained from cultivated trees, especially on the island of Chios, has a technical use as a gum or adhesive for securing bandages, and in the eastern Mediterranean region it is chewed to sweeten the breath.
Common in garigue, maquis and woods.
Mediterranean region, Canary Islands.
P.×saportae Burnat (*P. lentiscus×terebinthus*): Evergreen hybrid between the two species, recorded from several countries.

□□
■□ *Schinus molle* L. **Californian Pepper Tree, Peruvian Mastic Tree** *Anacardiaceae*
4–8m; April–August; ♄
Evergreen tree or shrub with slender, overhanging stems. Leaves long, narrow, aromatic, with 15–27 linear-lanceolate, entire or serrate, sessile leaflets, 2.5–6cm long and 3–8mm broad. Flowers small, yellowish white, 5-petalled, in much-branched, hanging panicles. Fruits pink, 6–7mm in diameter, remaining on the tree throughout the winter, tasting of pepper. Often planted as a decorative tree, occasionally becoming naturalised. Native in central and S. America.
S. terebinthifolia Raddi resembles *Pistacia terebinthus* L.: branches not pendent. Leaves with only 2–4 pairs of leaflets, 1–2cm broad, leaf-axis winged in the upper part. Fruits shining, red (planted in S.W. Europe and naturalised in places, native in S. America).

□□
□■ *Acer monspessulanum* L. **Montpelier Maple** *Aceraceae*
Up to 6(–12)m; April–May; ♄
Deciduous shrub or tree. Leaves with stalks 2–6cm long, coarse, shining above, rather grey-green beneath, softly hairy, becoming hairless, divided halfway into 3 usually entire lobes, 3–8cm long. Flowers few together, the clusters at first erect, later somewhat pendent. Petals 5, yellow-green, 4–5mm long. Fruits becoming hairless, with almost parallel wings.
Deciduous woods, thickets.
Mediterranean region (absent from the Balearic Islands and Crete), rarely extending into central Europe; S.W. Asia.
The evergreen species *A. sempervirens* L. is similar: Leaves with stalks only 1cm long, and with the blade 3-lobed or undivided, more undulate and sometimes toothed on the margin, greener beneath, hairless, 2–5cm long. Flowers in erect clusters. Wings of the fruit almost parallel or diverging at an acute angle (Greece to S. Anatolia).

Box family *Buxaceae*
Buckthorn family *Rhamnaceae*

■☐ *Buxus sempervirens* L. **Box** *Buxaceae*
☐☐ 2–5(–8)m; March–April; ♄
Evergreen shrub or small tree. The opposite, shortly stalked, leathery leaves are a shining dark green above and paler beneath, with the margin somewhat recurved, 1.5–3cm long. Flowers in clusters in the leaf-axils, each cluster consisting of a central, whitish, female flower, with usually 5 or 6 petals, surrounded by several sessile, greenish yellow male flowers with 4 petals. Diameter of inflorescence about 5mm. Style less than half as long as the capsule that finally becomes dark brown. The plant contains poisonous alkaloids.
Evergreen and deciduous woods, cultivated since ancient times in many garden forms.
Mediterranean region to W. and central Europe, S.W. Asia, elsewhere escaping from cultivation and growing wild.
B. balearica Lam.: stems stouter, leaves 2.5–4cm long, less shining above and paler green. Inflorescence about 10mm in diameter, male flowers stalked. Style almost as long as the capsule (Sardinia, Balearic Islands, locally in S. and E. Spain, N.W. Africa).

☐■ *Paliurus spina-christi* Mill. **Christ's Thorn, Jerusalem Thorn** *Rhamnaceae*
☐☐ 2–3m; May–September; ♄
Deciduous shrub with rather overhanging, zigzag stems, hairy when young. Leaves alternate, shortly stalked, arranged almost in 2 ranks, with an obliquely ovate, indistinctly crenate-serrate, 3-veined, pale green blade, 2–4cm long. The pairs of stipules are modified into spines, the longer one straight, the shorter one curved. Flowers greenish yellow, with 5 petals, about 2mm across, in small racemes in the leaf-axils. Fruits unmistakable, yellow-brown, dry, surrounded by a membranous, wavy margin, 1.5–3cm in diameter. Possibly used for Christ's crown of thorns.
Open woods, thickets, hedges.
Mediterranean region (absent from the large islands), eastwards to central Asia.

☐☐ *Ziziphus lotus* (L.) Lam. *Rhamnaceae*
■☐ 0.5–2.5m; April–August; ♄
An impenetrable, deciduous, spiny shrub, with zigzag, hairless, pale grey stems. Leaves alternate, very shortly stalked, ovate-oblong to broadly elliptic, 1–2cm long, with shallowly rounded, glandular teeth on the margin. At the point of attachment of each leaf are 2 spines, one long and straight, the other short and curved. Flowers with 5 petals, yellow-green, 3–4mm, solitary or few together in the leaf-axils, flower-stalks much longer than the calyces. Fruit almost spherical, 0.8–1cm, fleshy, yellow-orange when ripe, edible but insipid in taste.
Dry pastures, steppes.
Southern edge of the Mediterranean region, in Europe only in S. Spain, Sicily and Greece.

☐☐ *Rhamnus alaternus* L. **Mediterranean Buckthorn** *Rhamnaceae*
☐■ 1–3(–5)m; March–April; ♄
Evergreen, spineless shrub, the male and female flowers on separate plants. Leaves very variable, alternate (compare *Phillyrea latifolia* L. with opposite leaves, see p. 178), lanceolate to ovate, pointed or rounded, distantly toothed or entire, dark green above with prominent veins, pale green beneath, 1–6cm long, with a stalk 1–8mm long. Inflorescence a raceme, flowers without petals, but with usually 5 yellowish sepals, about 4mm long. Fruits about 5mm, red at first, later black.
Garigue, maquis, woods, mainly on chalk, also grown as an ornamental shrub.
Mediterranean region, Canary Islands.
The variable, deciduous or evergreen species *R. lycioides* L. is spiny: leaves opposite and clustered, linear or obovate. Calyx with 4 pointed segments (Mediterranean region, absent from Corsica, Italy and Yugoslavia).

Mallow family *Malvaceae*

■□ *Lavatera cretica* L.
□□ 0.2–1.5m; March–June; ☉, ☉
Plant erect or ascending, with star-shaped hairs. Lower leaves up to 20cm, long stalked, roundish to heart-shaped in outline, with 5–7 short, rounded, crenate-serrate lobes. Flowers in groups of 2–8 in the leaf-axils, their stalks of varying length, but shorter than the leaf-stalk, entirely without simple hairs. Petals 1–2cm long, lilac, deeply notched. Sepals 6–8mm, broadly triangular-ovate, pointed, surrounded by an outer calyx consisting of 3 broadly ovate, pointed segments, 6mm long, and united only at the base. Partial fruits 7–12, smooth or lightly ribbed, rounded on the edges.
Waysides, waste ground, fallow land.
Mediterranean region, W. Europe, northwards to S.W. England, Canary Islands.
One species similar to the above and often mistaken for it is *Malva sylvestris* L. It is variable in form and has both simple and star-shaped hairs. Segments of the outer calyx oblong-lanceolate, much narrower than in *Lavatera cretica*, and free to the base. Partial fruits sharply edged, wrinkled (Europe, N. Africa, S.W. Asia).

□■ *Lavatera arborea* L. **Tree Mallow**
□□ 1–3m; April–June; ☉
Plant woody in the lower part, the young growth felted with star-shaped hairs. Leaves roundish, with 5–7 short lobes and heart-shaped at the base, up to 20cm, with long stalks. Flowers 2–7 in racemes, their stalks shorter than the leaf-stalk. Petals 15–20mm long, lilac, with darker veins and base. Sepals about 4mm long, triangular, pointed, surrounded by an outer calyx twice as long, consisting of 3 segments united at the base that become considerably enlarged. Partial fruits 6–8, hairless or felted, angular.
Coastal rocks, waste ground, also cultivated as an ornamental plant, occasionally escaping and growing wild.
Coasts of W. Europe, N.W. Africa, Canary Islands.

□□ *Lavatera maritima* Gouan **Sea Mallow**
■□ 0.3–1.2m; February–May; ♄
All the younger parts of the shrub densely white-felted with star-shaped hairs. Leaves almost circular in outline and cut squarely at the base, usually shallowly 5-lobed, at most 7×8cm, with stalks 6–30mm long. Flowers with stalks longer than the leaf-stalk, solitary or in pairs, with pale pink or lilac petals, 1.5–3cm long, often purple at the base. Segments of the outer calyx almost free, 3–8mm long, shorter than the sepals, the latter triangular-ovate, pointed, enlarging in fruit. Partial fruits 9–13, hairless, with sharp edges.
Rocks, especially near the coast.
Western Mediterranean region, eastwards to Italy.
L. oblongifolia Boiss.: plant with yellowish woolly felt. Leaves ovate-lanceolate or ovate-oblong, about twice as long as broad, not lobed, with stalks 1.5cm long. Partial fruits smooth and usually hairless, rounded (S. Spain).

□□ *Lavatera olbia* L.
□■ 0.6–2m; March–June; ♄
Shrub, the younger parts densely felted with star-shaped hairs. Leaves 6–15cm, 3 to 5-lobed, with the middle lobe somewhat longer, the upper ones oblong-ovate, pointed, only shallowly lobed. Flowers solitary in the leaf-axils, with stalks 2–7mm long, forming a long, spike-like inflorescence, the corolla consisting of pink to purple petals, 1.5–3cm long. Segments of outer calyx 3, united at the base, ovate, pointed, about as long as the more pointed sepals. Partial fruits about 18, felted or rough, rounded.
Waysides, waste ground, thickets.
Western Mediterranean region, eastwards to Italy.
L. bryoniifolia Mill. is similar, but the upper leaves are 3-lobed and spear-shaped. Outer calyx forming a sheath round the base of the flower-stalk, its segments shorter than the sepals. Partial fruits hairless (eastern Mediterranean region, westwards to Sicily).

Mallow family *Malvaceae*

■□ *Malva cretica* Cav.
□□ 10–40cm; April–June; ☉
A delicate, erect species with rough, spreading hairs. Leaves stalked, the lower ones more or less circular, crenate, the upper usually palmately divided into 3–5 crenate-serrate segments. Flowers solitary in the leaf-axils, their stalks having both simple and star-shaped hairs. Petals pink or pale lilac, 11–13mm, 1–1½ times as long as the lanceolate, pointed sepals. The 3 segments of the outer calyx free, narrowly linear. Partial fruits hairless, with small cross-ribs. In ssp. *althaeoides* (Cav.) Dalby the flower-stalks have only simple hairs, and the petals are twice as long as the sepals.
Garigue, stony pastures, fallow land.
S. Europe, Asia Minor, in Spain ssp. *althaeoides*.

□■ *Gossypium hirsutum* L. **Cotton**
□□ Up to 1.5m; August–September; an annual in cultivation
A plant much branched from the base with woody, hairy stems covered with black oil-glands. Leaves long-stalked, heart-shaped, with 3–7 broadly ovate, pointed lobes. Flowers shortly stalked, solitary in the leaf-axils, at first yellow, later fading to purple, up to 5cm long. Filaments of stamens 4–6mm, the upper ones longer than the lower. Below the 5-lobed calyx are the 3 broadly ovate-triangular segments of the outer calyx, about 4.5cm long, their teeth more than 3 times as long as broad. Capsule 4–6cm, containing 8–10 seeds densely covered with long hairs. The hairs on the seeds are made into cotton, and the fatty oil extracted from the seeds is used in making margarine and for technical purposes.
This is the most frequently grown species of cotton, found world-wide nowadays including the Mediterranean region, where it sometimes escapes and becomes naturalised. Probably native in Peru.
G. herbaceum L.: plant hairless or sparsely hairy. Flowers yellow, dark purple at the base. filaments 1–2mm, about the same length. Segments of outer calyx 2–2.5cm, teeth usually less than 3 times as long as broad (cultivated in the eastern Mediterranean region and elsewhere, occasionally escaping and growing wild; probably native in Pakistan).

□□ *Hibiscus rosa-sinensis* L.
■□ 1–5m; April–September; ♄
Deciduous shrub or small tree with broadly ovate, pointed, hairless leaves, shining above. Margin of leaves irregularly and coarsely serrate in the upper half. Flowers long-stalked, solitary in the leaf-axils, with a scarlet corolla, 10–15cm across. Petals 5, not notched at the tip. The long, red, protruding stylar column bears 5 large, red stigmas and numerous stamens. Segments of outer calyx usually 7, narrow. Many garden forms, white, yellow, pink, brownish or multi-coloured, sometimes with double flowers.
Grown as a decorative shrub in the warmer countries of the world, in places escaping and growing wild. Probably native in China, but not found as a wild plant.
The autumn-flowering *H. syriacus* L. is cultivated in numerous forms in gardens, sometimes escaping and growing wild: leaves short-stalked, 3-lobed, ovate-rhombic, with star-shaped hairs on the under side. Petals white to red or purple, with a dark mark at the base (native in S. and E. Asia).

□□ *Hibiscus trionum* L. **Bladder Hibiscus**
□■ 10–60cm; June–September; ☉
A prostrate to erect, branched plant, with bristly hairs. Leaves stalked, all except the lowest ones digitately divided almost to the base into pinnately cut segments. In the leaf-axils are solitary, long-stalked flowers, open only in the morning, with an outer calyx of 10–13 narrowly linear segments fringed with bristles, and a membranous inner calyx about twice as long, 5-lobed, with prominent, dark, stiffly hairy veins, enlarged and inflated, bladder-like, at fruiting time. Petals 5, ovate-circular, pale yellow with a dark purple patch at the base, 2–3cm long.
Cultivated and fallow land.
Eastern Mediterranean region, frequently becoming naturalised in the west, S.E. Europe, S.W. Asia.

Daphne family *Thymelaeaceae*

■☐ *Daphne gnidium* L.
☐☐ 0.5–2m; June–October; ♄
Shrub little branched, the erect stems densely covered with hairless, linear to lanceolate, pointed, blue-green leaves, 2–5cm long, 3–8mm broad, and lasting for one year. Flowers with 4 perianth-segments, yellowish white, appearing amongst the leaves at the ends of the stems; flower-stalks and tube hairy. Fruits ovoid, fleshy, bright red, later almost black, and like the leaves very poisonous. Used as a medicine in ancient times.
In the undergrowth of maquis and woods.
S. Europe, N.W. Africa, Canary Islands.
D. laureola L.: leaves up to 12cm long, obovate-lanceolate, leathery and dark green, clustered at the ends of the stems. Flowers in small racemes in the leaf-axils, greenish yellow and hairless, opening in February until May. Fruits black (S. and W. Europe, N.W. Africa, spreading into central Europe and becoming naturalised there).

☐■ *Daphne sericea* Vahl (incl. *D. collina* Sm., *D. vahlii* Keissler)
☐☐ Up to 0.5–1.5m; February–April; ♄
Evergreen shrub with hairy young shoots. Leaves evergreen, leathery, oblong-obovate, narrowed into an indistinct stalk, 2–6cm long and 0.6–2cm broad, recurved at the margin, appressed hairy beneath, hairless above. Flowers rose-purple, more or less strongly scented, in small heads of 5–15 at the ends of the stems, surrounded by small, ovate, silky-hairy bracts. Perianth 12–14mm long, 4-lobed with a long, white-felted tube. Fruits reddish brown. Plant poisonous. The Italian form illustrated is sometimes treated as a separate species, *D. oleaefolia* Lam.
Stony pastures, maquis, woods, mainly in coastal areas.
Central Italy, Sicily, Crete, Turkey, Lebanon.
D. oleoides Schreb. occurs in the mountains of Mediterranean countries: shrub 30–60cm high, with small leaves, hairless on both sides when mature. Flowers scented, without bracts, in groups of 2–6, white or yellowish white, rarely pink on the outer side.

☐☐ *Thymelaea hirsuta* (L.) Endl. (*Passerina hirsuta* L.)
■☐ 0.4–1m; October–May; ♄
A small, much-branched shrub, with erect, ascending or over-hanging stems bearing small, scale-like, rather fleshy, overlapping leaves, 3–8mm long, shining dark green and hairless above, and white-felted beneath like the young shoots. Flowers consisting of a 4-lobed perianth, 4–5mm long, with silky white hairs on the outer surface, yellowish and hairless within, unisexual or bisexual, in groups of 2–5 forming dense inflorescences.
The plant is locally common in the garigue, extending into desert areas.
Mediterranean region.

☐☐ *Thymelaea tartonraira* (L.) All. (*Passerina tartonraira* (L.) Schrad.)
☐■ 20–50cm; March–May; ♄
Small subshrub, with numerous, spreading, leathery, obovate to narrowly oblong leaves, 10–18mm long and 2–7mm broad, sessile on the upper parts of the stems, and usually silky-hairy on both sides like the young shoots. Unisexual and bisexual, inconspicuous flowers in groups of 2–5 in the leaf-axils, surrounded by small bracts. Perianth 4-lobed, with white hairs on the outer side, yellowish within, 5–6mm long. Several subspecies are distinguished by the density of the hairs and the size of the leaves, 2 being endemic on Crete and Corsica.
Garigue, sandy and rocky places, often near the coast.
S. Europe, Asia Minor, N.W. Africa, absent in some areas.
T. myrtifolia (Poir.) D.A. Webb occurs in the Balearic Islands, and has leaves less than 1cm long, covered with woolly felt. Other endemic species are found mainly in the Iberian peninsula.

St John's Wort family *Hypericaceae*
Rockrose family *Cistaceae*

■□
□□ *Hypericum hircinum* L. **Stinking Tutsan** *Hypericaceae*
0.3–1.5m; May–September; ♄
A hairless, evergreen shrub, the erect stems with opposite, sessile, ovate-lanceolate leaves, 2–7.5cm long, without red or black glands, often smelling like goat when rubbed. Flowers clustered at the ends of the stems, with 5 yellow petals 10–18mm long, and the stamens with yellow anthers grouped in 5 bundles and protruding from the flowers. Styles 3, 3–5 times as long as the ovary. Sepals only 3–6mm long, ovate-lanceolate, soon falling. Fruit leathery, ellipsoid, 8–13mm long.
Damp, shady places, often by streams.
Mediterranean region, in the west only naturalised.
H. androsaemum L. is also shrubby but is without the goat-like smell: petals 6–10mm, as long as or only a little longer than the persistent calyx, stamens shorter. Styles shorter than the ovary. Fruit fleshy, red at first, later black (Mediterranean region, eastwards to Iran).

□■
□□ *Hypericum balearicum* L. *Hypericaceae*
0.5–1.2m; July–October; ♄
Small shrub with erect stems, 4-angled at least when young. Leaves more or less leathery, opposite, sessile, ovate-oblong, 10–12×6–8mm, undulate on the margin, and covered with large resin-glands like the stems. Flowers solitary, terminal, the yellow petals 10–15mm long, 3 times as long as the roundish sepals that spread out at fruiting time. Stamens in 5 bundles, styles 5. Capsule ovoid to pyramid-shaped.
Open woods.
Native only in the Balearic Islands, but naturalised in Italy (Liguria).
Numerous other species occur, often restricted to small areas, especially in the eastern Mediterranean region.

□□
■□ *Cistus parviflorus* Lam. *Cistaceae*
0.3–1m; March–May; ♄
A much-branched, low-growing, rounded shrub. Leaves broadly stalked, ovate-elliptic, indistinctly 3-veined, grey-felted on both sides with dense, star-shaped hairs, 1–3cm long. Flowers 1–6, densely clustered on stalks 5–10mm long, with a pale pink corolla only 2–3cm in diameter and 5 sepals. Style absent, and stigma therefore sessile, shorter than the stamens.
Garigue near the coast, mainly on chalk.
From Lampedusa eastwards to S. Anatolia and Cyprus.

□□
□■ *Cistus incanus* L. (*C. villosus* auct. vix L., incl. *C. polymorphus* Willk.) *Cistaceae*
0.3–1m; April–June; ♄
Shrub with ovate-lanceolate leaves, more or less green or grey-green on both sides, with sunken, pinnate veins above, 20–50×8–30mm, leaf-stalk 3–15mm long, more or less broadened at the base. Flowers with stalks 3–15mm long, in loose clusters of 1–7, the corolla rose-red, 4–6cm across, style as long as the stamens. Sepals 5, ovate-lanceolate, long-pointed. A variable species, the plant illustrated being ssp. *creticus* (L.) Heyw.: leaves only 15–25×8–15mm, distinctly undulate on the margin, often with glandular hairs on flower-stalks and young shoots (eastern Mediterranean region, westwards to Sardinia, S. Italy, N.W. Africa). Ssp. *incanus* has larger, flat leaves and long white hairs on stems, flower-stalks and sepals that hide the star-shaped hairs (from Corsica and W. Italy eastwards) and ssp. *corsicus* (Loisel.) Heyw. has star-shaped hairs on stems, flower-stalks and calyces, and only a few simple hairs (islands in the western Mediterranean region).
Garigue, maquis.
Mediterranean region, absent from France and the Iberian peninsula.
C. heterophyllus Desf.: similar, but leaves smaller, with stalks only 1–2mm long, and the veins hardly sunken (Spain near Cartagena, N.W. Africa).

Rockrose family *Cistaceae*

■□
□□ *Cistus albidus* L. **Grey-leaved Cistus**
0.4–1m; April–June; ♄
A dense shrub with opposite, white-felted leaves, flat, not undulate, half clasping the stem, 2–5cm long and 0.5–2cm broad, with 3 parallel, distinctly prominent veins on the underside. Flowers 1–7 on stout stalks 5–20mm long. Petals 5, as in all *Cistus* species, rose-red, 2–3cm long, irregularly folded in bud, and still looking wrinkled even when fully open, falling after a few hours. Style as long as the stamens. Sepals 5, broadly ovate, felted.
Common in garigue, lower growing maquis, open woods, mainly on chalk.
Western Mediterranean region, eastwards to N. Italy, Corsica, Sardinia.
C. crispus L. is similar, but has somewhat smaller, dark red flowers on stalks 1–5mm long, and wavy, sessile leaves. Plant only 30–60cm high, aromatic (western Mediterranean region).

□■
□□ *Cistus monspeliensis* L. **Narrow-leaved Cistus**
0.3–1m; April–June; ♄
A dense, strongly scented shrub with sticky glands. Leaves sessile, narrowly lanceolate, 3-veined, 4–8mm broad and 2–5cm long, dark green, becoming brown in mid-summer, slightly hairy above, densely felted beneath with star-shaped hairs. Flowers white, 2–3cm in diameter, in groups of 2–8 all facing to one side. Style very short. Sepals 5, the outer ones broadly wedge-shaped at the base.
Maquis and garigue on acid rock, frequently dominating large expanses, flourishing in areas consumed by fire.
S. Europe, N.W. Africa, Canary Islands.

□□
■□ *Cistus salvifolius* L. **Sage-leaved Cistus**
0.3–1m; April–June; ♄
A dense, aromatic, but non-sticky, grey-green shrub. Leaves stalked, ovate or elliptic, very wrinkled, and with star-shaped hairs on both sides, rounded at the base, 1–4×0.5–2cm. Flowers white, with stalks 1–10cm long, solitary or up to 4 together, 3–5cm in diameter. Style very short, Sepals 5, the outer ones heart-shaped at the base.
Garigue, maquis, particularly in areas with acid rock.
Mediterranean region, eastwards to the Caucasus.
C. populifolius L.: Leaves stalked, hairless, green and smooth above, 4–10cm long and 3–6.5cm broad, heart-shaped at the base. Flowers 4–6cm in diameter (Iberian peninsula, France, Morocco).

□□
□■ *Cistus ladanifer* L. **Gum Cistus**
Up to 2.5m; April–June; ♄
A tall, erect, aromatic shrub with sticky glands. Leaves almost sessile, linear-lanceolate, 4–8(–12)cm long and 6–25mm broad, 3-veined for ⅓ of their length, shining dark green and hairless above, densely white-felted beneath. Flowers solitary, very large, 7–10cm in diameter, with white petals, often with a dark red mark at the base, and 3 sepals. Style very short. Capsule 6 to 10-celled.
Woods, maquis.
France, Iberian peninsula, N.W. Africa, Canary Islands.
Other shrubby species with 3 sepals growing only up to 1m or 1.5m high are *C. laurifolius* L.: leaves as in *C. ladanifer*, but shortly stalked, ovate to ovate-lanceolate, 3–9×1–3cm. Flowers 4–8 at the ends of the stems, long-stalked, 5–6cm in diameter, with white petals. Capsule 5-celled (S.W. Europe, Corsica, central Italy); and *C. clusii* Dunal: leaves linear with recurved margins, 1-veined, 10–25×1–2mm. Flowers 3–6(–12) at the ends of the stems, 2–3cm in diameter, with white petals. Flower-stalks and the 5–8mm long sepals with long, white hairs (Spain, Balearic Islands, S. Italy, Sicily, N.W. Africa). *C. libanotis* L. is very similar: flower-stalks and the 8–10mm long sepals hairless but sticky (Iberian peninsula, N.W. Africa).

Rockrose family *Cistaceae*

■□ *Halimum halimifolium* (L.) Willk.
□□ 0.3–1.5m; April–June; ♄
A silver-grey shrub, much-branched, with erect stems and abundant inflorescences. The elliptic-oblong leaves are opposite and shortly stalked, only the uppermost ones sessile, without stipules, 1–4×0.5–2cm, densely covered with scales and short, star-shaped hairs. Flowers 2–3cm across, the 5 yellow petals often having a dark mark at the base. Sepals 5, densely covered with scales, the 2 outer sepals very small.
On sandy soils near the coast, sometimes forming colonies, maquis, woods.
Western Mediterranean region, eastwards to Italy, absent from France.
Other species, with only 3 sepals, occur mainly in the Iberian peninsula and in Morocco, for example *H. lasianthum* (Lam.) Spach: up to 1m high, inflorescence with long, silky hairs, sepals often with purple bristles, and *H. commutatum* Pau: up to 50cm high, leaves like those of Rosemary, up to 3mm broad. Flowers pale yellow, solitary or few together at the ends of the stems. Sepals hairless. There are also some similar, white-flowered species.

□■ *Tuberaria guttata* (L.) Fourr. **Annual Rockrose, Spotted Rockrose**
□□ 5–30cm; March–June; ☉
A delicate, erect, hairy plant, very variable in form with several subspecies. Leaves of the basal rosette, which have often withered by flowering-time, and the lower stem-leaves oblong-elliptic, without stipules, the upper ones more linear-lanceolate, with or without stipules, all opposite. Inflorescences loose, composed of flowers 1–2cm across with long, thin stalks, the 5 petals yellow, usually with a dark brown spot within. The 2 outer sepals much smaller and narrower than the 3 inner ones. Fruit-stalks spreading or bending downwards. Capsule shorter than the sepals.
Grassy pastures on sand, garigue.
Mediterranean region, W. Europe, Canary Islands, rare in central Europe.
T. praecox Grosser is also an annual: Petals barely exceeding the sepals, unspotted (central Mediterranean region, in coastal areas). The perennial *T. lignosa* (Sweet) Samp. (*Helianthemum tuberaria* (L.) Mill.) has a plantain-like basal rosette. Flowers about 3cm across, unspotted (western Mediterranean region, Canary Islands, eastwards to Italy, Sicily).

□□ *Helianthemum lavandulifolium* Mill.
■■ 10–50cm; April–June; ♄
An easily recognisable species amongst the 30 or so comprising the genus *Helianthemum*, most of which are confined to small areas in the western Mediterranean region. An erect, densely felted subshrub with opposite, linear-lanceolate leaves, 1–5cm long and 3–8mm broad, recurved at the margin, grey-felted above and white-felted beneath, and narrowly linear stipules that sometimes quickly fall. Characteristic of the plant are the 3–5 times forked inflorescences, the branches of which are coiled like a snail when young but straighten out later and are then covered with flowers. Flowers yellow, 1.5–2cm across, sepals fringed with hairs, the 2 outer ones narrowly lanceolate, the 3 inner much larger, ovate-lanceolate, longer than the flower-stalks. Fruit-capsules shorter than the calyx.
Garigue, stony pastures, also open woods, mainly on chalk.
Mediterranean region, absent from the islands in the west and from most of Italy.

□□ *Helianthemum caput-felis* Boiss.
□■ 10–30cm; March–April; ♄
A small, much-branched subshrub, covered with grey-white felt. Leaves opposite with deciduous stipules, elliptic or lanceolate, shortly stalked, thick, 6–15×2–10mm, with dense star-shaped hairs on both sides and the margins considerably recurved. Inflorescence dense with 5–10 yellow, stalked flowers, petals 9–12mm, longer than the calyx with its characteristically long, spreading hairs; the outer, broadly ovate and pointed sepals are curved back and give the bud the apearance of a cat's paw.
Garigue, open woods, on chalk.
Spain (province Alicante), Balearic Islands, Sardinia, N.W. Africa, rare.

Rockrose family Cistaceae
Tamarisk family Tamaricaceae

■□ *Helianthemum salicifolium* (L?) Mill. *Cistaceae*
□□ 5–30cm; March–June; ☉
A usually branched, ascending, slightly woody plant. Leaves opposite, shortly stalked, ovate-lanceolate, softly hairy and green, sometimes with recurved margins, 5–30×3–10mm. Stipules narrowly lanceolate, ¼–½ as long as the leaves. Inflorescence loose, 5 to 20-flowered, the flowers in the axils of bracts, with the petals yellow, 5–12mm long, about as long as the sepals, or absent. The 2 outer sepals, narrowly lanceolate, are about half as long. Flower-stalks thin, spreading horizontally and turning upwards at the end, at least as long as the calyx.
Grassy pastures, garigue, and into semi-desert areas.
Mediterranean region, Canary Islands, S.W. Asia.
Two other annual species with similar distributions are *H. ledifolium* (L.) Mill.: flower-stalks erect, thick, at most as long as the calyx, and *H. aegyptiacum* (L.) Mill.: calyx membranous, inflated, with red veins, fruit-stalks recurved.

□■ *Fumana arabica* (L.) Spach *Cistaceae*
□□ 10–30cm; March–June; ♃
Leaves of this prostrate or ascending, dwarf shrub all about the same size, 5–12×0.8–5mm, oblong–elliptic and usually flat, alternate, with small stipules, glandular-hairy or becoming hairless, green or greyish when young. Yellow flowers, 1–1.5cm long, appear solitarily or up to 7 in a raceme at the ends of the stems, the 2 outer sepals much smaller and narrower than the 3 membranous, green-veined inner ones. Capsule 6–8mm long, with (6–)8–12 seeds, splitting into 3 parts when ripe.
Stony pastures, garigue, maquis, especially on chalk.
S. Europe, from Sardinia and Sicily eastwards, S.W. Asia, N. Africa.
F. ericoides (Cav.) Gand.: leaves all equal, linear, without stipules. Flowers appearing among the leaves at the ends of the stems (S. Europe, N.W. Africa).

□□ *Fumana thymifolia* (L.) Spach ex Webb *Cistaceae*
■□ 10–30cm; April–June; ♃
Dwarf shrub, with usually ascending stems, the needle-like leaves with stipules and small leafy shoots in the axils, opposite at least below, 5–11×0.5–1mm, hairless, hairy or glandular-hairy, often recurved at the margin. Leaves in the region of the inflorescence much smaller. The 3–9 flowers long-stalked, with yellow petals 5–8mm long, and 5 sepals, the 2 outer ones very small, the 3 inner ones large, membranous, and distinctly green-veined. Capsule 4–5mm, with 6 seeds, splitting into 3 parts when ripe. A variable species.
Garigue, stony pastures.
Mediterranean region.
F. laevipes (L.) Spach is similar: leaves all alternate, even narrower, 4–8×0.3–0.4mm (S. Europe, N.W. Africa).

□□ *Tamarix africana* Poir. *Tamaricaceae*
□■ 2–6m; April–June, also in autumn; ♄
Shrub or small tree with black or dark purple bark. Leaves scale-like, lying close to the stems, 1.5–4mm long, pointed, with a translucent margin. White or pale pink, almost sessile, 5-petalled flowers form catkin-like inflorescences 3–6cm long and 5–8mm broad, before or at the same time as the leaves, usually on stems of the previous year. Petals 2–3mm long. Bracts triangular, usually longer than the calyx. Seeds with a tuft of hairs.
River-banks, flat coasts, also grown as an ornamental plant.
Western and central Mediterranean region, eastwards to Italy, Canary Islands.
T. gallica L. is similar, with blue-green leaves and fairly loose inflorescences 3–5mm broad on leafy stems of the current year. Petals 1.5–2mm (western Mediterranean region, frequently planted). *T. parviflora* DC.: Flowers 4-petalled, arranged in inflorescences 1.5–3cm long and 3–5mm broad. Petals up to 2mm, bracts almost entirely membranous (eastern Mediterranean region, cultivated elsewhere). There are numerous other species, not always easy to identify, especially in the east.

Sea Heath family *Frankeniaceae*
Gourd family *Cucurbitaceae*
Cactus family *Cactaceae*

■□
□□ *Frankenia thymifolia* Desf. *Frankeniaceae*
5–30cm; April–May; ♄
A small, much-branched subshrub, the stems densely covered with fine hairs. Leaves opposite, sessile, needle-like, recurved at the margin, and completely covered with a white crust,
2–3.5mm. Flowers solitary or few together, sessile, in the leaf-axils at the ends of the stems,
all facing the same way, with 5 purple petals, about 7mm long, the sepals more or less densely
hairy.
On saline soils, salt-steppes.
Spain, N.W. Africa.
F. laevis L., **Sea Heath**: Plant prostrate. Leaves 2–5mm long, flowers 4–6mm, along the stems
(western Mediterranean region, W. Europe, Canary Islands). *F. pulverulenta* L.: annual.
Leaves obovate, flat, flowers in short spikes in the leaf-axils and at the ends of the stems
(Mediterranean region, Canary Islands, S.E. Europe, S.W. Asia).

□■
□□ *Ecballium elaterium* (L.) A. Rich **Squirting Cucumber** *Cucurbitaceae*
0.2–1m; April–September; ♃
A stiffly hairy, somewhat fleshy plant, with prostrate stems, no tendrils. Leaves long-
stalked, heart-shaped to triangular, usually toothed and wavy, up to 10cm long. Flowers yellowish, deeply 5-lobed, the male in clusters, the female solitary on stalks arising from the
leaf-axils, both sexes on the same plant. The green, roughly hairy, cucumber-shaped fruits,
up to 5cm long and extremely bitter, have an interesting method of seed-dispersal: when they
are ripe, they detach themselves from their stalks at the slightest touch and squirt out with
their seeds a liquid that should be treated with care, since it can cause inflammation of the
skin.
Waysides, waste ground, fallow land.
Mediterranean region, S.E. Europe, Canary Islands.

□□
■□ *Citrullus colocynthis* (L.) Schrad. (*Colocynthis vulgaris* Schrad.) **Bitter Cucumber, Bitter
Apple** *Cucurbitaceae*
30–50cm; June–August; ♃
A prostrate or climbing, roughly hairy plant, with tendrils. Leaves stalked, ovate-oblong in
outline, pinnately divided into 3–5 sinuately lobed segments. Flowers unisexual, stalked,
solitary in the axils of the leaves, with a greenish-yellow corolla divided almost to the base
into 5 ovate, pointed lobes, about 5mm long. Ovary with scattered, coarse hairs. Fruit spherical, yellow or mottled, 4–12cm in diameter, with dry, very bitter pulp. Formerly used as a
strong purgative.
Sandy soils, especially near the coast, waysides.
Southern Mediterranean region, Canary Islands, to S.W. Asia and India.
The frequently cultivated **Water Melon**, *C. lanatus* (Thunb.) Mansf. belongs to the same
genus. It has a usually red, juicy pulp (native in S. Africa).

□□
□■ *Opuntia ficus-indica* (L.) Mill. **Prickly Pear, Barbary Fig** *Cactaceae*
2–5m; April–July; ♄
A much-branched, fleshy plant, sometimes tree-like, with flat obovate-oblong stem-joints
20–50×10–20cm. Small cushions of yellow, barbed bristles, soon falling, sometimes with 1 or
2 stout, pale spines less than 1cm long amongst them, arise in the axils of small, deciduous
leaves. Flowers 6–10cm in diameter, with numerous yellow petals and stamens, clustered on
the margins of the stem-joints. Fruits fig-like, 5–9cm long, yellow to red, also bearing cushions of bristles, and with a depression at the end. The juicy pulp is edible. Cultivated for its
fruits and as an impenetrable hedge-plant, often escaping and in places becoming
naturalised (native in tropical America).
O. maxima Mill.: Stem-joints with 1–4 spines up to 3cm long, end of the fruit flat (probably
native in Mexico) and *O. vulgaris* Mill.: only up to 50cm high, spines solitary or absent, up to
5cm long (native in N. America) are similar.

Loosestrife family *Lythraceae*
Myrtle family *Myrtaceae*

■□ *Lythrum junceum* Banks. & Sol. *Lythraceae*
□□ 20–70cm; April–September; usually ♃
A hairless plant, prostrate or ascending, branched at the base, with angular stems bearing usually alternate, sessile, ovate-oblong to linear-oblong leaves, 1–2×0.2–1cm. Flowers solitary in the leaf-axils, with a 6-petalled, purple corolla 5–6mm long, and a 12-toothed floral-cup of about the same length, narrowing evenly to an often red-spotted base. There are 3 types of flower, differing in the length of the style. Stamens 12, of varying lengths, at least some protruding.
Swampy places, river-banks.
Mediterranean region, Canary Islands.
L. acutangulum Lag. (western Mediterranean region) and *L. flexuosum* Lag. (central Spain) are similar and often confused with the above species. Both are much smaller, annual species, with the floral-cup of one colour.

□■ *Myrtus communis* L. **Myrtle** *Myrtaceae*
□□ 1–5m; June–August; ♄
An evergreen, hairless shrub, the firm, entire, shortly stalked leaves opposite, occasionally in whorls of 3, 1–5cm long, ovate-lanceolate, pointed, and dotted with translucent glands. Flowers aromatic like the leaves, up to 3cm in diameter, always solitary in the leaf-axils on stalks up to 3cm long, with 5 white petals and numerous stamens. Fruit a blue-black berry, about 1cm long when ripe. Myrtle played a large part in Greek mythology and is used for bridal wreaths even today. Because of its high ethereal oil content it is also used medicinally for respiratory problems and as a spice.
Maquis, woods, also cultivated in many forms as an ornamental plant, sometimes escaping and growing wild.
Mediterranean region, Canary Islands, eastwards to central Asia.

□□ *Eucalyptus globulus* Labill. **Blue Gum** *Myrtaceae*
■□ 20–40m; February–July; ♄
Distinguished from the many other *Eucalyptus* species cultivated in the Mediterranean region by its solitary flowers and fruit-capsules over 1cm long. The bark of this tall tree comes off in long strips. Juvenile leaves opposite, each pair at right-angles to the next, ovate to lanceolate, sessile, blue-green, adult leaves alternate, stalked, sickle-shaped to lanceolate, bright green, 10–30cm long and 3–4cm broad. Flower-buds covered with a blue-green bloom. Petals and sepals united, coming off as a lid (operculum) and releasing the numerous white or pink stamens. Fruits top-shaped, 1.5–3cm, with 4 ribs. The leaves are a source of eucalyptus oil that is used in the treatment of respiratory problems.
Planted extensively in the Mediterranean region and in the Canary Islands since the 19th century to dry up swampy areas and as a quick-growing source of wood, also grown as an ornamental tree. Native in Tasmania.

□□ *Eucalyptus camaldulensis* Dehnh. (*E. rostratus* Schlecht. non Cav.) *Myrtaceae*
□■ Up to 15m; June–September; ♄
A quick-growing tree with smooth, white bark, coming off in plates. Juvenile leaves opposite, each pair at right-angles to the next, narrowly to broadly lanceolate, rather blue-green, adult leaves lanceolate, pointed, fairly straight, 12–22×0.5–1.5cm. Flowers 5–10 in small umbels, on round stalks 10–15mm long. The beaked lid, formed by the united petals and sepals, falls off releasing the numerous yellowish white stamens. Fruit distinctly stalked, hemispherical, 7–8×5–6mm, with a broad rim, and the central part opening into 4 protruding segments.
Cultivated in the Mediterranean region and the Canary Islands, native in Australia.
Other frequently grown species include *E. tereticornis* Sm.: Bark smooth and white, umbels on round stalks 5–12mm long. Fruit broadly top-shaped, 6–9×8–10mm, and *E. resinifer* Sm.: Bark reddish, fibrous. Umbels on compressed to angular stalks 1.5–2cm long. Fruit 5–8mm, ovoid to hemispherical.

Pomegranate family *Punicaceae*
Carrot family *Apiaceae* (*Umbelliferae*)

■□ *Punica granatum* L. **Pomegranate** *Punicaceae*
□□ 2–7m; May–September; ♄
A hairless, often spiny shrub or small tree with 4-angled twigs. Leaves opposite, firm and shining, but deciduous, ovate or lanceolate, 2–8cm long, entire. Flowers 1–3 at the ends of the stems, bright red like the fleshy calyx and the floral-cup, with 5–7 crumpled petals, 2–3cm long, and numerous stamens. Fruit apple-shaped, the rind leathery, reddish brown. Numerous seeds, each surrounded by juicy, edible pulp. Formerly a symbol of fertility, and often featured in textile designs, also the rind used in the preparation of a medicine to expel tapeworms.
Grown for its fruit and as a decorative tree, occasionally with double flowers, sometimes becoming naturalised in hedges, thickets and maquis.
Widely cultivated in the Mediterranean region, perhaps originating in the east, native in S.W. Asia.

□■ *Eryngium maritimum* L. **Sea Holly** *Apiaceae*
□□ 15–60cm; June–September; ⚃
Plant covered in a blue-green bloom, with erect, stout stems branched above, frequently forming a hemispherical bush. Basal leaves stalked, with the blade almost circular in outline, 3- to 5-lobed, sinuately toothed with stout spines on the margin. Upper leaves with a broad base, sessile, less divided. Flowers in small heads, 1.5–3cm across, surrounded by 4–7 elliptic to obovate, broadly spiny-toothed bracts, 2–4cm long. Flowers blue, exceeded by the 3-pointed bracteoles about 12mm long. Fruits about 15mm long, densely covered with pointed scales.
Sandy beaches, dunes.
Coasts of the Mediterranean and the Black Sea, W. and N. Europe, northwards to 60° latitude.

□□ *Eryngium amethystinum* L. **Blue Eryngo** *Apiaceae*
■□ 20–70cm; July–October; ⚃
An erect plant with a thick stem, tinged steel-blue almost everywhere in the upper part. Basal leaves usually persistent, leathery, blade 10–15cm, obovate in outline, bipinnately divided with spiny-toothed, linear-lanceolate segments. Stalks of the stem-leaves broadened, entire. Flowers blue, in small heads 1–2cm across, exceeded by the 5–9 linear-lanceolate bracts, 2–5cm long, bearing 1–4 pairs of small spines on the margin. Outer bracteoles 3-pointed. Fruit sparsely scaly.
Stony and grassy pastures, garigue.
Eastern Mediterranean region, westwards to Italy and Sicily.
E. creticum Lam.: Basal leaves long-stalked, undivided, crenate-serrate, soon withering. Flower-heads 0.5–1cm across, numerous. Bracts 1–3cm long, with 1 or 2 pairs of spines. Bracteoles 3-pointed (eastern Mediterranean region). *E. dilatatum* Lam.: basal leaves persistent, leathery, 3-lobed above, generally coarsely spiny-toothed. Flower-heads 0.5–1.5cm across. Bracts 1–3cm long, with 3–6 pairs of spines. Bracteoles usually entire (western Mediterranean region).

□□ *Echinophora spinosa* L. *Apiaceae*
□■ 20–80cm; June–October; ⚃
A stout, grey-green, more or less hairy plant. Leaves 2 to 3-pinnate, fleshy and stiff, the segments keeled below and furrowed above, with a spiny tip. Umbels with 4–8 hairy rays and 5–10 spiny bracts and bracteoles. Petals white, rarely pink, hairy on the back, the outer ones larger than the inner. Sepals spiny, persistent. Each partial umbel with a central bisexual flower surrounded by a number of male flowers, the stalks of which are united with the ovary and form a covering round the fruit.
Sandy beaches.
S. Europe, N.W. Africa.
E. tenuifolia L. is yellow-flowered: Plant more or less grey-felted. Leaf-segments flat, without spines. Umbels 2 to 5-rayed (from S. Italy and Sicily eastwards).

Carrot family *Apiaceae* (*Umbelliferae*)

■□
□□
Scandix pecten-veneris L. **Shepherd's Needle**
15–50cm; April–July; ☉
Stem ascending or erect, branched from the base, finely grooved, and with short, stiff, spreading hairs. Leaves 2 to 4-pinnate, ovate-oblong in outline, with narrow, pointed lobes. Umbel with only 1–3 rays. Petals white, the outer ones often somewhat enlarged. Bracts absent, bracteoles entire or with teeth pointing forwards. Fruit 1.5–8cm long, with a stout beak, strongly laterally compressed and bristly on the margin that is much longer than the seed-bearing part and distinct from it. Very variable in form.
Cultivated and fallow land.
Mediterranean region, Canary Islands, northwards to Scotland and Sweden (in earlier times more common there), S.W. Asia. Other species found in the Mediterranean region are *S. australis* L.: fruit only 1.5–4cm long, the beak not very distinct from the seed-bearing part, and *S. stellata* Banks & Sol. that has obviously pinnate bracteoles.

□■
□□
Bifora radians Bieb.
20–40cm; April–July; ☉
Plant smelling of bed-bugs, like Coriander. Stem erect, hairless, branched almost from the base, angular and furrowed, bearing 1–3 times pinnately divided leaves, oblong in outline, lobes of the lower leaves flat, lobes of the upper ones thread-like. Umbel-rays 3–8, up to 2.5cm long. Outer petals of the marginal flowers greatly enlarged, deeply 2-lobed, the inner flowers only male, with slightly unequal petals. Calyx small, without teeth, distinguishing it from Coriander in the flowering state. Bracts absent or 1 only, bracteoles 2 or 3, awl-shaped, on one side. Fruit consisting of 2 almost spherical partial fruits. Style 1–1.5mm.
Cultivated and fallow land.
S. Europe, introduced further north and becoming naturalised, S.W. Asia.
B. testiculata (L.) Roth: Lobes of the upper leaves flat. Umbel-rays 1–3(–5), up to 1cm long. Petals of all flowers small and nearly equal. Style only 0.2mm long (Mediterranean region, Canary Islands, S.W. Asia).

□□
■□
Crithmum maritimum L. **Rock Samphire**
10–60cm; July–October; ♃
An easily recognisable species, even when not in flower, hairless, woody at the base, with 1 to 2-pinnate leaves, triangular in outline, blue-green and fleshy, the linear, pointed segments 1–7cm long. Umbels with 8–30 fairly stout rays. Flowers with small, yellow-green petals, curled up at the tips. Bracts and bracteoles numerous, bent downwards in fruit. Fruits 5–6mm, ovoid-oblong, strongly ribbed, hairless, yellowish to reddish. Leaves sometimes used in salads or as a spice.
Rocky coasts, near the sea-spray.
Mediterranean coast, also coasts of the Atlantic and the Black Sea, Canary Islands.

□□
□■
Foeniculum vulgare Mill. ssp. *piperitum* (Ucria) Cout. (*F. piperitum* (Ucria) Sweet) **Bitter Fennel**
0.5–2.5m; July–September; ☉
A tall plant with a grooved stem, covered in a blue-green bloom. Leaves oblong-triangular in outline, 3 to 4-pinnate. Lobes of leaves awl-shaped, somewhat fleshy and firm, hardly longer than 1cm. Leaf-sheaths only 1–3cm long, the uppermost with the blade absent or rudimentary. Umbels shortly stalked, with 4–10 rays of unequal length, bracts and bracteoles absent, the terminal umbel often overtopped by the lateral ones. Flowers yellow, the 5 petals with blunt, curled-up tips. Sepals absent. Partial fruits with 5 distinct but unwinged ribs, sharp-tasting.
Roadsides, river-banks, fallow land.
Mediterranean region, Canary Islands, S.W. Asia.
Ssp. *vulgare*, **Fennel**, is grown almost everywhere in Europe. Lobes of leaves more than 1cm long, not rigid. Umbels with 12–25 rays, the terminal umbel not exceeded by the lateral ones. Fruits with a sweetish-spicy taste, used for flavouring and for medicinal purposes. **Florence Fennel** is derived from var. *azoricum* (Mill.) Thell.

Carrot family *Apiaceae* (*Umbelliferae*)

■☐ *Smyrnium olusatrum* L. **Alexanders**
☐☐ 0.5–1.5m; March–May; ☉
A stout, hairless plant, often with opposite branches in the upper part, smelling and tasting of Celery. Basal leaves stalked, the blade divided into 3 leaflets, sometimes each leaflet further divided into 3 leaflets. Leaflets rhombic-ovate, crenate-serrate, sometimes lobed. Stem-leaves divided into 3 leaflets or merely 3-lobed, on short, broadened stalks fringed on the margin, all shining dark green. Umbels convex, long-stalked, with 5–18 rays, bracts and bracteoles small and quickly falling or absent. Petals greenish yellow. Fruits 6–8mm, broadly ovoid with prominent, wing-like ribs, black and shining when ripe. The name 'Alexanders' is a corruption of 'Parsley of Alexandria', the English translation of the mediaeval Latin name for the plant. The young shoots and leaves were formerly eaten as a vegetable, but nowadays the cultivation of Celery has taken its place.
Hedges, waysides, waste ground, especially in damp places.
Mediterranean region, Canary Islands.
S. perfoliatum L.: Stems narrowly winged on the angles. Upper leaves ovate to heart-shaped, crenate-serrate, clasping the stem (Mediterranean region). *S. rotundifolium* Mill. is similar: stems round, grooved. Upper leaves entire or very slightly toothed (from Corsica and Sardinia to Asia Minor).

☐■ *Bupleurum lancifolium* Hornem.
☐☐ 15–75cm; April–August; ☉
Stem erect, bent from side to side, with spreading branches bearing blue-green, entire, ovate-or oblong-lanceolate leaves, the lower ones narrowed at the base, 5–15×1–4cm, the middle and upper ones apparently pierced by the stem, all with 5–9 parallel, interconnected veins. Umbel-rays usually 2 or 3, without bracts. Bracteoles usually 5, united at the base, spreading, yellow-green, almost circular, pointed, much longer than the many-flowered partial umbels. Petals yellow, very small, curling up at the tip. Fruit 2–5mm, ovoid, densely warted between the ribs.
Cultivated and fallow land.
Mediterranean region, Canary Islands, S.W. Asia.
B. rotundifolium L. is similar: leaves elliptic-ovate to almost circular. Umbel-rays usually 5–10. Bracteoles ovate, pointed. Fruit 3mm, smooth between the ribs (Mediterranean region, central and E. Europe, S.W. Asia).

☐☐ *Bupleurum spinosum* Gouan
■☐ 15–30cm; July–August; ♄
A rounded, much-branched shrub, spiny because of the rigid and pointed, withered upper parts of the stem bearing the umbel-rays that remain 2–3 years on the plant. Leaves linear-lanceolate, grey-green, with 3–5 parallel veins. Umbels with 2–7 rays, the 5 bracts awl-shaped and 1-veined, 2mm long. Petals yellow, small with a curled-up tip. Fruits 3–4.5mm, ovate-oblong, ribbed.
Stony pastures in the mountains, often forming colonies.
Sp..in, N.W. Africa.

☐☐ *Bupleurum fruticosum* L. **Shrubby Hare's Ear**
☐■ 1–2m; April–September; ♄
An aromatic, bushy shrub, with reddish stems and evergreen, leathery, almost sessile leaves, blue-green beneath, obovate-lanceolate, and 5–8cm long. Midrib prominent, ending in a small, sharp point, main lateral veins reaching the leaf-margin. Umbels of yellow flowers with 5–25 stout rays, 5 or 6 bracts and 5 or 6 bracteoles, all bending downwards and soon falling. Fruits 7–8mm, oblong, with narrowly winged ribs.
Rocks, garigue, also grown as an ornamental shrub.
Mediterranean region, sporadic.
B. gibraltaricum Lam. is similar: leaves narrower, main lateral veins not reaching the leaf-margin, bracts persistent (Spain, N.W. Africa). Other shrubby and herbaceous species occur in the region, including some annuals.

Carrot family *Apiaceae* (*Umbelliferae*)

■□ *Ammi majus* L. **False Bishop's Weed**
□□ 0.3–1m; June–September; ☉
A hairless plant, erect and branched, with a finely grooved stem and very variable leaves, the lower ones often simple or divided into 3 leaflets, the middle and upper ones 2 to 3-pinnate with lanceolate to linear lobes, edged with cartilaginous teeth. Umbels long-stalked, with 15–30(–60) thin rays, spreading when in flower and fruit. Bracts numerous, usually 3-parted or pinnately divided with thread-like lobes, bracteoles with a membranous margin. Petals white, unequally 2-lobed. Partial fruits sickle-shaped, 1.5–2mm long, with 5 weak ribs.
Cultivated and fallow land, waysides.
Mediterranean region, Canary Islands, S.W. Asia, introduced elsewhere and becoming naturalised.
A. visnaga (L.) Lam.: all leaflets with narrowly linear and entire lobes. Umbel-rays up to 150, drawn together, nest-like, at fruiting time, becoming thick and hard, and used to make toothpicks. An important medicinal plant, especially in cases of asthma and angina pectoris (southern Mediterranean region, Canary Islands, S.W. Asia).

□■ *Ferula communis* L. **Giant Fennel**
□□ 1–3m; April–June; ♃
A very stout, tall plant with leaves several times pinnate, the linear segments flat, 1.5–5cm long (in ssp. *communis* not broader than 1mm and green on both sides, in ssp. *glauca* (L.) Rouy & Cam. up to 3mm broad and grey-green beneath). Lower leaves 30–60cm, long-stalked, the upper ones with conspicuously large leaf-sheaths, the uppermost with only the leaf-sheath remaining. Inflorescence large and much-branched, the fruit-bearing umbels shortly stalked or sessile, surrounded by long-stalked, infertile, lateral umbels. Bracts absent, bracteoles soon falling. Fruit elliptic, about 1.5cm long, compressed, with lateral wings.
Garigue, pastures, on chalk, often near dwellings.
Mediterranean region.
F. tingitana L.: leaf-segments not longer than 1cm, with distinctly recurved margins (Iberian peninsula, N. Africa, Near East).

□□ *Tordylium apulum* L.
■□ 20–50cm; April–June; ☉
Stem erect, branched, with dense, soft, spreading hairs at the base, and scattered hairs above. Leaves pinnate, the lower ones with circular to ovate, deeply crenate leaflets, the upper ones with entire, linear segments. Umbel-rays 3–8. Marginal flowers each having 1 white petal, enlarged and uniformly deeply 2-lobed. Bracts and bracteoles awl-shaped, short. Fruit almost round, flat, 5–8mm, with vesicular hairs and a whitish, crenate, thickened margin.
Cultivated and fallow land, waysides.
Mediterranean region.
T. maximum L.: marginal flowers with 2 or 3 of the petals unequally 2-lobed, umbel-rays 5–15. Fruit bristly, with a smooth, thickened edge (S. and S.E. Europe, Asia Minor). *T. officinale* L.: umbel-rays 8–14, marginal flowers with 2 of the petals unequally 2-lobed. Fruit 2–3mm, with vesicular hairs and a wrinkled, thickened margin (S.E. Europe).

□□ *Thapsia villosa* L.
□■ 0.3–2m; May–June; ♃
A species having a hairless, stout, finely grooved stem and 3–4 times pinnately divided, woolly hairy leaves, ovate in outline, and 20–35cm long. Terminal segments 5–15(–30)mm, ovate-oblong, with regular, finely pointed teeth. Leaf-stalk of the upper stem-leaves inflated and without a blade. Umbels large, yellow, with 9–24 rays, usually completely lacking in bracts and bracteoles. Fruit flat, elliptic, 8–15mm, with lateral wings 2–3mm broad, deeply notched at the top and the base.
Stony and grassy pastures.
Iberian peninsula, S. France, N.W. Africa.
T. garganica L.: terminal segments of leaves linear, entire or with 1 or 2 teeth. Fruit 15–25mm, with lateral wings 3–6mm broad (southern Mediterranean region).

Heath family *Ericaceae*

■□ *Erica arborea* L. **Tree Heath**
□□ 1–4(–15)m; March–May; ♄
Evergreen shrub or small tree, up to 15m high in the Canary Islands, the young stems densely covered with white hairs. Leaves needle-like, 3–5mm long, usually 4 in a whorl, hairless, dark green, the edges of the leaves rolled under, completely covering the lower surface. Inflorescences with numerous flowers, flower-stalks hairless, with 2 or 3 bracteoles below the middle. Corolla white, 2.5–4mm, bell-shaped with 4 lobes, the dark brown anthers having appendages at the base and enclosed within the flower. Stigma white, more or less spherical. Evergreen woods, maquis, mainly on acid soils.
Mediterranean region, Canary Islands, mountains of central Africa.
E. scoparia L. Flowers in May and June: A slender shrub, up to 6m high, with usually hairless young stems, and leaves 4–7mm long in whorls of 3 or 4. Flowers 1.5–3mm, greenish white, inconspicuous. Anthers without appendages, enclosed within the flower. Stigma red (western Mediterranean region, eastwards to Italy, Canary Islands).

□■ *Erica multiflora* L.
□□ Up to 80(–250)cm; August–December; ♄
Evergreen shrub with erect, hairless branches. Leaves needle-like, 6–11mm long, in whorls of 4 or 5. Inflorescences dense, usually terminal, up to 5cm long. Corolla 4–5mm, bright pink, bell-shaped with 4 lobes, on long, thin, reddish stalks. Anthers without appendages, usually with their 2 parts parallel and touching, dark red, protruding from the corolla.
In the undergrowth of open, evergreen woods and maquis, mainly on chalk.
Mediterranean region, eastwards to Yugoslavia.
E. manipuliflora Salisb. (*E. verticillata* Forsk. non Bergius) is closely related: a prostrate or ascending shrub up to 50cm, leaves 4–8mm, in whorls of 3 or 4. Anthers protruding from the corolla, their 2 parts separated and spreading (eastern and central Mediterranean region, also flowering in the autumn).

□□ *Arbutus unedo* L. **Strawberry Tree**
■□ 1.5–3(–12)m; October–March; ♄
Evergreen shrub or small tree with dull brown, fissured bark. Young stems glandular-hairy. Leaves shining, thick, lanceolate and sharply serrate, 4–11cm long and 1.5–4cm broad. Leaf-stalks less than 1cm long. Flowers about 9mm, white to pink or tinged greenish, bell-shaped with recurved lobes, in pendent panicles. Calyx 1.5mm with roundish lobes. Fruits at first yellow, later dark red, strawberry-like, with a warted surface, up to 2cm in diameter, edible but insipid in taste. In many districts used to make jam or a liqueur.
Maquis and evergreen woods, mainly on soils lacking in chalk.
One of the characteristic plants in the evergreen vegetation of the Mediterranean.
Mediterranean region, on the Atlantic coast of western Europe northwards to Ireland.

□□ *Arbutus andrachne* L. **Eastern Strawberry Tree**
□■ 3–5m; February–April; ♄
Evergreen shrub or small tree, the trunk and branches often twisted, and the strikingly smooth, red-brown bark peeling off in large pieces. Young stems hairless. Leaves thick, slightly grey-green beneath, elliptic, almost entire, 3–6cm broad, less than twice as long as broad, and with stalks 1.5–3cm long. Only the leaves on young stems are serrate and hairy. Panicles erect, glandular-hairy, flowers white, urn-shaped with recurved lobes, about 7mm long. Calyx 2.5mm with ovate-rhombic lobes. Berries 8–12mm, orange, with a network of grooves.
Maquis and evergreen woods.
Eastern Mediterranean region, westwards to S. Albania and Greece.
A. × *andrachnoides* Link: a hybrid between the 2 *Arbutus* species, found everywhere where the parent species grow together and some plants flower at the same time. Usually has orange-coloured bark and at least slightly glandular-hairy young stems.

Primrose family *Primulaceae*

■□ *Cyclamen hederifolium* Ait. (*C. neapolitanum* Ten.) **Sowbread**
□□ 8–12cm; August–November: ♃
Corm large, 3–15cm, rooting mainly from the top and sides. Leaves only appearing in late summer or autumn after flowering, oblong to heart-shaped, often lobed or 5- to 9-sided, with an irregularly toothed, slightly cartilaginous margin. Flowers long-stalked, pale pink or white, the reflexed corolla-lobes about 2cm long, with ear-like appendages at the base and with dark purple blotches divided into 2 parts. Style scarcely protruding from the corolla. Fruit-stalk spirally twisted from the tip.
Deciduous woods, thickets, extending into the mountain zone.
S. Europe, from S. France to the Aegean, W. Anatolia.
C. graecum Link: flowers in late autumn, corm rooting only from the base. Leaves with a thickened, toothed margin, rarely angled or lobed. Corolla-lobes with ear-like appendages. Fruit-stalk twisted spirally from the middle or the base (Greece, Aegean, Cyprus, Asia Minor).

□■ *Cyclamen repandum* Sibth. & Sm.
□□ 10–20cm; March–May; ♃
Corm hairy, 1.5–3.5cm, rooting only from the base. Leaves appearing before the flowers in spring, broadly heart-shaped, pointed, with a deeply toothed to sinuate margin. Flowers usually rose-red, more rarely white or pink and darker around the throat (var. *rhodense* Meikle), the reflexed lobes 1.5–3cm long, without ear-like appendages. Style protruding. Fruit-stalk twisted spirally from the tip.
In the undergrowth of shady, usually evergreen woods and maquis.
Mediterranean region, from France and N.W. Africa to the Aegean.
Other spring-flowering species without ear-like appendages: *C. creticum* Hildebr., corolla pure white, the lobes 1.6–2.5cm long (Crete), and *C. balearicum* Willk.: Corolla white with pink veins, lobes 1–1.8cm (S. France, Balearic Islands). The Cyclamen grown as ornamental house-plants are derived from *C. persicum* Mill., that occurs in the eastern Mediterranean region. Corolla white or pink, darker around the throat, the reflexed lobes 2.5–4.5cm. Fruit-stalk curved but not spirally twisted.

□□ *Anagallis foemina* Mill. (*A. caerulea* Schreb. non L.) **Blue Pimpernel**
■□ 5–30cm; April–October; ☉, ☉
Stem 4-angled, prostrate, ascending or erect, with opposite, sessile, ovate-lanceolate to lanceolate leaves dotted with glands. Flowers long-stalked in the upper leaf-axils, with a spreading, always blue corolla. Corolla-lobes 5, 4–6mm long, with small teeth towards the tip, and a few, usually 4-celled, glandular hairs, the lobes not overlapping so that the sepals are visible from above for almost their whole length in an open flower. Calyx as long as the bud and covering it completely.
Cultivated and fallow land, garigue.
Mediterranean region, Canary Islands, occasionally introduced into central Europe and elsewhere.
A. arvensis L., **Scarlet Pimpernel**, is widespread: Flowers vermilion, pink or blue, the last form dominant in the Mediterranean region and often confused with *A. foemina*. Corolla-lobes with numerous 3-celled, glandular hairs, overlapping in the lower half so that only the tips of the sepals are visible from above in the open flower. Calyx only ⅔ as long as the bud and not covering it entirely.

□□ *Anagallis monelli* L. (*A. linifolia* L.) **Shrubby Pimpernel**
□■ 10–50cm; March–June; ♃
An ascending or erect plant with round stems, woody at the base. Leaves opposite, sessile, often with small, sterile shoots in the axils, linear-lanceolate or elliptic. Flowers in the axils of the upper leaves, on stalks 2–5cm long. Corolla bright blue with 5 spreading lobes, 5–12mm long, and partially or completely coloured red at the base. Stamens with numerous purple or yellow basal hairs. Calyx 4–6mm. Very variable in leaf-shape and flower-size.
Fallow and cultivated land, waysides.
Iberian peninsula, Sardinia, Sicily, N.W. Africa.

Sea Lavender family *Plumbaginaceae*

■□ *Plumbago europaea* L. **European Plumbago**
□□ 0.3–1m; July–October; ♃
An erect plant with stiff, spreading branches. Stem furrowed. Leaves alternate, undulate, glandular toothed, mealy beneath, the lower ones stalked and ovate, the middle ones lanceolate, sessile, lobed at the base and clasping the stem. Flowers numerous, purple or pink, in spike-like inflorescences. Corolla-tube slender, 1½ times as long as the calyx, the 5 lobes spreading out like the spokes of a wheel. Calyx 5-toothed, 5–7mm, with large, conspicuous, stalked glands on the ribs.
Waysides, waste ground, fallow land.
Mediterranean region, S.W. Asia.
A frequently grown species belonging to the same genus is *Plumbago auriculata* Lam. (*P. capensis* Thunb.), a decorative shrub, arching over or climbing, up to 1.5m high, with delicate blue flowers about 2.5cm across (native in S. Africa).

□■ *Limonium sinuatum* (L.) Mill. (*Statice sinuata* L.) **Winged Sea Lavender**
□□ 15–40cm; April–September; ♃
A roughly hairy plant, with a basal rosette of pinnately divided leaves with rounded lobes, 3–15cm long and about 1.5cm broad. Stem ascending to erect, with 4 rather undulate wings, 1–3mm broad, that end in 3 linear-lanceolate appendages at the nodes. Inflorescence-branches with 3 wings, broadening above, the appendages of which surround the spikes, the latter composed of 2 or 3-flowered, upward-pointing spikelets and bracts. Calyx 10–14mm, the blue-purple, wrinkled, papery margin almost entire. Corolla-lobes small, yellowish white.
Sandy and rocky coasts, also in saline areas inland. An ornamental plant, often used for dried flower arrangements.
Mediterranean region, Canary Islands.

□□ *Limonium angustifolium* (Tausch) Degen (*L. vulgare* Mill. ssp. *serotinum* (Rchb.) Gams)
■□ 30–70cm; July–October; ♃
Plant hairless, all leaves basal, lanceolate-spathulate, gradually tapering into the stalk and forming a sheath at the base, with a stout midrib and thin, pinnate, alteral veins, usually pointed, 10–15×1.5–4cm. Inflorescence large, with sparse, often backward-curving branches, sterile branches few or absent. Spikes 1–2cm long, with 6–8 spikelets per centimetre, each consisting of 2 flowers. Outer bract herbaceous, about half as long as the middle one. Corolla 6–8mm.
Saltmarshes on flat coasts.
One of the few *Limonium* species distributed throughout the entire Mediterranean region, with *L. vulgare* Mill. ssp. *vulgare* in W. and N. Europe.
In the whole region, on flat and rocky coasts, there are well over 100 species, often difficult to distinguish, and usually with basal rosettes of small leaves. Many species are restricted to certain parts of the coast, and only a few are more widely distributed, such as *L. oleifolium* Mill. with several subspecies: leaves 1-veined, 3–5cm long. Inflorescence with many sterile branches. Flower-spikes 2–4cm long, with 4 curved and compressed spikelets per centimetre. The easily recognisable species *L. articulatum* (Lois.) Kuntze has jointed stems, resulting from constriction at the nodes. Leaves withered at flowering time (Corsica, Sardinia).

□□ *Limoniastrum monopetalum* (L.) Boiss.
□■ 0.3–1.2m; June–August; ♄
A small much-branched shrub with salt glands. Leaves blue-green, fleshy, spathulate and narrowed towards the base with a sheath clasping the stem. Flowers solitary or in pairs in branched, spike-like inflorescences, very fragile in a dry state. Corolla pink, 1–2cm in diameter, the tube about as long as the 5 lobes. Calyx 5-toothed, enclosed by 3 overlapping bracts.
Sandy beaches, saltmarshes.
S. Europe (absent from the Balkan peninsula), Crete, N. Africa.

Storax family *Styracaceae*
Olive family *Oleaceae*

Styrax officinalis L. **Storax** *Styracaceae*
2–7m; April–May; ♄
Deciduous shrub or small tree, stems with star-shaped hairs. Leaves alternate, broadly ovate to ovate-lanceolate, entire, 3–7cm long, grey-green beneath. Flowers with stalks 1–2cm long, scented, 3–6 together on short-shoots, white, about 2cm long, with a very short corolla-tube and 5–7 overlapping, lanceolate lobes. Calyx cup-shaped, almost entire or with 5 small teeth. Fruit leathery, white-woolly, with persistent calyx. The only representative of this family in the Mediterranean region.
Open woods, thickets, river-banks.
Eastern Mediterranean region, westwards to central Italy, naturalised in S. France.

Fraxinus ornus L. **Manna Ash, Flowering Ash** *Oleaceae*
6–15m; April–June; ♄
Deciduous tree with smooth, grey bark. Leaves opposite, each pair at right-angles to the next, with 5–9 leaflets on a stalk about 30cm long. Leaflets on mature trees 3–8cm long, irregularly serrate, ovate-lanceolate, pointed, distinctly stalked. Flowers scented, in erect, later arching panicles, appearing before the leaves. Petals white, usually 4, united in pairs at the base, linear, usually 6(–10)mm long (other species of Ash have no petals). Stamens 2, with long filaments. Fruit dark brown, tongue-shaped, pendent, 2–4cm long. The dried juice (manna), obtained from incisions in the bark, is used as a laxative.
Warm, mixed deciduous forests, extending into the mountain zone, occasionally grown as a decorative tree. Formerly also planted as a source of manna, and for its leaves that were used as fodder.
S. Europe, northwards into Czechoslovakia, Asia Minor.
F. angustifolia Vahl is similar to our native Ash, but the leaf-buds are dark brown, and the sessile leaflets have an equal number of serrations and lateral veins (river-banks, woods in the Mediterranean region, S.W. Asia).

Phillyrea angustifolia L. *Oleaceae*
Up to 2.5m; March–May; ♄
Evergreen shrub with hairless or only finely hairy young stems. Leaves all similar, opposite, linear to lanceolate, 3–8cm long and at most 1.5cm broad, dark green, leathery, entire or rarely distantly toothed, with 4–6 pairs of inconspicuous lateral veins making a small angle with the midrib. Flowers scented, in short racemes in the leaf-axils, with a greenish white, 4-lobed corolla, the lobes about 2mm long. Calyx thick, brownish, cut for about ¼ of its length into 4 rounded lobes. Fruits fleshy, blue-black in September–October, 6–8mm, with persistent styles.
Maquis, open woods, mainly on chalk.
Western and central Mediterranean region, eastwards to Yugoslavia and Albania, Canary Islands.

Phillyrea latifolia L. *Oleaceae*
Up to 5(–15)m; March–May; ♄
Evergreen shrub or small tree with the young stems covered in a downy felt. Leaves dark green and leathery, opposite (in contrast to *Rhamnus alaternus*, see p. 144), variable in form: juvenile leaves 2–7×1–4cm, ovate or heart-shaped to ovate-lanceolate, more or less dentate or serrate. Adult leaves only 1–6×0.4–2cm, broadly lanceolate, entire or finely serrate with 7–11 pairs of conspicuous lateral veins, making a wide angle with the midrib. Flowers as in *P. angustifolia* in small racemes in the leaf-axils, but the 4-lobed calyx thin, yellowish, cut for up to ¾ of its length into triangular lobes. Fruits fleshy, blue-black, 7–10mm, the styles soon falling.
Maquis, open woods, mainly on chalk.
Mediterranean region, Canary Islands.
Phillyrea media L., with all its leaves like the adult ones of *P. latifolia* L., is not regarded as a separate species by many authorities.

Olive family *Oleaceae*
Gentian family *Gentianaceae*
Periwinkle family *Apocynaceae*

■□
□□ *Olea europaea* L. **Olive** *Oleaceae*
Up to 15m; May–June; ♄

Evergreen tree, gnarled in age, with a broad crown and grey, fissured bark. Leaves 2–8cm long and 0.5–1.5cm broad, oblong-lanceolate, short-stalked, leathery, dark green above, and shining silver-grey beneath. Flowers small, scented, yellowish white, 4-lobed, arranged in a panicle. Fruits 1–3.5cm, fleshy, with a hard stone, green at first, brownish to blue-black when ripe. Olives are harvested October–November. See also p. 25.

The most frequently cultivated tree in the entire Mediterranean region.

Wild plants occurring in the woods and maquis are designated var. *sylvestris* Brot. (var. *oleaster* DC.). They are distinguished by having smaller leaves, spiny stems, and small, bitter fruits containing little oil.

□■
□□ *Blackstonia perfoliata* (L.) Huds. (*Chlora perfoliata* (L.) L.) **Yellow-wort** *Gentianaceae*
10–60cm; May–September; ☉

An erect, hairless plant, with a simple stem or branched in the inflorescence. Basal leaves ovate, blunt-tipped, stem-leaves opposite, ovate-triangular, pointed, more or less joined in pairs. Flowers yellow, 8–15(–35)mm, with a short corolla-tube and 6–8(–12) spreading lobes. Calyx deeply divided into 6–12 narrow segments. There are several subspecies that are sometimes considered as separate species.

Damp places in woods, maquis, on waysides, especially on sand.

Mediterranean region, Canary Islands, W. and central Europe, S.W. Asia.

The similar species *Centaurium maritimum* (L.) Fritsch has 4 or 5 corolla-lobes (Mediterranean region, W. Europe northwards to N.W. France, Canary Islands).

□□
■□ *Centaurium spicatum* (L.) Fritsch (*Erythraea spicata* (L.) Pers.) *Gentianaceae*
10–55cm; June–September; ☉, ☉

Plant hairless, stem erect, branched from the base or the middle, with a basal rosette of broadly ovate leaves, sometimes soon falling. Stem-leaves numerous, opposite, sessile, elliptic-oblong to ovate-lanceolate, the upper ones lanceolate, 3 to 5-veined. Flowers 12–14mm, sessile, in erect, spike-like, leafy inflorescences. Corolla pink, with 5 spreading lobes, 4–5mm long. Calyx with appressed, linear teeth, about as long as the corolla-tube.

Saltmarshes, damp hollows in dunes, cultivated land.

Mediterranean region, Canary Islands, eastwards to central Asia.

C. tenuiflorum (Hoffm. & Link) Fritsch: stem usually without a distinct basal rosette, but with erect branches in the upper part. Inflorescence a dense cluster of flowers 12–14mm long, with stalks at least 2mm long (Mediterranean region, W. Europe, Canary Islands, S.W. Asia). In addition, there are 2 species that also occur in central and N. Europe, *C. erythraea* Rafn with several subspecies and *C. pulchellum* (Sw.) Druce.

□□
□■ *Nerium oleander* L. **Oleander** *Apocynaceae*
1–4m; July–September; ♄

A robust, evergreen shrub. Leaves leathery, mostly in whorls of 3 or 4, more rarely opposite, lanceolate, narrowing into the stalk, up to 15cm long and 2cm broad. Flowers in terminal inflorescences, corolla rose-red or white, 3–4cm in diameter with a funnel-shaped tube and 5 spreading lobes cut off obliquely at the end, and with jagged scales in the throat. Calyx of 5 united sepals, densely glandular-hairy within. Fruits conspicuous, erect, reddish brown 8–18cm long. Seeds with a tuft of long, brown hairs. This very poisonous plant with milky juice contains glycosides that have an effect on the heart, and it is therefore of medicinal use.

River-banks, intermittently dry stream-beds, on stony soils.

Frequently cultivated, sometimes in the double-flowered forms, as a hedge-plant and for ornament.

Mediterranean region.

Periwinkle family *Apocynaceae*
Milkweed family *Asclepiadaceae*

■□
□□ *Vinca difformis* Pourr. (*V. media* Hoffm. & Link) **Intermediate Periwinkle** *Apocynaceae*
Creeping up to 2m; February–May; ♃
A far-creeping plant with ascending or erect flowering-stems up to 30cm high. Leaves ever-green, opposite, ovate-lanceolate, shortly stalked, hairless on the margins, 2.5–7×1.5–4.5cm. Flowers solitary in the upper leaf-axils, their stalks shorter than the accompanying leaf. Corolla pale blue, with a funnel-shaped tube 1.2–1.8cm long, and the limb spreading out flat, 3–4.5cm in diameter, its 5 lobes pointed or cut off obliquely. Calyx-lobes very narrowly trian-gular, 5–14mm long, hairless. Ssp. *sardoa* Stearn from Sardinia has minute hairs on the leaf-margins and calyx-lobes, and flowers 6–7cm across.
Shady and damp hedges, ditches and thickets.
Western Mediterranean region, eastwards to Italy.
Two species with a fringe of hairs on the leaf-margins and calyx-lobes are *V. major* L. with blue-purple flowers, 3–5cm across (western and central Mediterranean region, Canary Islands, often naturalised elsewhere) and *V. balcanica* Pénzes with flowers only 2.5–3.5cm across, and leaves not more than 3.5×2cm (Balkan peninsula).

□■
□□ *Gomphocarpus fruticosus* (L.) Ait.f. **Bristly-fruited Silkweed** *Asclepiadaceae*
1–2m; May–September; ♄
An erect and branched plant, woody at the base, with milky juice. Leaves opposite, often in whorls of 3, shortly stalked, linear-lanceolate, 2–10×0.3–1cm, curled up at the margin and green on both sides. Flowers stalked, pendent, in umbel-like inflorescences arising from the leaf-axils and at the ends of the stems, with a white, 5-lobed corolla. Corolla-lobes ovate-oblong, fringed at the margin, recurved, corona fleshy. Fruit-capsule inflated, ovate, pointed, 4–6×2–3cm, softly spiny. Seeds with silky hairs. Poisonous plant.
River-banks, damp places, usually near the coast, also grown as an ornamental plant.
In the whole of the Mediterranean region and the Canary Islands, and naturalised in places elsewhere, native in S. Africa.

□□
■□ *Cynanchum acutum* L. **Stranglewort** *Asclepiadaceae*
1–3m; June–September; ♃
A twining, blue-green plant with milky juice. Leaves thin, opposite, heart-shaped, deeply notched at the base, with the stalk 1–5cm long. Flowers scented, in stalked clusters in the leaf-axils. Corolla white or pink, 8–12mm in diameter, with 5 spreading lobes and a small corona divided into 10 segments. Calyx 5-lobed, finely hairy. Fruit usually a single follicle, 8×1cm, smooth. Seeds with long, silky hairs. Poisonous plant.
Saline soils, in hedges and on river-banks near the coast.
Mediterranean region, Canary Islands, eastwards to central Asia, absent from Corsica and Sardinia.

□□
□■ *Vincetoxicum hirundinaria* Med. (*V. officinale* Moench, *Cynanchum vincetoxicum* (L.) Pers.) *Asclepiadaceae*
0.2–1.2m; June–September; ♃
Stem erect, with numerous opposite, more or less hairy leaves, broadly ovate to ovate-lanceolate, pointed, sometimes heart-shaped at the base, with stalks 5–10mm long. Flowers in small clusters in the leaf-axils, with a white or yellow 5-lobed corolla, 3–10mm across, and a small corona formed by appendages of the stamens. Fruit a pair of follicles, about 6×0.8cm, smooth. Seeds with a tuft of white hairs. A very variable species with many subspecies. Yellow-flowered forms predominate in the Mediterranean region, as for example the plant illustrated, ssp. *intermedium* (Lor. & Barr.) Markg.: stem 50–60cm. Corolla 6–9mm across, the lobes hairy within (S. France. N.E. Spain). Poisonous plant.
Grassy pastures, waste ground, edges of woods.
Europe, N.W. Africa, Asia Minor, Caucasus.

Bedstraw family *Rubiaceae*

■□ *Putoria calabrica* (L. f.) DC.
□□ 30–80cm; April–September; ♄
A much-branched, prostrate subshrub with a strong smell. Leaves opposite, shortly stalked, lanceolate, 1–2cm long and 2–4mm broad, recurved at the margin, leathery, becoming black on drying. Stipules small, ovate. Flowers in terminal clusters, the pink, narrowly funnel-shaped corolla 1–1.5cm long, with 4 spreading, linear-lanceolate lobes, 3–6mm long. Stamens protruding. Fruit about 5mm, red to black.
Rock-crevices, especially in limestone.
Mediterranean region, absent from France and the western Mediterranean islands.

□■ *Crucianella maritima* L.
□□ 10–40cm; May–September; ♃
A hairless, prostrate or ascending plant, woody at the base, with smooth, whitish stems. Leaves leathery, blue-green with a white margin, 4–10×1–4mm, ovate-lanceolate and sharply pointed, in whorls of 4, often closely overlapping on young stems. Inflorescence a spike, 2–4cm, the narrowly funnel-shaped flowes 10–13mm long, with 5 short, converging lobes, arising singly in the axils of separate, ovate, fringed bracts, 3–7mm broad, and protruding beyond them. At the base of the flowers are 2 shorter, folded bracteoles, more or less joined at the base.
Established dunes and rocks.
Mediterranean region, absent from the Balkan peninsula and Asia Minor.
Two annual species that occur in almost the entire Mediterranean region are *C. angustifolia* L.: leaves usually in whorls of 6–8, inflorescence 2–8cm long, corolla 4-lobed, not protruding beyond the separate bracts, and *C. latifolia* L.: leaves in whorls of 4–6. Inflorescence about 15cm long, the 4-lobed corolla somewhat longer than the bracts, that are usually united at the base.

□□ *Valantia hispida* L.
■□ 5–20cm; March–June; ☉
A delicate, inconspicuous, slightly fleshy plant. Stem branched from the base, ascending or erect, with rough, spreading hairs especially in the upper part, and compound spike-like inflorescences at the ends. leaves in whorls of 4, narrowly obovate to lanceolate, more or less pointed, 2–10×1–3.5mm. Flowers in threes forming small inflorescences in the leaf-axils, the middle one bisexual with a yellowish, 2-lobed corolla, the 2 lateral ones male, 3-lobed, their stalks bent downwards at fruiting-time, sometimes joined and thickened, enclosing the fruit, with 15–25 straight bristles on the back.
Flat, stony and sandy places, also on walls.
Mediterranean region, Canary Islands, S.W. Asia, absent from the northern Balkan peninsula.
V. muralis L.: stem more or less softly hairy only in the upper part. Leaves usually smaller, blunt, stalks with a prominent horn on the back, bristles hooked (Mediterranean region).

□□ *Rubia peregrina* L. **Wild Madder**
□■ 0.3–2.5m; April–August; ♄
Stem 4-angled, climbing, woody at the base and perennial, rough like the leaf-margins and midribs because of small, recurved spines or sometimes smooth. Leaves firm, leathery, dark green, sessile, narrowly or broadly ovate-lanceolate, 15–60×3–20mm, in whorls of 4–8, lateral veins inconspicuous. Inflorescences many-flowered, terminal and in the leaf-axils, distinctly longer than the leaves. Corolla 4–6mm broad, greenish yellow, with usually 5 bristle-tipped lobes. Fruit a black berry, 4–6mm.
Maquis, woods, hedges.
S. and W. Europe, northwards to Ireland, N.W. Africa, Canary Islands, m.W. Turkey.
R. tenuifolia D'Urv.: inflorescences not longer than the leaves, flowers 7–8mm (eastern Mediterranean region). *R. tinctorum* L.: stem withering to the ground in autumn, with soft, pale green, shortly stalked leaves, net-veined beneath. Corolla yellow, the lobes pointed but not bristle-tipped. Cultivated in earlier times as the source of a dye (madder), nowadays occurring wild throughout the Mediterranean region (native in Asia).

Convolvulus family *Convolvulaceae*

■□ *Calystegia soldanella* (L.) R. Br. **Sea Bindweed**
□□ Creeping to 1m; April–October; ⌕
A hairless plant of sandy beaches, with long creeping, not twining, stems. Leaves dark green and rather fleshy, kidney-shaped, long-stalked, similar to those of the Alpine Snowbell, *Soldanella alpina* L. Flowers funnel-shaped, 3–5cm long, pink, solitary in the leaf-axils. A pair of broad, ovate bracts encloses the calyx, distinguishing this plant from species of *Convolvulus*.
Coastal dunes.
Mediterranean coasts, also coasts of the Black Sea, Caspian Sea, the Atlantic and the North Sea, sporadically as far north as Scotland and Denmark, nowadays distributed over most of the world.

□■ *Convolvulus cantabrica* L. **Pink Convolvulus**
□□ 10–50cm; May–July; ⌕, ♄
An ascending or erect plant with several stems, woody at the base, and bearing spreading hairs at least in the lower part. Basal leaves spathulate-oblong, narrowed into a stalk, the upper ones oblong-lanceolate and sessile. Inflorescences long-stalked, longer than the accompanying leaf. Flowers 1–3(–7) on short stalks bearing 2 bracts. Corolla funnel-shaped, pink, 1.5–2.5cm long, with silky hairs on the outer surface of the folds. Calyx-lobes with long, woolly hairs. Capsule hairy.
Garigue, maquis, grassy pastures, waysides.
Mediterranean region, S.E. Europe, S.W. Asia.
Some species have narrowly oblong leaves, such as *C. lineatus* L.: plant with dense, silky hairs, inflorescence-stalks shorter than the accompanying leaves (Mediterranean region, E. Europe, S.W. Asia). Several species have clusters of flowers: *C. cneorum* L., flowers white (western and central Mediterranean region), *C. oleifolius* Desr., flowers pink (eastern Mediterranean region, N. Africa) and *C. lanuginosus* Desr., flowers pink, capsules hairless (S.W. Europe, N.W. Africa).

□□ *Convolvulus tricolor* L. **Dwarf Convolvulus**
■□ 20–60cm; March–June; usually ☉
Plant hairy, stems ascending to erect, with sessile, obovate-oblong leaves. Flowers solitary, on stalks as long as or longer than the accompanying leaves and bearing 2 minute bracteoles. Corolla funnel-shaped, 1.5–4cm long, tricoloured, yellow at the base, white in the middle and blue at the edge. Sepals entirely green, in 2 distinct parts, with long hairs. Capsule hairy. In ssp. *tricolor* the calyx-lobes are not longer than the tube, in ssp. *cupanianus* (Sa'ad) Stace they are distinctly longer (native only in Sicily).
Cultivated land, waysides.
S. Europe, N.W. Africa, Canary Islands, cultivated elsewhere and then sometimes escaping and growing wild.
The following species also have sessile leaves, *C. meonanthus* Hoffmanns. & Link: sepals not in 2 distinct parts, their margins membranous. Corolla 14–22mm, capsule hairless (western Mediterranean region) and *C. pentapetaloides* L. with the corolla only 7–10mm long (S. Europe, S.W. Asia). Particularly large, often brightly coloured, funnel-shaped flowers are a characteristic of the subtropical genus *Ipomoea*, several species of which are cultivated as ornamental plants. *I. sagittata* Poir., however, is considered to be native in the Mediterranean region.

□□ *Convolvulus siculus* L. **Small Blue Convolvulus**
□■ 10–40cm; March–May; ☉
A delicate plant, branched at the base, at first prostrate, then ascending. Leaves ovate, pointed, heart-shaped or rounded at the base, with thin stalks. Flowers usually solitary on thin stalks that are shorter than the accompanying leaves. Corolla funnel-shaped, blue with a yellow tube, distinctly 5-lobed, 7–12mm. Just below the hairy sepals are 2 lanceolate bracteoles. Ssp. *agrestis* (Schweinf.) Verdc. (only Sardinia and N. Africa) has, by contrast, linear bracteoles, situated well below the sepals. Fruit hairless.
Fallow land, open stony places.
Mediterranean region, Canary Islands.

Convolvulus family *Convolvulaceae*
Borage family *Boraginaceae*

■☐ *Convolvulus althaeoides* L. **Mallow-leaved Bindweed** *Convolvulaceae*
☐☐ Stem up to 1m long; April–June; ♃
Stem prostrate or twining. Leaves stalked, at least the upper ones deeply lobed and heart-shaped to arrow-shaped at the base. The conspicuous, pink, funnel-shaped flowers, 2.5–4cm long, arise singly or up to 3 together in the leaf-axils, on stalks that are longer than the accompanying leaves. There are 2 subspecies: ssp. *althaeoides*, a plant with spreading hairs, the lower leaves crenately lobed, the upper ones irregularly and more or less deeply lobed, but rarely as far as the midrib, segments of the outer calyx 8–10mm, and ssp. *tenuissimus* (Sibth. & Sm.) Stace, hairs appressed, uppermost leaves lobed to the midrib, the segments fairly narrow, segments of the outer calyx 4–7mm.
Waysides, cultivated land, fallow fields.
Mediterranean region, Canary Islands; ssp. *tenuissimus* is more common in the east.

☐■ *Heliotropium europaeum* L. **Heliotrope** *Boraginaceae*
☐☐ 5–40cm; June–October; ☉
A softly hairy, green to grey plant with an ascending or erect, branched stem. Leaves ovate to elliptic, entire, up to 5.5cm long and 2.8 cm broad, and with stalks up to 3.5cm long. Flowers scentless, sessile, in bractless, simple or forked, many-flowered inflorescences that are coiled at first but unroll later. Corolla white, 2–4mm across, with 5 spreading lobes. Calyx divided almost to the base, persistent, with spreading lobes. Nutlets 4, separate, wrinkled, hairless or hairy. A variable species.
Cultivated land, waste ground, waysides.
Mediterranean region, Canary Islands, S.E. Europe, naturalised in places, occasionally as far as central Europe.
H. suaveolens Bieb.: flowers scented, 4–8mm across (S.E. Europe, S.W. Asia). *H. supinum* L.: stem prostrate. leaves with white hairs beneath, stalks up to 1.5cm long. Calyx divided at most to a ¼ of its length, enclosing the solitary nutlet at fruiting time and falling with it. Corolla only 1mm across (Mediterranean region, Canary Islands, eastwards to India).

☐☐ *Neatostema apulum* (L.) Johnst. (*Lithospermum apulum* (L.) Vahl) *Boraginaceae*
■☐ 3–30cm; March–June; ☉
Plant stiffly erect, with one or more stems, branched above from the same point. Basal leaves linear to narrowly spathulate, narrowed into the stalk, the numerous stem-leaves linear and sessile, all with spreading bristly hairs especially on the margins, up to 7×0.5cm. Flowers almost sessile, in dense inflorescences, leafy right to the tip, and curved backwards. Corolla yellow, about 6mm long, with 5 hairy lobes. Calyx about 4mm, its 5 pointed lobes slightly shorter than the tube, bristly on the outside, with soft white hairs within. Nutlets beaked, warted, light brown.
Open, stony grassland, garigue.
Mediterranean region, Canary Islands.

☐☐ *Buglossoides purpurocaerulea* (L.) Johnst. (*Lithospermum purpurocaeruleum* L.) **Purple**
☐■ **Gromwell** *Boraginaceae*
15–70cm; April–June; ♃
Stem erect, with spreading hairs, arising unbranched from the rhizome, with several usually prostrate, rooting, non-flowering shoots. Leaves bright green, lanceolate, the lower ones narrowed into a short stalk, the upper ones sessile, 3.5–8×0.7–1.5cm, with rough appressed hairs, and only the midrib visible beneath. Flowers almost sessile in usually 3 terminal clusters, surrounded by leaf-like bracts. Corolla funnel-shaped, hairy on the outer surface, red-purple at first, then bright blue, 5-lobed, 14–19mm long, with 5 bands of short hairs in the throat. Calyx 6–8.5mm, with pointed lobes, bristly. Nutlets 3.5–5mm, smooth and shining, white.
Submediterranean deciduous oak woods and thickets in the mountain zone.
S. Europe, spreading out into the dry and warm areas of central and W. Europe, S.W. Asia.

Borage family *Boraginaceae*

■□
□□ *Lithodora hispidula* (Sibth. & Sm.) Gris. (*Lithospermum hispidulum* Sibth. & Sm.)
10–35cm; March–May; ♄
A much-branched shrub forming large cushions, the stem short and stiff, with appressed white bristles (lens needed). Leaves sessile, dark green, leathery, narrowly oblong-ovate, up to 15×4.5mm, flat or slightly upturned at the margin, the bristles on the upper side long, spreading, and thickened at the base, those on the lower side short and appressed. Flowers solitary or up to 4 together, blue-purple, with a long, funnel-shaped corolla, hairless on the outside, the tube 1.2cm long, opening out into 5 lobes about 1cm in diameter. Calyx 7mm, with bristly hairs. Nutlets usually 1, finely warted, white.
Garigue, pine woods.
Aegean, Anatolia, Cyprus, Cyrenaica.
There are several species with small areas of distribution. One of these with the corolla hairy on the outside is *L. rosmarinifolia* (Ten.) Johnst., with leaves 1–6cm long, linear, and recurved at the margin (S. Italy, Sicily, Algeria).

□■
□□ *Onosma echioides* L. **Golden Drop**
15–40cm; May–July; ♃, ♄
A bristly hairy, grey-green plant, the bristles arising from small tubercles, surrounded by 10–20 bristles about ⅕ as long. Stems several, erect, woody at the base, also non-flowering shoots with only tufts of leaves. Basal leaves linear-lanceolate, narrowed towards the base, 20–70×2–7mm. Inflorescence only slightly branched with almost sessile flowers. Bracts about as long as the calyces, which are divided almost to the base into linear-lanceolate lobes and enlarge after flowering from 1 to 1.5cm. Corolla pale yellow, tubular, 1.8–2.5cm long, with 5 short lobes.
Stony and grassy pastures on chalk and serpentine rock.
Italy, Sicily, western part of the Balkan peninsula.
There are numerous species with their distribution confined to small areas, especially in the eastern Mediterranean region.

□□
■□ *Cerinthe major* L. **Honeywort**
15–60cm; March–June; ☉
An erect, blue-green plant, almost hairless. Lower leaves shortly stalked, spathulate, fringed at the margin, and often covered with white dots, the upper ones sessile, ovate, heart-shaped at the base and clasping the stem. Flowers in clusters, the bracts usually tinged red-purple, as long as or longer than the calyx. Corolla tubular, straight, yellow, often tinged purple at the base or entirely purple, up to 3cm long and 8mm broad, more than twice as long as the calyx. Corolla-lobes sharply recurved at their tips, much shorter than the corolla-tube.
Cultivated and fallow land, waysides.
Mediterranean region.
Cerinthe retorta Sibth. & Sm.: corolla only 1–1.5cm long and 3–5mm broad, curved above, pale yellow with purple tips to the lobes (Balkan peninsula, W. Anatolia).

□□
□■ *Alkanna tinctoria* (L.) Tausch **Dyer's Alkanet**
10–30cm; April–June; ♃
A prostrate or ascending plant with grey hairs but no glands. Lower leaves stalked, linear-lanceolate, 6–15cm long and up to 2.5cm broad, the upper ones sessile with a heart-shaped base. Bracts scarcely longer than the calyx, which is 5-parted almost to the base. Flowers in clusters that are dense at first but later become considerably elongated. Corolla bright blue, hairless outside, tubular, opening out funnel-shaped to a diameter of 6–8mm. Calyx as long as the corolla-tube or only slightly shorter. Nutlets warted. The outer layer of the root, when dried, contains the red dye alkannin. Genuine alkanna comes from the **Henna** bush (*Lawsonia inermis* L.).
Sandy beaches, stony pastures, fallow land.
Mediterranean region, northwards to Slovakia.
Other, mainly yellow-flowered species of *Alkanna* are endemic in the Balkan peninsula, but the only one occurring in the western Mediterranean region is *A. lutea* DC.: plant an annual, glandular-hairy. Corolla 5–7mm in diameter. Bracts at least twice as long as the calyx.

Borage family *Boraginaceae*

■☐ *Echium italicum* L. **Pale Bugloss**
☐☐ 0.3–1m; April–August; ☉
Plant erect, densely covered with spreading whitish to yellowish bristles. Basal leaves
lanceolate, 20–35cm long and 1.5–4cm broad, narrowed at the base, stem-leaves sessile.
Inflorescence spike-like or branched forming a pyramid. Corolla whitish, flesh-coloured or
pale blue, 10–12mm long, narrowly funnel-shaped and oblique at the end, finely hairy outside. Stamens 4–5 with pale filaments, protruding considerably from the corolla. Calyx 6–
7mm, divided almost to the base into narrow, lanceolate lobes.
Fallow land, pastures.
S. Europe, S.W. Asia.
E. asperrimum Lam. (*E. italicum* ssp. *pyrenaicum* Rouy) is similar: corolla 13–18mm, flesh-
coloured. Stamens with red filaments (western Mediterranean region).

☐■ *Echium plantagineum* L. (*E. lycopsis* L. p.p.) **Purple Viper's Bugloss**
☐☐ 20–60cm; April–July; ☉, ☉
Plant usually branched, with soft bristles. Basal rosette plantain-like, the leaves long-
stalked, ovate, with prominent midrib and lateral veins, 5–14cm long. Stem-leaves oblong-
lanceolate, the upper ones sessile with a more or less heart-shaped base. Inflorescence
usually branched, corolla blue, later purple-red, 18–30mm long, broadly funnel-shaped and
oblique at the end, the outer surface hairy only on the margin and the veins. Stamens 2, protruding. Calyx 7–10mm, divided almost to the base into narrow, lanceolate lobes, enlarging
to 15mm at fruiting-time.
Waysides, waste ground, sandy places near the coast.
Mediterranean region and W. Europe, northwards to S.W. England, Canary Islands.
Echium vulgare L. is similar; plant covered with rough hairs, basal leaves lanceolate,
narrowed into the stalk, without prominent lateral veins. Corolla only 10–19mm, with 4 or 5
stamens protruding from it (almost the whole of Europe, Asia).

☐☐ *Echium creticum* L.
■☐ 20–90cm; April–July; ☉
Stem erect, with spreading bristly hairs and an under-layer of short, appressed, downward-
pointing hairs. Basal leaves 8–18cm long and 1–2.5cm broad, lanceolate, narrowed into
the stalk, stem-leaves narrowed at the base, sessile. Inflorescence more or less branched,
panicle-like. Corolla 1.5–4cm long, broadly funnel-shaped, oblique at the end, the outer surface evenly covered with fine hairs, remaining red-purple or becoming bluish-purple or blue,
with 1 or 2 stamens protruding. Calyx 7–9mm, divided almost to the base into narrow,
lanceolate lobes, enlarging at fruiting-time to 12–19mm. There are several subspecies.
Waysides, fallow land, waste ground.
Western Mediterranean region.
Another red-flowered species is *E. angustifolium* Mill. (incl. *E. diffusum* Sibth. & Sm.): plant
with grey bristles, leaves only 3–8mm broad. Corolla 16–22mm long with 4 or 5 protruding
stamens (eastern Mediterranean region).

☐☐ *Nonea vesicaria* (L.) Rchb. (*N. nigricans* (Desf.) DC.)
☐■ 10–50cm; March–May; ☉,
An ascending or erect plant, not much branched, with rough bristles and short glandular
hairs. Leaves sessile, more or less stem-clasping higher up, lanceolate, 3–20cm long. Corolla
8–12mm, with a cylindrical tube, and 5 short, blunt, brown-purple lobes, 3–5mm across.
Anthers attached above the middle of the tube but not protruding. Calyx 5–7mm, enlarged at
fruiting-time to 10–15mm, open, the teeth about as long as the tube. Nutlets with a wrinkled
surface and collar-like basal ring.
Open sandy and stony places.
Iberian peninsula, Balearic Islands, Sicily, N.W. Africa.
N. ventricosa (Sibth. & Sm.) Griseb.: flowers pale yellow or white, the calyx greatly enlarged
at fruiting-time and its teeth converging (S. Europe, eastwards to Syria).

Borage family *Boraginaceae*

■□ *Anchusa azurea* Mill. (*A. italica* Retz.) **Large Blue Alkanet**
□□ 0.2–1.5m; April–August; ♃
An erect plant, much-branched above, and densely covered with stiff, white hairs. Leaves lanceolate, the lower ones 10–30cm long and 1.5–5cm broad, narrowed into the stalk, the upper ones sessile. Bracts shorter than the calyx. Clusters of bright blue to violet flowers combine to form large, showy panicles, their stalks up to 10mm long at fruiting-time. Corolla-tube 6–10mm long, about as long as the calyx, which is divided almost to the base into linear, pointed lobes. Corolla with 5 lobes spreading out flat, 10–15mm and more in diameter, with a white ring in the centre consisting of scales with long hairs. Nutlets oblong, 7–10mm, swollen and densely warted.
Cultivated and fallow land, waysides.
Mediterranean region, Canary Islands, eastwards to Iran, occasionally cultivated in northern and central Europe as an ornamental plant, sometimes escaping and becoming naturalised.
There are about 20 species in Europe, many of them confined to small areas of the Mediterranean region. One species with a wider distribution is *A. undulata* L.: plant with appressed hairs and spreading bristles. Lower leaves usually sinuately toothed and undulate. Corolla-tube 7–13mm, 1½ times to twice as long as the calyx, which is divided to the middle into blunt lobes (Mediterranean region).

□■ *Borago officinalis* L. **Borage**
□□ 20–70cm; April–September; ☉
A stout, erect, bristly hairy plant with a basal rosette of ovate to lanceolate leaves, 5–20cm long, narrowed into a winged stalk. Upper stem-leaves sessile, clasping the stem. Flowers on stout stalks 5–30mm long, nodding, with a very short corolla-tube and lanceolate, pointed lobes spreading out flat, 2–3cm across, bright blue, rarely white, in lax, branched inflorescences. Anthers dark violet. Calyx more than ½ as long as the corolla. A pot-herb, formerly used in folk medicine to treat coughs and to purify the blood.
Cultivated and fallow land, waysides, waste ground.
Mediterranean region, Canary Islands, probably native only in the west, but cultivated elsewhere as a herb plant, and sometimes escaping and growing wild.
B. pygmaea (DC.) Chater & Greut. (*B. laxiflora* Poir.), is more like a *Campanula* in appearance. It grows only in damp places in Corsica, Sardinia and Capraia.

□□ *Cynoglossum creticum* Mill. (*C. pictum* Ait.) **Blue Hound's Tongue**
■□ 20–80cm; April–July; ☉, ☉
Plant densely and evenly covered with soft hairs, the stem usually branched above. Leaves lanceolate, 5–15cm long, the lower ones in a rosette, narrowed into a long stalk, the upper ones sessile, more or less half stem-clasping, often without prominent lateral veins. Flowers on short, later recurved stalks, in bractless clusters. Corolla 7–9mm, at first pink, later pale blue, with conspicuously dark veins, the 5 roundish, hairless lobes about as long as the tube. Calyx 6–8mm, divided almost to the base into 5 oblong, blunt lobes. Nutlets 5–7mm, rounded without a thickened edge, densely covered with hooked spines.
Fallow land, waysides, garigue.
Mediterranean region, Canary Islands, S.W. Asia.

□□ *Cynoglossum cheirifolium* L.
□■ 10–40cm; April–June; ☉
Stem erect, felted, branched in the upper part. Leaves felted on both sides, oblong-lanceolate to narrowly spathulate, without visible lateral veins, the upper ones sessile, but not clasping the stem. Inflorescence with bracts and with the flowers pale red at first, later purple to blue. Corolla about 8mm long, the 5 hairless lobes shorter than the tube. Calyx-lobes ovate, felted, 5–7mm. Nutlets 5–8mm in diameter, with a distinctly thickened margin, densely covered with hooked spines or almost smooth.
Open, rocky places.
Western Mediterranean region, eastwards to Italy and Sicily, absent from Corsica.

Verbena family *Verbenaceae*
Mint family *Lamiaceae (Labiatae)*

■□
□□ *Vitex agnus-castus* L. **Chaste Tree** *Verbenaceae*
1-6m; June–November; ♄
A robust shrub with 4-angled, grey-felted young stems. Leaves deciduous, long-stalked, palmately divided into 5–7, almost entire leaflets, up to 10cm long, white-felted beneath, hairless above. Flowers small, scented, blue, more rarely pink, with a hairy, 2-lipped corolla in terminal, branched, spike-like inflorescences. Stamens distinctly protruding. Fruits small, fleshy, reddish black, used in earlier times as a spice like pepper and also as an anti-aphrodisiac, and nowadays used medicinally in the treatment of hormone disorders.
River-banks, damp places, also planted as a decorative shrub.
Mediterranean region, S.W. Asia.

□■
□□ *Ajuga chamaepitys* (L.) Schreb. **Ground-pine** *Lamiaceae*
5-20cm; March–October; ☉, ☉, ♃
Plant with aromatic smell. Stem usually branched at the base, ascending, hairless to densely hairy. Leaves crowded, usually divided into 3 linear segments, 0.5–2mm broad, the segments themselves sometimes 3-lobed. Flowers solitary or in pairs in the leaf-axils, with a yellow corolla, 7–15mm long, often with red-brown markings, the upper lip very small, the lower lip much longer and 3-lobed, the middle lobe larger and notched at the end, the corolla-tube with a ring of hairs within. Filaments of stamens hairy, protruding. A very variable species with several subspecies, especially in the east.
A weed of vineyards and fields, and on dry grassland.
Mediterranean region, eastwards to central Asia, already naturalised a long time ago in the warmer areas of central Europe.
A subspecies with a more easterly distribution, ssp. *chia* (Schreb.) Arc., has leaf-segments 1.5–3mm broad and the corolla 18–25mm long.

□□
■□ *Ajuga iva* (L.) Schreb. *Lamiaceae*
5-20cm; April–October; ♃
A prostrate or ascending, branched, hairy plant, woody at the base. Leaves numerous, linear-oblong, 3–6mm broad, entire to weakly lobed. Flowers 2–4 together in the leaf-axils, forming a dense inflorescence. Corolla purple, pink or yellow, 1.2–2cm long, with a ring of hairs within. Upper lip very short, lower lip 3-lobed, the middle lobe larger and notched at the end. Filaments hairy, protruding from the corolla.
Stony pastures, garigue, dry grassland.
Mediterranean region, Canary Islands.

□□
□■ *Teucrium fruticans* L. **Tree Germander** *Lamiaceae*
0.3-1.5m; February–June; ♄
Evergreen shrub with 4-angled, white-felted stems. Leaves with short stalks, lanceolate to ovate, flat, white-felted beneath, becoming hairless above, dark green and shining. Flowers stalked, in pairs in the upper leaf-axils, forming a long inflorescence. Corolla pale blue to lilac, 1.5–2.5cm long, the upper lip absent, the lower lip 5-lobed with an elongated middle lobe, throat without a ring of hairs. Filaments distinctly protruding. Calyx short, bell-shaped, white-felted on the outside.
Evergreen thickets near the coast.
Western Mediterranean region, eastwards to Yugoslavia, also cultivated as an ornamental shrub, often escaping and growing wild.
T. brevifolium Schreb. is closely related: a small shrub, up to 60cm high. Leaves grey-felted on both sides, linear-oblong with recurved margins. Flowers blue, solitary in the leaf-axils, about 1cm long (eastern Mediterranean region). *T. marum* L. has purple flowers, about 1cm long, in narrow, spike-like inflorescences. Shrub 50cm high, with white-felted stems. Leaves 1cm long, linear-lanceolate to rhombic with recurved margins, grey-felted beneath. An ancient medicinal plant (Balearic Islands, Corsica, Sardinia and several other islands). There are numerous endemic species of *Teucrium*, found only in small areas, especially in the western Mediterranean region.

Mint family *Lamiaceae* (*Labiatae*)

■□ *Teucrium pseudochamaepitys* L. **Ground-pine Germander**
□□ 20–50cm; April–July; ♃, ♄
A small, usually hairy species, somewhat woody at the base, the simple, erect stem very leafy. Leaves deeply divided into 3–5 linear, entire, pointed lobes. Flowers stalked, in whorls of 2, almost all facing in the same direction and forming a loose inflorescence. Corolla 10–15mm long, white, pale rose or purple, the upper lip absent, the lower lip 5-lobed. Throat without a ring of hairs, filaments distinctly protruding. Calyx much shorter than the corolla, bell-shaped, not enlarged at the base, the 5 teeth of equal length, longer than the calyx-tube. Stony pastures, garigue, grassy pastures.
Iberian peninsula, S. France, N.W. Africa.

□■ *Teucrium polium* L. **Felty Germander**
□□ 5–45cm; April–August; ♃, ♄
A small subshrub with ascending or erect stems, covered all over with a dense felt of white, greenish or sometimes golden, branched hairs. Leaves opposite or in tufts, very shortly stalked, 7–27mm, oblong or narrowly obovate, with a recurved or flat margin, with 2–5 rounded teeth on each side. Flowers in dense, simple or compound heads, with leaf-like, crenate or entire bracts, and white, more rarely red flowers. Corolla about 5mm long with a 5-lobed lower lip, the upper lip absent, hairy or hairless outside, the throat without a ring of hairs. Calyx 3–5mm, the 5 equal teeth hidden by hairs. A very variable species.
Stony pastures, garigue, open woods.
Mediterranean region, eastwards to southern central Russia and S.W. Asia.

□□ *Prasium majus* L.
■□ 0.5–1m; February–June; ♄
An irregularly branched shrub, often climbing, hairless or sparsely hairy. Leaves 2–5cm long with stalks 1–1.8cm long, ovate, pointed, shining dark green, the margin serrate to crenate and the base heart-shaped or cut off squarely. Whorls composed of only 1 or 2 white or pale lilac flowers, 17–23mm long. Corolla with a ring of scale-like hairs in the tube, the upper lip arched, the lower lip 3-lobed with a broad middle segment. Calyx 10-veined, enlarged at fruit-ing-time up to 25mm, weakly 2-lipped, the 5 lobes ending in a short bristle.
Garigue, maquis, evergreen woods, especially near the coast.
Mediterranean region, Canary Islands, absent from France.

□□ *Marrubium incanum* Desr. (*M. candidissimum* auct. non L.)
□■ 20–60cm; June–August; ♃
Stem white-felted, woody at the base, and usually with short, erect, non-flowering stems. Leaves densely felted, oblong-ovate, wedge-shaped at the base, crenate-serrate, grey-green above, whitish beneath. Leaf-stalk shorter than the blade. Flowers in dense, many-flowered, false whorls, standing above each other but clearly separated, with numerous, awl-shaped bracteoles curving upwards. Corolla white, hairy on the outside, protruding slightly from the calyx. Upper lip flat, 2-lobed for ⅓ of its length, lower lip 3-lobed. Calyx felted with star-shaped hairs, strongly 10-ribbed, with 5 awl-shaped teeth, about the same length, 3–4mm long, at first erect, later spreading out like a star. Calyx-tube 6–7mm long with a ring of hairs in the throat.
Stony grassland, garigue, pasture and fallow land.
Italy, Sicily, Balkan peninsula southwards to Albania, sometimes introduced.
M. vulgare L. is widely distributed: leaves broadly ovate, rounded or heart-shaped at the base, becoming hairless above. Calyx with 10 spreading, curved teeth (Eurasia, Canary Islands, N. Africa). The red-flowered *M. alysson* L. occurs in the southern Mediterranean: Leaves long wedge-shaped, almost sessile. The 5-toothed calyx protrudes beyond the corolla. There are other species, especially in the eastern Mediterranean region.

Mint family *Lamiaceae (Labiatae)*

■□
□□ *Sideritis romana* L.
10–30cm; May–July; ☉
A more or less densely softly hairy, erect plant, with a simple stem or branched in the lower part. Leaves opposite, 10–25×5–12mm, oblong-ovate, coarsely crenate-serrate, green, the lower ones stalked, the upper ones sessile, with 6-flowered false whorls, without bracteoles, in the axils. Flowers with a white, yellow or purple, 2-lipped corolla, 7–10mm long, the upper lip undivided, flat. The typical 2-lipped calyx, about as long as the corolla, distinctly 10-veined, the upper tooth broadly ovate, and, like the 4 lanceolate lower ones, bearing a sharp bristle and spreading out at fruiting-time.
Grassy pastures, garigue, maquis.
S. Europe, N.W. Turkey, N.W. Africa.
Another annual species is *S. montana* L.: calyx-teeth almost equal, corolla yellow or dark brown with a yellow lower lip (Mediterranean region, S.W. Asia).

□■
□□ *Phlomis samia* L.
Up to 1m; June–September; ♃
A tall, erect plant, most parts with glandular hairs, and with star-shaped hairs forming a dense felt. Basal leaves with stalks up to 18cm long, fairly thick, lanceolate-ovate, the base heart-shaped or arrow-shaped, crenate-serrate at the margin, 8–23×5–15cm. Flowers in false whorls of 12–20, the purple corolla 30–35mm long, with a helmet-shaped upper lip and 3-lobed lower lip. Calyx 18–25mm, with awl-shaped teeth 6–12mm long. Bracteoles awl-shaped, 20–26mm.
Pine, fir and cedar woods of the mountain zone.
S. Yugoslavia, Greece, Asia Minor.
Also red-flowered but without glandular hairs is *P. herba-venti* L.: plant herbaceous, only up to 70cm high. Bracteoles awl-shaped, corolla 1.5–3cm (Mediterranean region, E. Europe, S.W. Asia), and 2 shrubby species growing up to 2m high: *P. purpurea* L., bracteoles more or less lanceolate, 2–5mm broad, corolla about 2.5cm (western Mediterranean region) and *P. italica* L. (only in the Balearic Islands).

□□
■□ *Phlomis lychnitis* L.
20–65cm; May–July; ♄
A small shrub, covered with a felt of star-shaped hairs. Leaves linear-lanceolate, net-veined and wrinkled above, white-felted beneath, narrowed into an indistinct stalk, 5–11cm long. Inflorescence composed of 4–8 false whorls, some distance apart from each other, each consisting of 4–10 flowers arising in the axils of 2 bracts, broadly ovate at the base and with a pointed tip. Corolla yellow, 2–3cm long, with a hairy, helmet-shaped upper lip and 3-lobed lower lip. Calyx with 5 equal, straight teeth bearing long hairs like the linear bracteoles.
Garigue, grassy pastures.
Iberian peninsula, France.
Species with a distinct leaf-stalk include *P. crinita* Cav. (Spain, N.W. Africa), *P. cretica* C. Presl (Greece, Crete, Rhodes) and *P. fruticosa* L.: shrub up to 1.3m high. Flowers 23–35mm long, in whorls of 14–36, with ovate-lanceolate bracteoles (central and eastern Mediterranean region, also grown as an ornamental plant).

□□
□■ *Stachys cretica* L. (*S. italica* Mill.)
20–80cm; May–July; ♃
Stem erect, and usually simple, white-felted. Leaves opposite, the lower ones stalked, oblong-ovate, the base wedge-shaped, or squarely cut to weakly heart-shaped, finely crenate, 3–10×1–3cm, densely grey or white-felted on the under side, grey-green above, the surface visible under a thin covering of felt. Upper leaves sessile with dense, many-flowered false whorls in their axils. Bracteoles linear-lanceolate, about as long as the calyx-tube, calyx-teeth without glands and ending in a stiff bristle. Flowers almost sessile, with a red, hairy, 2-lipped corolla, 15–20mm long. There are several subspecies, the one illustrated being ssp. *salviifolia* (Ten.) Rech. f.
Garigue, grassy pastures, fallow land.
S. Europe from France eastwards to S.W. Asia.
S. byzantina C. Koch: leaves narrowed at the base, the upper side white-felted, completely covered by the hairs (native in S.W. Asia, often cultivated as an ornamental plant).

Mint family Lamiaceae (Labiatae)

■□ *Prunella laciniata* (L.) L. (*P. alba* Pall. ex Bieb.) **Cut-leaved Self-heal**
□□ 5–30cm; June–August; ⚥
Plant more or less densely hairy, with the stem ascending to erect. Basal leaves stalked, ovate-oblong to elliptic, at least the upper leaves pinnately divided or with long, narrow teeth, the uppermost pair situated directly below the inflorescence. Flowers usually in groups of 6 in closely set false whorls that are surrounded by 2 roundish bracts. Corolla yellowish white, more rarely pink or purple, 15–17mm long, with a helmet-shaped upper lip and a 3-lobed lower lip. Calyx 2-lipped, the upper lip cut squarely at the end with 3 short teeth, the 2 teeth of the lower lip linear-lanceolate, fringed with hairs.
Grassy pastures, open woods.
Mediterranean region, extending into the warmer areas of central Europe, S.W. Asia.
In addition to the widespread, purple-flowered species *P. grandiflora* (L.) Scholl. found also in central Europe, and *P. vulgaris* L., **Common Self-heal**, native throughout most of Europe including the British Isles, there is in S.W. Europe *P. hyssopifolia* L. with mainly sessile, entire leaves. All 4 species hybridise with each other.

□■ *Satureja thymbra* L.
□□ 10–40cm; April–May; ♄
A small, much-branched, aromatic shrub, the stem with hairs directed backwards. Leaves sessile, oblong to obovate, pointed, folded, 9–14×3–5mm, with short bristly hairs and glandular dots, and with short shoots in the leaf-axils. Flowers with a red, 2-lipped corolla, 8–12mm long, in dense, spherical, false whorls. Calyx 4–7mm, 10-veined, with long, white, spreading hairs, the 5 almost equal calyx-teeth pointed, somewhat shorter than the tube, which is hairless within. Bracteoles lanceolate, about as long as the calyces and covering them.
Garigue, mainly on chalk.
Eastern Mediterranean region, extending to S. Sardinia.

□□ *Satureja montana* L. **Winter Savory**
■□ 10–40cm; July–September; ⚥
An aromatic, dwarf shrub. Leaves opposite, sessile, linear to lanceolate, broadest above the middle, sharply pointed, leathery, dotted with dark glands, with short bristles on the margin, 5–30×1–5(–7)mm, usually longer than the stem-sections. Flowers in small, stalked, closely set false whorls, mostly facing the same way, the lower ones exceeded by the 1–2cm long bracts. Corolla 6–14mm, white, pink or purple, 2-lipped. Calyx hairy in the throat, 10-veined, the lower calyx-teeth usually somewhat longer than the upper ones, but at most as long as the tube. Bracteoles small, about half as long as the calyx. Variable in form, especially in the Balkan peninsula. A culinary herb.
Stony and grassy pastures.
S. Europe, absent from the islands.
In contrast, **Summer Savory**, *S. hortensis* L. is an annual: Leaves soft and bluntly pointed, shorter than the stem-sections. Flowers 4–7mm, at least the lower calyx-teeth longer than the tube (S. Europe, Anatolia, cultivated elsewhere).

□□ *Micromeria nervosa* (Desf.) Benth.
□■ 10–40cm; March–May; ♄
A small subshrub, the ascending or erect stems with appressed backward pointing hairs. Leaves very shortly stalked, opposite, ovate, pointed at the tip and cut squarely at the base, 7–10×4–5mm, the under side with prominent veins, without glandular dots. The spike-like inflorescences are composed of 4 to 20-flowered, stalked, false whorls, which are about as long as the accompanying leaves. Bracteoles minute. Flowers with a purple, 2-lipped corolla, 4–6mm long. The conspicuous calyx is 3–4mm long, with long, dense, spreading hairs outside and woolly within.
Stony pastures, garigue, especially on chalk.
Southern Mediterranean region.
M. graeca (L.) Benth. ex Rchb.: leaves ovate-oblong with a wedge-shaped base, narrower above and with recurved margins, 5–12×2–7mm. Whorls of flowers more or less loose. Variable in form, with early and late-flowering subspecies (Mediterranean region).

Mint family Lamiaceae (Labiatae)

■□ *Thymus capitatus* (L.) Hoffmanns. & Link (*Coridothymus capitatus* (L.) Rchb. f.)
□□ 20–50cm; May–September; ♄
A strongly aromatic, often rounded, dwarf shrub, with white-felted stems. Leaves narrowly linear-lanceolate, almost triangular in cross-section, not recurved at the margin, fringed with hairs at the base, 6–10×1–1.2mm, often withering away during the dry season. Tufts of smaller, persistent leaves in the leaf-axils. Flowers in dense ovoid heads, the rose-red corollas up to 10mm long. Calyces, in contrast to all other *Thymus* species, flattened on the back and with 20–22 veins, 2-lipped, the upper lip shorter than the lower one, all the teeth fringed with hairs. Bracts greenish, ovate to lanceolate, fringed with hairs, and overlapping.
Garigue, mainly on chalk.
Mediterranean region, absent from France.

□■ *Thymus longiflorus* Boiss.
□□ 10–30cm; April–May; ♄
An aromatic dwarf shrub. Leaves sessile or very shortly stalked, linear, with recurved margins, grey-felted, at most fringed with long hairs at the base, 8–12×0.8–1mm. Inflorescence up to 2.5cm, forming heads at the ends of the stems, with conspicuous, overlapping, purple, leathery bracts, up to 13×9mm, broadly ovate, pointed, and fringed at the margin. Corolla purple, about 15mm long, protruding far beyond the 2-lipped, cylindrical, 10 to 13-veined calyx which is only 5–7mm long. Upper calyx-teeth narrowly lanceolate.
Stony pastures, garigue.
S.E. Spain.

□□ *Thymus vulgaris* L. **Thyme**
■□ 10–30cm; April–July; ♄
A strongly aromatic dwarf shrub. Leaves grey-green, densely felted, linear to elliptic with a prominent midrib and recurved margin, not fringed with hairs, 3–8×0.5–2.5mm, barely longer than the tufts of leaves in the leaf-axils. Inflorescence a head or interrupted spike of false whorls arising from the axils of leaf-like bracts. Corolla whitish to pale purple, 4–6mm long. Calyx cylindrical, 10 to 13-veined, 3–4mm long, stiffly hairy, 2-lipped, the upper teeth as long as broad, not fringed. Often used as a culinary herb and as a cough medicine.
Garigue on chalk; giving its name to the Spanish 'tomillares' and often the dominant plant covering large areas.
Western Mediterranean region, eastwards to Italy, cultivated elsewhere.
T. zygis L.: leaves fringed at the base, corolla whitish. Used like the ordinary Thyme as a medicinal plant (western Mediterranean region). There are numerous other species confined to small areas, especially in the Iberian peninsula.

□□ *Rosmarinus officinalis* L. **Rosemary**
□■ 0.5–2m; January–December; ♄
A strongly aromatic, evergreen shrub with brown stems. Leaves sessile, narrowly linear, 1.5–4cm long, leathery, the margins rolled under, the upper side bright green, the under side white-felted. Inflorescences consisting of small racemes in the axils of the leaves, the stalks densely covered with star-shaped hairs. Corolla blue, sometimes rather pale, more rarely white or pink, 10–12mm long, 2-lipped, the upper lip 2-lobed, erect to recurved, the lower lip 3-lobed with a large middle lobe. The 2 stamens distinctly protruding. Calyx bell-shaped, 2-lipped, enlarged at fruiting-time, 5–7mm, almost hairless and with prominent veins. The leaves are used as a culinary herb, and the ethereal oil is used medicinally in embrocations and bath mixtures to improve the circulation of the blood.
Garigue, maquis, open woods.
Mediterranean region, Canary Islands, cultivated elsewhere.
R. eriocalix Jord. & Fourr.: a usually prostrate shrub with grey stems. Leaves 5–15mm long. Long, glandular hairs in the inflorescence (Spain, N.W. Africa).

Mint family Lamiaceae (Labiatae)

■□ *Lavandula stoechas* L. **French Lavender**
□□ 0.3–1m; March–June; ♄
A small shrub, the leaves grey-felted on both sides, oblong-lanceolate, 1–4cm long, the margins rolled under. Inflorescence a stalked, dense false spike, composed of 6 to 10-flowered whorls in the axils of rhombic to heart-shaped, felted bracts, 4–8mm long. Standing above the whole spike is a cluster of oblong-ovate, purple, upper bracts, 1–5cm long, which make this species unmistakable. Corolla 2-lipped, 6–8mm, dark purple. Calyx 4–6mm, 13-veined, the upper tooth ending in an obcordate appendage, 1–2mm broad.
Garigue, open maquis and pine woods on siliceous rocks.
Mediterranean region.
L. viridis L'Hér. has a cluster of green bracts, 8–20mm long. Flowers white. Appendage of calyx 2.5–3.5mm broad (south-western Mediterranean region).

□■ *Lavandula dentata* L. **Toothed Lavender**
□□ 0.3–1m; April–July; ♄
An aromatic subshrub with grey-felted stems. Leaves linear, 1.5–3.5cm long, the margins rolled under and more or less deeply crenate, grey-green above, grey-felted beneath. Inflorescences spike-like, 2.5–5cm long, with long stalks. Lower bracts ovate-rhombic, pointed, 5–8mm, the upper ones coloured a conspicuous purple, ovate, pointed, 8–15mm long, without flowers in the axils. False whorls 6 to 10-flowered, the blue-purple, 2-lipped corolla about 8mm long, calyx 5–6mm, 13-veined, the upper tooth with a large appendage at the end.
Garigue, mainly on chalk.
Spain, Balearic Islands, N.W. Africa, occasionally cultivated elsewhere, sometimes escaping and growing wild.

□□ *Lavandula angustifolia* Mill. ssp. *angustifolia* (*L. officinalis* Chaix, *L. vera* DC.) **Common**
■□ **Lavender**
0.2–1m; June–August; ♄
A strongly scented subshrub with linear-lanceolate, entire leaves, 2–4cm long. Young leaves white-felted, later becoming hairless and green. Flowers in long-stalked, simple, spike-like inflorescences, 2–8cm long, interrupted in the lower part. False whorls with 6–10 flowers and broadly ovate, pointed, membranous and strongly veined bracts. Bracteoles minute or absent. Corollas 10–12mm, 2-lipped, blue-purple, calyces usually grey-purple, 4.5–6mm long, 13-veined, with an indistinct appendage at the end of the upper tooth. The ethereal oil from the flowers has a wide application in the perfume industry and also in medicine.
Garigue and stony pastures extending into the mountains, various forms being grown in fields as a source of the ethereal oil.
S. Europe, cultivated elsewhere, occasionally escaping and growing wild; ssp. *pyrenaica* (DC.) Guinea occurs only in N.E. Spain.
L. latifolia Med. (*L. spica* auct. non L.) is similar: leaves broader, with a very dense covering of short, white hairs when young, later becoming hairless and grey-green. Bracts linear-lanceolate, without distinct lateral veins. Bracteoles awl-shaped, 2–3mm long. Corolla 8–10mm, calyx 13-veined. Has a camphor-like smell (S. Europe, eastwards to Yugoslavia). *L. lanata* Boiss. is endemic in the mountains of S. Spain: leaves remaining felted with white hairs. Bracteoles bristle-like, 2–5mm long, corolla 8–10mm, calyx 8-veined.

□□ *Lavandula multifida* L. **Cut-leaved Lavender**
□■ 0.2–1m; March–June; ♄
Subshrub with sparsely hairy leaves, bipinnately divided. Stems grey-felted, sometimes also with long hairs. Inflorescences 2–7cm long, spike-like, long-stalked, sometimes branched at the base, composed of 2-flowered false whorls. Bracts heart-shaped to ovate, membranous. Corolla blue-purple, 2-lipped, up to 12mm long, calyx about 5mm, 15-veined, the upper tooth without an appendage. Not as aromatic as the other species of lavender.
Garigue, stony pastures, fallow land.
Iberian peninsula, S. Italy, Sicily, N. Africa, Canary Islands.

Mint family *Lamiaceae (Labiatae)*

■☐ *Salvia officinalis* L. **Sage**
☐☐ 20–60cm; May–July; ♄
An aromatic subshrub with ascending to erect stems covered with a felt of spreading hairs. Leaves opposite, stalked, usually simple, oblong-ovate to narrowly elliptic, more or less narrowed at the base, wrinkled, very finely crenate on the margin, densely white-felted at first, later becoming hairless especially on the upper side. Bracts ovate-lanceolate, long pointed, with false whorls in their axils, arranged one above the other, each consisting of 5–10 shortly stalked flowers, and bracteoles that soon fall. Corolla pale purple, more rarely white, 2–3.5cm long, with an almost straight upper lip and 3-lobed lower lip. Calyx often tinged purple, bell-shaped, 10–14mm long, 2-lipped, hairy and dotted with glands, with 5 pointed teeth, 5–8mm long, the middle tooth of the upper lip distinctly smaller and shorter than the 2 lateral ones. The leaves are used medicinally to treat excessive perspiration, also inflammation of the mouth and the respiratory organs. A culinary herb.
Garigue and stony pastures, especially in the karst region of Yugoslavia.
Probably native in the Balkan peninsula, often cultivated and sometimes becoming naturalised.
S. grandiflora Etl. is closely related: leaves rounded to heart-shaped at base. Flower-stalks 5–10mm (Balkan peninsula, S.W. Asia). There are numerous endemic species, especially in the eastern Mediterranean region.

☐■ *Salvia lavandulifolia* Vahl
☐☐ 0.3–1m; July–August; ♄
An aromatic subshrub with erect or ascending stems. Leaves stalked, ovate to elliptic, the younger ones whitish grey. Flowers in 6 to 8-flowered false whorls, usually arranged some distance apart on a hairless axis, often almost sessile. Corolla 2–2.5cm long, pale blue-purple, the upper lip almost straight and the lower lip 3-lobed. Calyx often tinged purple, gland-dotted, without glandular hairs but often with simple hairs, 8–12mm long, divided for about ¼ of its length into 5 teeth of about equal size, broad at the base and pointed at the tip. There are 4 subspecies.
Stony pastures in the mountain zone.
Spain, S. France, N.W. Africa.

☐☐ *Salvia triloba* L.f. **Three-lobed Sage**
■☐ 0.3–1.5m; March–June; ♄
An aromatic shrub, the stems felted with appressed white hairs but without glands. Leaves opposite, stalked, narrowly ovate, simple, or with 2 or more, rarely 4, small lateral lobes at the base, grey-green and wrinkled above, grey-felted beneath. Inflorescences spike-like, composed of 2 to 6-flowered false whorls in the axils of small bracts. Corolla 16–25mm long, blue-purple, pink or more rarely white, with a fairly straight upper lip and a 3-lobed lower lip. Calyx bell-shaped, weakly 2-lipped, 5–8mm, often tinged purple, with simple or glandular hairs, the 5 triangular teeth about 2mm long. A variable species. The leaves are used in the same way as those of *S. officinalis.*
Garigue, maquis.
Eastern Mediterranean region, westwards to S. Italy and Sicily.

☐☐ *Salvia verbenaca* L. **Wild Clary**
☐■ 10–80cm; almost throughout the year; ♃
Plant herbaceous, the stems more or less glandular hairy in the upper part. Leaves of the basal rosette long-stalked, oblong to ovate, dull green, coarsely crenate, more or less lobed, 5–10cm long and 2–4cm broad, wrinkled above. Stem-leaves shortly stalked or sessile, bracts ovate, pointed, about 6mm long. Inflorescence a fairly lax or dense spike, often branched. Flowers stalked, in groups of 4–10 in false whorls. Corolla 6–15mm, 2-lipped, sometimes remaining closed, pale blue to purple. Calyx bell-shaped, with prominent veins and long white hairs, enlarging to 8–10mm at fruiting-time. A very variable species.
Fallow and cultivated land, waysides.
Mediterranean region and W. Europe, Canary Islands, introduced almost everywhere else in the world.

Nightshade family *Solanaceae*

■□ *Lycium europaeum* L. **Tea-tree**
□□ 1–4m; April–September; ♄
A much-branched, spiny shrub. Leaves shortly stalked, often in tufts, somewhat fleshy, narrowly spathulate and entire, 20–50cm×3–10mm. In the leaf-axils are shortly stalked pale purple or white flowers, usually in pairs, 11–13mm long, the narrowly funnel-shaped corolla with 5 round lobes, 3–4mm. Filaments hairless. Calyx 2–3mm, 5-toothed, later 2-lobed. Berries reddish. Plant possibly poisonous. Hedges, thickets, waysides.
Mediterranean region, Canary Islands, probably introduced in some places.
L. intricatum Boiss. (including *L. schweinfurthii* Damm.): leaves 3–15×1–6mm. Flowers longer, 13–18mm, with the calyx only 1.5–2mm. Berries red or black (local in the extreme south of Europe, N. Africa, Canary Islands, S.W. Asia). *L. afrum* L.: leaves not more than 2mm broad. Flowers brown-purple, 20–22mm, the calyx 5–7mm long, deeply cut into 5 lobes. Berries purple (grown as an ornamental plant, naturalised in places in the western Mediterranean region, native in S. Africa).

□■ *Hyoscyamus albus* L. **White Henbane**
□ⁿ 20–80cm; March–September; ☉, ☉, ⚄
Plant erect, sticky, and covered with glandular-woolly hairs. All leaves stalked, ovate, bluntly sinuately toothed. Flowers 3cm across, only the lowest ones stalked, in dense, leafy spike-like inflorescences, the flowers mostly facing the same way. Corolla tubular to bell-shaped, almost regular, with 5 lobes, glandular hairy outside, usually yellowish white, the throat green or purple. Anthers not or only slightly protruding. Calyx densely glandular-woolly, 2–2.5cm long at fruiting-time. Plant poisonous.
Waste ground, on walls, near settlements.
Mediterranean region, Canary Islands, eastwards to S. Russia and Iraq.
Our native Henbane, *Hyoscyamus niger* L., found throughout almost the whole of Europe, has sessile, stem-clasping leaves and dingy yellow flowers usually with a network of purple veins. *H. reticulatus* L. has sessile but not stem-clasping leaves, and purple flowers with a network of dark-coloured veins (eastern Mediterranean region, S.W. Asia).

□□ *Hyoscyamus aureus* L. **Golden Henbane**
■□ 20–60cm; March–June; ☉, ⚄
A sticky, glandular-woolly plant with erect, prostrate or hanging stems. All leaves stalked, ovate or roundish, irregularly lobed and with pointed teeth. Flowers up to 4.5cm long, all shortly stalked, in lax, few-flowered, leafy clusters. Corolla funnel-shaped, with 5 irregular, wide-spreading lobes, golden yellow with a purple throat. Anthers distinctly protruding. Calyx up to 3cm at fruiting-time, densely woolly below. Plant poisonous.
On walls and rocks, usually near settlements.
Eastern Mediterranean region, westwards to the Aegean and Crete, S.W. Asia.

□□ *Solanum sodomeum* L. **Apple of Sodom**
□■ 0.5–3m; May–September; ♄
An extremely spiny, much-branched shrub with star-shaped hairs. Leaves stalked, ovate in outline, 5–13cm long, pinnately divided almost to the midrib, with rounded, undulate lobes. Leaf-veins, like the stems, with stout, straight, yellowish spines up to 1.5cm long. Inflorescence few-flowered, the flowers stalked. Corolla blue-purple, the 5 lobes spreading out like a star, 2.5–3cm in diameter. Fruit a berry, at first mottled whitish and green, later bright yellow to brown, 2–3cm in diameter. Plant poisonous.
Waysides, waste ground, sandy beaches.
Naturalised in S. Europe, N.W. Africa, native in S. Africa.
Two species from S. America that have become naturalised in places are *S. bonariense* L.: shrub up to 2m, slightly spiny only when young. Leaves ovate-lanceolate, usually undivided, with scattered star-shaped hairs. Flowers 2–4 together, white or pale blue, 2.5–3.5cm in diameter (western Mediterranean region) and *S. elaeagnifolium* Cav.: plant shrubby or herbaceous, 30–60cm high, densely covered with star-shaped hairs and with scattered reddish spines. Leaves linear to oblong, more or less undivided. Flowers solitary or up to 5 together, corolla purple, 2.5–3.5cm across (eastern Mediterranean region).

Nightshade family *Solanaceae*
Foxglove family *Scrophulariaceae*

■□
□□ *Mandragora autumnalis* Bertol. **Mandrake** Solanaceae
10–20cm; September–November, rarely also March–April; ⚇
Root thick, fleshy, often forked. Leaves stalked, ovate-oblong, undulate at the margin, lying flat on the ground in a rosette. In the centre are shortly stalked flowers with an erect, bell-shaped, purple corolla, 3–4cm long, the 5 lobes broadly triangular. Calyx much enlarged at fruiting-time, as long as or longer than the yellow to orange, ovoid, 2.5–3m long berry. Since ancient times the root, which contains poisonous alkaloids, has played an important role in relieving pain and inducing sleep, and also more recently as a magic charm, because of its resemblance to the human figure.
Fallow and cultivated land, waysides.
Southern Mediterranean region.
Mandragora officinarum L. (*M. vernalis* Bertol.) has greenish white flowers only 2.5cm long with narrow, triangular lobes. Calyx much shorter than the roundish, yellow berry (flowers February–May; N. Italy, W. Yugoslavia).

□■
□□ *Nicotiana glauca* R.C. Graham **Shrub Tobacco** Solanaceae
2–6m; April–October; ♄
A hairless, blue-green shrub, only slightly branched. Leaves alternate, ovate and pointed or ovate-lanceolate, entire, 5–25cm, the long leaf-stalk unwinged. Flowers in loose terminal panicles. Corolla hairy outside, yellow, 2.5–4.5cm long, tubular, with 5 very short, blue lobes. Calyx 10–15mm with 5 triangular, pointed teeth. Anthers not protruding. Fruit-capsules elliptic, 7–10mm.
Waysides, waste ground, ruins, also grown as an ornamental plant.
Naturalised in the Mediterranean region and the Canary Islands, native in S. America.
Two related species of tobacco-plants, many cultivated varieties of which are grown in the Mediterranean region, are herbaceous and have green, glandular-hairy leaves: *N. rustica* L., with unwinged leaf-stalks and greenish yellow flowers, and *N. tabacum* L., with sessile or slightly stem-clasping leaves or with short, winged leaf-stalks, and cream or pink flowers.

□□
■□ *Verbascum phoeniceum* L. **Purple Mullein** Scrophulariaceae
0.3–1m; April–July; ☉, ⚇
Stem erect, usually unbranched, densely glandular-hairy above, white-felted towards the base. Basal leaves with stalks 0.5–4cm long, long-ovate, 4–17×2.5–9cm, weakly crenate to sinuate on the margin, sparsely hairy or hairless. Stem-leaves few, smaller, sessile. Flowers in a long, loose inflorescence, with stalks 1–2.5cm long, each flower in the axil of a small bract. Corolla 5-lobed, 2–3.5cm across, dark purple (yellow in ssp. *flavidum* (Boiss.) Bornm., only in Macedonia and further eastwards). Stamens 4 or 5, with purple woolly hairs, the anthers all attached at their centre to the filaments and at right-angles to them.
Dry pastures, thickets.
From Italy eastwards to central Asia, rare in central Europe, cultivated as an ornamental plant, sometimes escaping and growing wild.
There are numerous species in the Mediterranean region, usually confined to small areas. The genus is concentrated in Asia Minor, where there are about 200 species.

□□
□■ *Verbascum sinuatum* L. Scrophulariaceae
0.5–1m; April–October; ☉
Plant covered with a grey or yellow felt of dense, short hairs. Leaves of the basal rosette oblong, barely stalked, sinuately lobed, coarsely toothed and more or less undulate on the margin, 15–35×6–15cm. Stem-leaves with a broad to heart-shaped base, sessile and slightly clasping the stem. Inflorescence branched, flowers 2–5 together, sessile in the axils of small bracts. Corolla 5-lobed, 1.5–3cm in diameter, yellow, with reddish markings inside at the base. Stamens 5, with purple, woolly hairs, the 2 lower ones hairless above, the anthers attached at their centre to the filaments and at right angles to them. Calyx 2–4mm.
Waysides, fallow land.
Mediterranean region, Canary Islands, S.W. Asia.
V. undulatum Lam.: leaves strongly undulate, the lobes almost overlapping. Flowers 2.5–5cm, the filaments with white hairs. Calyx 6–12mm (Balkan peninsula).

Foxglove family *Scrophulariaceae*

■□
□□ *Antirrhinum latifolium* Mill. **Large Snapdragon**
30–90cm; May–September; ⩜

Stem erect, usually glandular-hairy to the base. Leaves glandular or almost hairless, ovate, blunt at the tip and cut more or less squarely at the base, 20–70×8–32cm, 1½–2½ times as long as broad, the lower ones opposite, the upper ones alternate. Bracts ovate, 5–12mm. Flowers with stalks 3–8mm long in terminal clusters. Corolla 33–48mm, yellow, bag-shaped at the base, the upper lip 2-lobed, the lower lip 3-lobed with a swelling that closes the throat. Calyx deeply divided into 5 almost equal, ovate, blunt lobes, 7–9mm long. Capsule 13–17mm, oblong-ovate, glandular-hairy.
Stony pastures, walls.
North-western Mediterranean region from N.E. Spain to central Italy.
A. majus L. is very similar but the flowers are usually pink or purple: stem hairless, at least below. Leaves pointed, 2–12 times as long as broad, distinctly wedge-shaped at the base (western Mediterranean region, Canary Islands, cultivated elsewhere as an ornamental plant and becoming naturalised.) *A. siculum* Mill.: corolla yellow, only 17–25mm. Leaves 2–6mm broad, linear to narrowly elliptic (Sicily, S.W. Italy; an ornamental plant).

□■
□□ *Misopates orontium* (L.) Raf. (*Antirrhinum orontium* L.) **Weasel's Snout**
20–60cm; March–September; ☉

Stem erect with few branches, leaves opposite in the lower part and usually alternate above, narrowly linear or oblong-lanceolate, pointed, 2–5cm long and 2–7mm broad, shortly stalked. Flowers in a loose, terminal cluster, on short, glandular-hairy stalks, arising singly in the axils of long bracts. Corolla 2-lipped, 10–15mm long, pink, more rarely whitish, as long as or shorter than the calyx. Calyx-teeth up to 17mm, of unequal length. Fruit-capsules 8–10mm long, ovate, glandular-hairy and covered with small tubercles.
Cultivated and fallow land, waysides.
Mediterranean region, extending into central and W. Europe, Canary Islands, S.W. Asia.
The western Mediterranean *Misopates calycinum* Rothm. is similar, but has a larger, white corolla 18–22mm long, and the calyx shorter than the corolla.

□□
■□ *Cymbalaria microcalyx* (Boiss.) Wettst. (*Linaria microcalyx* Boiss.)
Up to 25cm long; March–May; ℏ

A prostrate or hanging plant, the thin, hairy stems and leaves persistent. Leaves usually opposite, long-stalked, kidney-shaped to semi-circular, with 3–5 round lobes. Flowers solitary in the leaf-axils, long-stalked. Corolla 9–13mm, pale violet with a spur 1–3mm long, a 2-lobed upperlip, and a 3-lobed lower lip with yellow swellings in the throat. Calyx 1–2mm, deeply 5-lobed, sparsely hairy or hairless. Fruit hairy, distinctly longer than the calyx. Several subspecies.
Rocks and walls near the coast.
Balkan peninsula, Aegean, S.W. Anatolia.
A species widely distributed in the Mediterranean region and the Canary Islands, and extending into central Europe is *C. muralis* G., M. & Sch. (*Linaria cymbalaria* (L.) Mill.): leaves with 5–9 often pointed lobes. Spur 1.5–3mm. Fruit hairless. *C. aequitriloba* (Viv.) A. Cheval.: leaves entire or with 3(–5) round lobes. Fruit hairless (islands in the western Mediterranean region). Endemic species occur in Corsica, Sardinia, Italy and the Aegean.

□□
□■ *Digitalis obscura* L. **Spanish Rusty Foxglove**
0.3–1.2m; April–July; ℏ

A hairless subshrub. Stem leafless below, but with leathery, closely set, linear-lanceolate leaves in the upper part, entire (ssp. *obscura*, see illustration) or deeply serrate (ssp. *laciniata* (Lindley) Maire). Leaves in long, terminal inflorescences, the flowers facing the same way. Corolla 2–3cm long, red-brown or yellow-orange, with darker markings inside, 2-lipped, with a bell-shaped tube. Bracts ovate-lanceolate, longer than the flower-stalks. Fruit pointed, longer than the calyx. Plant poisonous.
Stony pastures in the mountain zone.
Spain, N.W. Africa.

Foxglove family *Scrophulariaceae*

■□ *Digitalis laevigata* Waldst. & Kit.
□□ 0.6–1m; June–September; ♃, ♄
A tall, erect, hairless plant, woody at the base. Leaves lanceolate, the margin entire or toothed. Flowers in a loose, terminal inflorescence on a hairless axis, the flowers facing the same way. Corolla yellow, 1.5–3.5cm, veined red-brown, with a widely bell-shaped tube and a blunt, elongated lower lip, the middle lobe of which is 5–15mm long. Calyx-lobes ovate, pointed or tapering, with or without a very narrow, membranous margin. There are 2 subspecies, differing in the length of the flower and the middle lobe of the lower lip. Plant poisonous.
Woods in the mountain zone.
Balkan peninsula, northwards to Slovenia.
D. ferruginea L.: flowers yellowish or reddish brown with dark veins, 1.5–3.5cm, in a dense cluster. Calyx-lobes blunt with a broad, membranous margin. Inflorescence-axis hairless (eastern Mediterranean region, Italy). *D. lanata* Ehrh.: flowers yellowish white, with dark veins, 2–3cm. Calyx-lobes lanceolate, pointed, glandular-hairy. Inflorescence-axis densely glandular-hairy. Bracts lanceolate (Balkan peninsula). *D. leucophaea* Sibth. & Sm. is similar, but the flowers are only 1–2cm long, and the bracts are linear (N.E. Greece).

□■ *Parentucellia viscosa* (L.) Caruel (*Bartsia viscosa* L.) **Yellow Bartsia**
□□ 10–70cm; April–September; ☉
An erect, pale green semi-parasite, usually unbranched and sticky with glands. Leaves opposite, sessile, oblong-lanceolate, crenate-serrate, 10–45×3–15mm. Inflorescence 4-sided, spike-like, with bracts, in the axils of which are yellow, more rarely white flowers, 16–24mm long and soon falling. Upper lip of corolla shortly helmet-shaped, lower lip longer and much broader, 3-lobed. Calyx tubular, 10–16mm, the 4 linear-lanceolate lobes about as long as the tube. Capsule hairy, oblong, about as long as the calyx-tube.
Damp, grassy pastures, fallow land.
Mediterranean region, W. Europe, Canary Islands, eastwards to Iran.

□□ *Parentucellia latifolia* (L.) Caruel (*Bartsia latifolia* (L.) Sibth. & Sm.) **Southern Red Bartsia**
■□ 5–20cm; March–June; ☉
A small, erect, usually unbranched semi-parasite, tinged reddish, and sticky with glands. Leaves opposite, sessile, ovate, the upper ones almost as long as broad, fairly deeply toothed or lobed. Flowers in 4-sided, leafy, spike-like inflorescences, very short and dense at first. Corolla about 1cm long, reddish purple with a white tube, or completely white. Upper lip entire, lower lip 3-lobed, longer than the upper one. Calyx 6–10mm, the 4 calyx-teeth half as long as the tube. Capsule hairless.
Grassy pastures, fallow land.
Mediterranean region, Canary Islands, eastwards to Iran.
The eastern Mediterranean *P. flaviflora* (Boiss.) Nevski is similar but has yellow flowers.

□□ *Bellardia trixago* (L.) All. (*Bartsia trixago* L.)
□■ 10–80cm; April–July; ☉
A glandular, sticky semi-parasite. Stem usually simple and erect. Leaves opposite, sessile, oblong-lanceolate to linear, with a few blunt teeth, 15–90×1–15mm. Inflorescence dense, 4-sided, spike-like, with bracts in the axils of which are white flowers, 20–25mm long, usually tinged purple and yellow, or sometimes pure yellow and then easily confused with *Parentucellia viscosa* (see above). Corolla with a short, helmet-shaped upper lip and a longer and much broader, 3-lobed lower lip. Calyx 8–10mm, inflated and bell-shaped, the 4 triangular teeth less than ¼ as long as the tube. Capsule spherical, pointed, hairy, about as long as the calyx. Seeds ribbed lengthwise.
Garigue, pastures, fallow land.
Mediterranean region, Canary Islands, eastwards to Iran.

Globularia family *Globulariaceae*
Acanthus family *Acanthaceae*
Broomrape family *Orobanchaceae*

■☐ *Globularia alypum* L. **Shrubby Globularia** *Globulariaceae*
☐☐ 0.2–1m; October–April; ♄
A much-branched, evergreen shrub with shortly stalked, leathery, oblong-ovate leaves, pointed or sometimes 3-toothed at the end, arranged in clusters on the old stems. Flowers small, blue, in globular heads 1–2.5cm across, surrounded by overlapping, broadly ovate bracts fringed with hairs. Individual flowers tubular, the upper lip with 2 short teeth and the lower lip 3-lobed. Calyx-teeth with long hairs on the margin.
Garigue, stony pastures, sometimes the dominant plant.
Mediterranean region.
G. arabica Jaub. & Spach is similar (N. Africa, S.W. Asia). Several species occur in the southern European mountains, some creeping and shrubby, others herbaceous such as *G. punctata* Lap.

☐■ *Acanthus spinosus* L. **Spiny Bear's Breech** *Acanthaceae*
☐☐ 40–90cm; April–August; ♃
A robust, tall, sometimes hairy, thistle-like plant with an erect, simple stem. Basal leaves stalked, with an oblong, deeply pinnately cut, spiny-toothed blade up to 60cm long. Flowers in a dense, terminal, cylindrical spike, each flower in the axil of a spiny-toothed bract and 2 spiny bracteoles. Corolla about 4cm, white with purple veins, with a short tube and 3-lobed lower lip. Stamens 4. Calyx 4-lobed, the upper lobe greatly enlarged, often tinged purple, projecting over the corolla and replacing the missing upper lip. It is debatable whether the leaves of this species were the example for the ornaments on Corinthian columns.
Open woods, pastures.
S. Europe, westwards to Italy, Asia Minor, N.W. Africa.
A. mollis L.: leaves soft, segments not narrowed at the base, without spines (western and central Mediterranean region, Canary Islands). *A. balcanicus* Heyw. & Richards.: segments narrowed at the base, without spines (Balkan peninsula).

☐☐ *Cistanche phelypaea* (L.) Coutinho *Orobanchaceae*
■☐ 0.2–1m; March–May; ♃
A hairless species, without chlorophyll, parasitic mainly on the roots of shrubby members of the Chenopodiaceae. Stem simple, erect and stout, yellowish. Leaves ovate-lanceolate, blunt, brownish, with a membranous, more or less toothed margin. Flowers in a dense spike, 10–20cm long, each with an ovate-lanceolate, irregularly crenate bract, about 2cm long, and 2 bracteoles appressed to the 13–18mm long, bell-shaped calyx that has 5 equal, blunt, broad lobes. Corolla yellow, 3–6cm long, with a curved, abruptly widened tube and 5 spreading, ovate to roundish, almost equal lobes. Anthers hairy.
Saline areas on the coast and inland.
Southern Iberian peninsula, Crete, N. Africa, Canary Islands.

☐☐ *Orobanche ramosa* L. **Branched Broomrape** *Orobanchaceae*
☐■ 5–30cm; April–September; ☉
Plant without chlorophyll, parasitic on the roots of other plants. Stem usually branched, thickened at the base, glandular-hairy, with scattered, ovate-lanceolate, scale-like leaves, 3–8mm long. Flowers in spikes 2–25cm long, each with a bract 6–8mm long and 2 linear-lanceolate bracteoles of about the same length which are appressed to the 4-toothed calyx. Corolla 10–22mm, glandular-hairy, narrowed and whitish above the ovary, curved and gradually widening towards the mouth, blue, purple, or rarely whitish. Lower lip with 2, upper lip with 3 roundish lobes. Filaments and anthers hairless or sparsely hairy at the base. A very variable species with several subspecies.
Grows on a number of economic plants, especially hemp and tobacco.
Mediterranean region, Canary Islands, S.W. Asia, eastwards to India.
O. lavandulacea Rchb. is similar: plant larger, 15–60cm, anthers hairy (Mediterranean region, frequently on *Psoralea bituminosa*).

Plantain family *Plantaginaceae*

■□ *Plantago serraria* L.
□□ 5–20cm; April–June; ♃
All leaves in a basal rosette, 6–15cm long, lanceolate, regularly shallowly or deeply serrate, hairless or hairy. Inflorescence-stalks numerous, curving upwards, as long as or longer than the leaves. Flowers inconspicuous in dense spikes 6–10cm long, corolla 4-lobed, hairy outside, each flower having a broadly membranous-edged bract that is shorter than the calyx-lobes.
Pastures, fallow fields.
S. Europe, N.W. Africa, absent from France, Corsica and some other areas.
P. coronopus L.: not or barely branched at the base. Leaves once or twice pinnately lobed or merely toothed. Corolla-lobes about 1mm long (with several subspecies widely distributed, mainly along the coasts of N. and W. Europe, the Mediterranean, Canary Islands, S.W. Asia).
P. macrorhiza Poir.: usually distinctly branched at the base, with several rosettes. Leaves fleshy, toothed or pinnately lobed. Corolla-lobes about 2mm long (central Mediterranean region).

□■ *Plantago subulata* L.
□□ 10–40cm; April–June; ♄
Older plants forming cushions, with small, branched, woody stems bearing dense rosettes of leaves. Leaves dark green, hairless or fringed at the margin, narrowly linear, about 1mm broad and triangular in cross-section. Inflorescence-stalks about as long as the leaves, straight or somewhat curving. Flowers inconspicuous in dense, cylindrical spikes 1–5cm long. Corolla 4-lobed, hairy outside.
Rocks near the coast.
S. Europe, N.W. Africa.
Closely related species include *P. holosteum* Scop. (*P. carinata* Schrad. ex Mert. & K.) with much longer inflorescence-stalks (Mediterranean region, sometimes indistinguishable from *P. subulata* L.) and *P. insularis* Gren. & Godr. which occurs in the mountains of Corsica, Sardinia and Sicily.

□□ *Plantago lagopus* L. **Hare's Foot Plantain**
■□ 10–40cm; April–June; ☉
Plant similar to our native Ribwort Plantain but usually an annual species. Leaves up to 30cm long, lanceolate, usually with a few teeth, hairless or hairy, in a basal rosette or more rarely alternate. Inflorescence-stalks 2–4 times as long as the leaves, grooved. Flowers inconspicuous in an ovoid to oblong spike. Corolla-tube hairless outside, with 4 long-pointed, often hairy lobes. Calyces and bracts with long silky hairs, so that the whole spike appears hairy.
Pastures, fallow fields, waysides.
Mediterranean region, Canary Islands, S.W. Asia.
P. albicans L.: plant perennial. Leaves 5–15×0.5–0.8cm, with long silky hairs. Flower-spikes much longer than the leaves, 3–10cm long, lax. *P. bellardii* All.: annual, leaves only 2–7×0.1–0.5cm, more or less densely hairy. Flower-spikes only slightly longer than the leaves, 1–2cm long, dense (both species in the Mediterranean region).

□□ *Plantago afra* L. (*P. psyllium* L. 1762, non L. 1753)
□■ 10–40cm; April–July; ☉
An erect or ascending plant, usually densely covered with glandular woolly hairs at least above, with opposite branches. Leaves opposite, sessile, linear-lanceolate, entire or with a few teeth. Flowers inconspicuous in long-stalked, ovoid to roundish heads in the upper leaf-axils. Floral bracts ovate-lanceolate, pointed, 3.5–8mm, all equal, without lateral veins. Seeds 2.5–5mm, boat-shaped, dark brown-red, used as a mild laxative because of their high mucilage content.
Fields, waste ground, waysides, garigue.
Mediterranean region, Canary Islands, S.W. Asia.
P. arenaria W. & K. (*P. psyllium* L. nom. ambig., *P. indica* L. nom. illegit.) is similar: the lowest 2 bracts 6–10mm, much larger than the upper ones, with lateral veins at the base. Plant more or less sparsely covered with minute glands (Mediterranean region, Asia).

220

Honeysuckle family *Caprifoliaceae*
Valerian family *Valerianaceae*
Scabious family *Dipsacaceae*

■□
□□ *Viburnum tinus* L. **Laurustinus** *Caprifoliaceae*
1–3(–7)m; January–June; ♄
Evergreen, much-branched shrub, the entire, leathery leaves shining dark green above, paler and sparely hairy beneath, elliptic, ovate-lanceolate or lanceolate, pointed, 3–10×1.5–7cm. Flowers arranged in dense, umbel-like clusters, 4–9cm across. Corolla 5–9mm in diameter, 5-lobed, pink outside and white within. Fruits metallic dark blue when ripe, 8mm across.
Shady, often damp places in the maquis and evergreen woods; also cultivated as an ornamental shrub.
Mediterranean region, rarer and sometimes absent in the east, Canary Islands.

□■
□□ *Lonicera implexa* Ait. *Caprifoliaceae*
1–2m; April–June; ♄
Twining, evergreen subshrub with hairless, blue-green stems. The opposite, sessile leaves are slightly lobed at the base, ovate-elliptic, pointed, 2–8×(0.5–)2–4cm, leathery, shining dark green above, blue-green beneath, with a translucent margin. Upper leaves on flowering stems united in pairs at the base, with whorls of 2–6 strongly scented flowers in their axils. Corolla 2-lipped, 2.5–4.5cm long, yellowish, later tinged red, the tube 3–4 times as long as the lobes.
Woods, maquis, hedges, also grown as a decorative shrub.
Mediterranean region, eastwards to Greece.
A similar but deciduous species is *L. etrusca* Santi, with leaves usually hairy beneath and long-stalked inflorescences of 8–12 flowers (Mediterranean region).

□□
■□ *Centranthus* (*Kentranthus*) *ruber* (L.) DC. **Red Valerian** *Valerianaceae*
30–80cm; April–September; ⅃
An ascending or erect, hairless, blue-green plant. Leaves opposite, 3–8×1–5cm, ovate-lanceolate, the upper ones sessile with a heart-shaped base, sometimes weakly irregularly toothed. Flowers pink, in clusters, corolla with a tube 7–10mm long, 5 unequal lobes and a thin spur 5–10mm long. One solitary, protruding stamen. Fruits with a tuft of feathery hairs.
Rock-crevices, scree, and on walls.
Mediterranean region, Canary Islands, also cultivated elsewhere as an ornamental plant, sometimes escaping and growing wild.
C. angustifolius (Mill.) DC.: leaves very narrow, 3–10cm×2–4mm. Corolla-tube 6–9mm, with a spur 2–4mm long (France, Italy, Switzerland, N.W. Africa); *C. calcitrapae* (L.) Dufresne: plant annual. Upper leaves deeply divided. Corolla-tube small, 1–3mm, with a bag-shaped swelling at the base (S. Europe, Asia Minor, N.W. Africa, Canary Islands).

□□
□■ *Cephalaria leucantha* (L.) Roem. & Schult. *Dipsacaceae*
0.2–1m; July–September; ⅃
A slender, erect plant, much-branched from the base. Leaves opposite, hairless, sometimes hairy, pinnately divided, the lowest ones with a large, serrate, terminal segment and long-stalked, the upper ones sessile, with uniformly narrow, lanceolate to linear segments, remotely serrate or lobed. Flowers in almost spherical, erect heds, 2–3cm across, with several rows of overlapping, ovate, blunt, whitish bracts with appressed hairs. Receptacular scales membranous, obovate-lanceolate, 7–9mm long. Flowers with a white or yellowish 4-lobed corolla, 10–15mm long. Calyx small, cup-shaped, sunk in a 4-sided, hairy outer calyx that has a membranous fringe round the top and is 6mm long at fruiting time.
Stony and grassy pastures, roadsides.
S. Europe, N.W. Africa.

Bellflower family Campanulaceae

■□ *Campanula hagielia* Boiss. (*C. sporadum* Feer)
□□ 10–40cm; April–June; ☉, ♃

A rock-plant, with usually several stems, and soft spreading hairs. Basal leaves ovate to heart-shaped, irregularly crenate-serrate, often with a pair of leaflets on the leaf-stalk or the whole leaf almost lyre-shaped. Lower stem-leaves similar, the upper ones sessile. Flowers at the end of the stems and in the leaf-axils, stalked. Calyx-lobes pointed, with large ovate appendages between them that completely cover the ovary. Corolla large, 20–30mm×10mm, broadly cylindrical to funnel-shaped. Style with 5 stigmas. Capsule opening by 5 pores. A very variable species in spite of its limited distribution.
Rock-crevices, especially in chalk.
W. Anatolia and adjacent Aegean Islands.
A closely related plant, often forming hybrids with the above species, is *C. lyrata* Lam.: plant more roughly hairy, especially the calyx-appendages. Corolla 12–25mm long (Asia Minor and European Turkey). Two softly hairy species, occurring in southern Greece, are *C. celsii* A. DC. and *C. rupestris* Sibth. & Sm., the latter having a style with 3 stigmas. There are numerous species found only in small areas, especially in the Balkan peninsula and Asia Minor, examples of which are provided by the plants illustrated.

□■ *Campanula pyramidalis* L.
□□ 0.3–1.5m; July–October; ☉, ♃

A hairless species, remarkable for its stiffly upright, tall growth. The long-stalked basal leaves have a broadly ovate, almost heart-shaped blade and a glandular crenate-toothed margin. Stem-leaves with progressively shorter stalks, weakly heart-shaped or narrowed at the base. Flowers 1–3 in the axils of the upper, lanceolate, bract-like stem-leaves, forming a long raceme or narrowly pyramidal panicle. Corolla widely bell-shaped, up to 3cm in diameter, divided almost to the middle into 5 triangular, pointed lobes, pale blue-violet, rarely white. The 5 calyx-lobes are narrowly triangular, and finally recurved, without appendages between them, much shorter than the corolla. Style with 3 stigmas. Capsule erect, with 3 pores, opening near the base.
Rocks, walls, waysides.
N. Italy, Balkan peninsula southwards to Albania.

□□ *Campanula versicolor* Andr.
■□ 20–40cm; June–September; ♃

A hairless plant, with stout, ascending or erect, simple or branched stems. Leaves leathery, without glands, crenate or toothed, the lower ones ovate to heart-shaped, stalked, the upper-most wedge-shaped at the base and almost sessile. Flowers in clusters, with a funnel-shaped corolla, 1.5–2.5cm long and 3cm broad, with 5 spreading, triangular lobes, pale violet or pale blue, dark violet inside at the base. Calyx-lobes narrowly lanceolate, without appendages. Style with 3 stigmas. Capsule erect. A variable species.
Rocks, extending into the mountain zone.
Balkan peninsula, S.E. Italy.

□□ *Trachelium caeruleum* L. **Throatwort**
□■ 0.3–1m; May–September; ♃ . ♄

An erect plant, woody at the base, the stem just below the inflorescence without leaves. Leaves except the uppermost stalked, ovate to broadly lanceolate, doubly serrate and fringed with fine hairs. Flowers in a lax, terminal cluster, 5–10cm across, blue-violet more rarely white, with a narrow corolla-tube, 6–8mm long, and 5 lobes. Style distinctly protruding. Ssp. *lanceolatum* (Guss.) Arc. has narrowly lanceolate leaves and winged leaf-stalks (only in Sicily).
Shady and damp rocks and walls.
Western Mediterranean region, absent from the Balearic Islands, Corsica and Sardinia, also cultivated as an ornamental plant, sometimes escaping and growing wild.
T. jacquinii (Sieb.) Boiss.: plant 10–35cm, stem leafy right up to the dense inflorescence. Only the lowermost leaves shortly stalked, the rest sessile (Greece, Aegean, Bulgaria).

Daisy family   *Asteraceae (Compositae)*

■☐ *Bellis annua* L. **Annual Daisy**
☐☐ 3–12cm; February–June; ☉
   Stem branched below and leafy, without an obvious rosette, roots very fine. Leaves tongue-
   shaped to spathulate, crenate-serrate or entire, up to 2.5cm long and 1.5cm broad. Flower-
   heads 0.5–1.5cm across, on thin stalks, with 2 rows of involucral bracts and white ray-florets,
   often tinged red beneath. Fruits compressed, hairy, without pappus.
   Grassy, sometimes damp places, also on sand.
   Mediterranean region, Canary Islands.
   Bellium bellidioides L.: equally small and delicate, but a perennial plant with runners. All
   leaves basal, narrowing into a long stalk, entire. Only one row of involucral bracts (Balearic
   Islands, Corsica, Sardinia).

☐■ *Bellis sylvestris* Cyr. **Southern Daisy**
☐☐ 10–30cm; September–May; ♃
   Leaves all in a basal rosette, the young ones with appressed hairs, oblong to narrowly
   obovate, 3–18cm long and up to 2.5cm broad, entire or remotely crenate-serrate, the blade
   narrowing very gradually into a scarcely distinct stalk, 3-veined. Flower-heads 2–4cm
   across, solitary on stout stalks, 10–45cm long, with 2 rows of more or less pointed involucral
   bracts, 7–12mm long, and white ray-florets often tinged purple-red on both sides. Fruits compressed, hairy, sometimes with short bristles.
   Woods, thickets, pastures, extending into the mountain zone.
   Mediterranean region.
   Our native Daisy, *B. perennis* L., also occurs in the Mediterranean region, but this has the
   leaf-blades abruptly narrowing into the stalk and with only one distinct vein. Flower-heads
   1.5–3cm across, with blunt involucral bracts, 3–5mm long.

☐☐ *Evax pygmaea* (L.) Brot.
■☐ 1–4cm; April–June; ☉
   A very low, grey-felted plant, branched at the base. Stem ascending, leafy, with a rosette in
   the upper part of oblong-obovate to spathulate, spreading leaves, 5–16mm long and 2–5mm
   broad, that surround a cluster of almost sessile flower-heads and are 2–3 times as long.
   Involucral bracts more than 30, yellowish, 3–4mm long, bristle-tipped. Only minute tubular
   flowers present. Fruit warted, rarely with a few hairs.
   Garigue and open grassy pastures near the coast.
   S. Europe, Asia Minor, N.W. Africa, Canary Islands.
   E. asterisciflora (Lam.) Pers.: rosette-leaves 15–40mm, oblong-lanceolate, about 4 times as
   long as the cluster of flower-heads (western Mediterranean region). In addition there are sev-
   eral species with a distribution restricted to small areas.

☐☐ *Helichrysum stoechas* (L.) Moench
☐■ 10–50cm; April–July; ♄
   Subshrub with sessile, white-felted leaves becoming hairless above, recurved at the margin.
   Flower-heads in dense clusters, 1.5–3cm across, with yellow tubular flowers and a bright yellow, globular to broadly ovoid involucre, 4–6mm across. Involucral bracts in several rows,
   loosely overlapping, without glands. Ssp. *stoechas*: Plant strongly aromatic, leaves narrowly
   linear, usually longer than 2cm; ssp. *barrelieri* (Ten.) Nym.: plant not or scarcely aromatic,
   leaves broadly linear to narrowly spathulate, usually shorter than 2cm. A variable plant.
   Common on sandy and rocky coasts, in garigue.
   Ssp. *stoechas* is found in S. Europe as far as W. Yugoslavia, and ssp. *barrelieri* from Sicily
   eastwards to Turkey and in N. Africa.
   H. rupestre (Rafin.) DC.: plant scentless. Leaves 3–8cm long. Inflorescence 3–7cm in diame-
   ter, involucre 4–7mm across, broadly ovoid in bud, later spreading (western and central
   Mediterranean region). *H. sanguineum* (L.) Kortel. has red involucral bracts (Turkey to
   Israel).

Daisy family *Asteraceae (Compositae)*

■□ *Helichrysum italicum* (Roth) Don f.
□□ 20–60cm; May–August; ♌
An aromatic subshrub, covered with grey-white felt when young. Leaves sessile, narrowly linear with a recurved margin, thinly felted above, becoming hairless. Flower-heads in dense clusters with yellow tubular flowers and a golden yellow, narrowly bell-shaped involucre that is distinctly longer than broad. Involucral bracts in several rows, closely overlapping, the outer ones ovate, the inner ones at least 5 times as long, and narrow. There are several subspecies: Ssp. *italicum* (*H. angustifolium* DC.): lower leaves 2–5cm long. Involucre 2–3mm across, outer involucral bracts without glands (S. Europe, N.W. Africa, Asia Minor). Ssp. *microphyllum* (Willd.) Nym.: lower leaves 0.5–1cm long. Involucre 2mm across, all the involucral bracts with glands (Coastal rocks of the western Mediterranean islands). Ssp. *serotinum* (Boiss.) Fourn.: lower leaves up to 4cm long. Involucre 3–4mm across, outer involucral bracts without glands. Flowering time somewhat later (western Mediterranean region).
Garigue, stony pastures.
S. Europe, N.W. Africa, Asia Minor.
Species restricted to small areas include *H. ambiguum* (Pers.) C. Presl (Balearic Islands), *H. saxatile* Moris (Sardinia, Pantelleria) and *H. heldreichii* Boiss. (Crete).

□■ *Phagnalon sordidum* (L.) Rchb.
□□ 15–40cm; May–July; ♌
A small subshrub with white-felted stems and linear leaves, 1–3cm long, with white woolly hairs on both sides and a recurved margin. At the end of the stem is a cluster of 2–6 sessile or shortly stalked heads of yellow tubular flowers and brownish, membranous, ovate, pointed involucral bracts, closely overlapping and appressed to the flower-heads.
Rocks, walls.
Western Mediterranean region, eastwards to Italy.
Hybrids with *P. rupestre* (L.) DC. and *P. saxatile* (L.) Cass. (see below) are not uncommon.

□□ *Phagnalon rupestre* (L.) DC.
■□ 15–50cm; March–July; ♌
A small subshrub with white-felted stems. Leaves 1–4cm long, narrowly ovate-lanceolate, the upper ones sessile with a broadened base, undulate and weakly toothed on the margin, more or less recurved, dark green above with rather cobwebby hairs, densely white-felted beneath. Flower-heads solitary, about 1cm long, long-stalked, with yellowish tubular flowers and closely appressed, hairless, brownish, membranous involucral bracts, the outer ones ovate to triangular and blunt.
Stony pastures, garigue.
Mediterranean region, Canary Islands, S.W. Asia.
P. graecum Boiss. & Heldr. (*P. rupestre* ssp. *graecum* (Boiss. & Heldr.) Hay.): Outer involucral bracts narrowly triangular to lanceolate, pointed (eastern Mediterranean region). *P. saxatile* (L.) Cass.: upper leaves linear, more or less recurved. Involucral bracts pointed, the outer ones later spreading or bent back (S. Europe, N.W. Africa, Canary Islands).

□□ *Inula crithmoides* L. **Golden Samphire**
□■ 10–90cm; August–October: ♃, ♌
Coastal plant with erect or ascending, leafy stems, sparsely branched but woody at the base. Leaves fleshy, hairless, linear, 2–4.5cm long and 2–4mm broad, entire or 3-toothed at the tip. Flower-heads of orange-yellow disc-florets and yellow ray-florets, 14–25mm long, much longer than the hemispherical involucre. Involucral bracts linear, the outer ones 3–4mm long, the inner ones 5–10mm long. Fruits 2–3mm long, the pappus of brownish white bristly hairs not joined at the base.
Sandy beaches, coastal rocks, saltmarshes.
Coasts of the Mediterranean and W. Europe, northwards to England and Ireland, inland also in E. Spain and N. Africa.

Daisy family *Asteraceae* (*Compositae*)

■□ *Inula verbascifolia* (Willd.) Hausskn. (*I. candida* ssp. *verbascifolia* (Willd.) Hay.)
□□ 10–50cm; July–August; ♃, ♄
Plant woody at the base and covered with white woolly felt. Basal leaves long-stalked, ovate-lanceolate and shortly wedge-shaped at the base, often pointed, entire or crenate, with prominent veins beneath, stem-leaves smaller. Flower-heads variable in size, with yellow tubular florets and yellow ray-florets, the latter either longer or, as in the plant illustrated (ssp. *heterolepis* (Boiss.) Tutin), shorter than the 7–12mm long involucre, which usually has spathulate, ovate or lanceolate bracts at its base. Fruits cylindrical, about 2mm long, with a pappus consisting of a single row of 10–15 bristly hairs, free at the base and about twice as long. There are several subspecies.
Rock-crevices, especially in limestone.
Italy (Gargano), Balkan peninsula, Asia Minor, Lebanon.
I. candida (L.) Cass. (*I. candida* ssp. *limonifolia* (Sibth. & Sm.) Hay.) is similar: leaves covered with a felt of appressed, silky hairs, gradually narrowing into the stalk, blunt. Veins on the under side not prominent. Involucre 8–9mm, longer than the ray-florets. Several subspecies (only in Greece and Crete).

□■ *Dittrichia viscosa* (L.) Greut. (*Inula viscosa* (L.) Ait.) **Aromatic Inula**
□□ 0.5–1.3m; August–November; ♃, ♄
An aromatic, glandular sticky plant, woody at the base, with erect, simple or branched, densely leafy stems. Lower leaves oblong-lanceolate, 3–7cm, entire or remotely toothed, the upper ones half stem-clasping. Inflorescence a leafy, narrowly pyramidal panicle, with numerous flower-heads abut 1.5cm in diameter. Disc-florets yellow-orange, ray-florets yellow, 10–12mm long, distinctly longer than the involucral bracts. Fruits 2mm long, hairy, abruptly narrowed at the end, the pappus-hairs united near the base.
Waysides, fallow land, also in the garigue, often covering large areas.
Mediterranean region, Canary Islands.
D. graveolens (L.) Greut. (*Inula graveolens* (L.) Desf.): plant an annual, 20–50cm high. Ray-florets 4–7mm, scarcely longer than the involucral bracts (Mediterranean region, S.W. Asia).

□□ *Pulicaria dysenterica* (L.) Bernh. **Fleabane**
■□ 20–100cm; July–October; ♃
Plant branched in the upper part. Leaves oblong-lanceolate, hairy and with sessile glands, somewhat undulate and remotely toothed on the margin, the lowest ones stalked and withering at flowering time, the others with a heart-shaped to arrow-shaped base clasping the stem. Flower-heads numerous, 1.5–3cm across, the golden yellow ray-florets radiating outwards, about 5mm longer than the involucre, which consists of linear-lanceolate, hairy, involucral bracts. Fruits with bristly pappus-hairs about 4mm long, which are surrounded at the base by a small ring of united scales, distinguishing this genus from *Inula*.
Damp places, marshes, by rivers and streams.
Mediterranean region, northwards to central Europe and eastwards to central Asia.
P. odora (L.) Rchb. has equally long ray-florets: plant with one or several flower-heads. Basal leaves green at flowering time (Mediterranean region). Several annual species have shorter ray-florets.

□□ *Pallenis spinosa* (L.) Cass.
□■ 10–60cm; April–August; ☉
Stem with spreading hairs, usually branched in the upper part. Leaves with appressed hairs, entire, the lower ones ovate-oblong, narrowed into a stalk, the upper ones sessile, half stem-clasping, pointed. Flowers in long-stalked heads, the lateral flower-heads standing higher than those in the middle. Outer involucral bracts spreading, leaf-like, 1.5–3.5cm long, lanceolate, spine-tipped, with parallel veins, much longer than the inner ones, and also far exceeding the 3-toothed ray-florets. The latter in 2 rows, 1–2cm long. Fruits, in contrast to those of *Asteriscus* species, flat and winged, 2–2.5mm long.
Waysides, fallow land.
Mediterranean region, Canary Islands.

Daisy family *Asteraceae* (*Compositae*)

■☐ *Asteriscus aquaticus* (L.) Less. (*Odontospermum aquaticum* (L.) Schultz Bip.)
☐☐ 10–40cm; April–August; ☉
Stem simple or with spreading branches above, pointing upwards. Leaves hairy, oblong-spathulate, the lower ones stalked, the upper ones sessile and half clasping the stem. Flower-heads solitary, 1.5–3cm across, with fairly short, sulphur-yellow ray-florets, 3-toothed at the tip, and tubular disc-florets. Outer involucral bracts with a long, blunt, leaf-like tip, 2–3 times as long as the ray-florets. Inner involucral bracts ovate, leathery, with or without a short, green tip. Fruits 1.5–2mm, silky hairy, with fringed pappus-scales, the outer ones more or less triangular, wingless.
Sandy, damp places near the coast.
Mediterranean region, Canary Islands.
A. pygmaeus (DC.) Coss. & Dur.: plant almost stemless, leaves all narrowing into a long stalk. Flower-heads 1.5cm across, pappus-scales hardly fringed (N. Africa, Canary Islands, S.W. Asia).

☐■ *Asteriscus maritimus* (L.) Less.
☐☐ 5–25cm; April–July; ♄
A roughly hairy dwarf shrub, with prostrate, ascending or sometimes erect stems, often covering large areas. Leaves entire, spathulate, narrowing gradually to the base. Flower-heads solitary at the ends of the stems, 3–4cm in diameter, rich yellow, the ray-florets 3-toothed at the tip, disc-florets cylindrical. Outer involucral bracts, like the upper stem-leaves, with a blunt, spathulate tip, almost as long as the ray-florets. Fruits more or less 3-sided, 1.5mm, wingless.
Stony pastures, often near the coast.
S. Europe, N.W. Africa, Canary Islands.

☐☐ *Xanthium strumarium* L. **Cocklebur**
■☐ 0.2–1m; July–September; ☉
Stem erect, usually much-branched from the base. Leaves green on both sides, shortly hairy, long-stalked, with a broadly ovate to triangular blade and a heart-shaped or wedge-shaped base, undivided or 3 to 5-lobed, coarsely serrate. Flower-heads unisexual, in clusters at the ends of the stems or in the leaf-axils, the male above the female. The latter 2-flowered, sunk into an ovoid involucre covered with straight or hooked spines and with 2 beaks at the end. There are several subspecies that hybridise with each other, regarded by some authors as separate species, e.g. the plant illustrated, ssp. *italicum* (Moretti) D. Löve: plant aromatic, stem often with violet markings. Fruiting heads yellow or brown when ripe, 1.5–3.5cm long. Spines 5–6mm long, stiff, distinctly hooked at the tip, closely set.
Waste ground, especially on sandy beaches, river-banks, waysides.
The species occurring throughout Europe and introduced elsewhere, ssp. *italicum* in the northern Mediterranean region. Origin unknown.

☐☐ *Xanthium spinosum* L. **Spiny Cocklebur**
☐■ 0.1–1m; August–October; ☉
An erect plant, much-branched from the base. Leaves alternate, sessile or shortly stalked, rhombic in outline, pinnately divided into 3–5 lobes, the middle one elongated, dark green above, only the main veins grey, pale grey-felted beneath. Where the leaf-stalk is attached to the stem there are 1 or 2 stout, straw-coloured spines, each divided into 3 parts. Male flowers in small, inconspicuous heads at the ends of the stems, the female in the leaf-axils, 2-flowered, sunk into an involucre that is covered with hooked spines. Ripe fruiting heads 10–12×6–8mm, with 2 straight beaks of unequal length at the end, and rather cobwebby hairs between the spines.
Waste ground, waysides.
Naturalised in the Mediterranean region and throughout the warmer regions of the world, native in S. America.

Daisy family Asteraceae (Compositae)

☐☐ *Anthemis tomentosa* L. **Woolly Chamomile**
☐☐ 5–30cm; March–June; ☉
A prostrate to ascending or more or less erect, branched plant, covered with white woolly felt, the main shoot shorter than the lateral ones. Leaves 2–5cm, ovate-oblong in outline, pinnate or bipinnate, the segments ovate to wedge-shaped, blunt. Flower-heads solitary on stalks that later thicken, 1.5–3.7cm broad, with yellow, tubular, disc-florets, and white ray-florets, 5–10mm long. Receptacular scales translucent, oblanceolate, pointed. Involucral bracts strongly hairy, the inner ones with a membranous margin. Fruits obconical, 1.5–2mm, with a narrow, membranous margin, sometimes with auricles, pappus absent. A variable species with several subspecies.
Sandy coasts, fallow land, also in rocky places in the mountains.
S. Europe, westwards to Italy and Sicily, Asia Minor.
A genus with numerous species occurring only in small areas.

☐☐ *Anacyclus clavatus* (Desf.) Pers. (*A. tomentosus* DC.)
☐☐ 10–50cm; May–July; ☉
An erect plant with appressed hairs, usually branched from the base. Leaves oblong, 2–3 times pinnate with narrow, finely pointed segments. Flower-heads solitary, their stalks thickened at the top at maturity, disc-florets yellow, ray-florets white, 7–14mm long. Receptacular scales obovate. Involucral bracts green, lanceolate, pointed, with a white or purple margin, silky hairy. Fruits 3–4mm, strongly compressed, the outer ones with broad, translucent wings, each with an erect, round lobe projecting beyond the end of the fruit. Pappus absent.
Waysides, fallow land, often near the coast.
S. Europe, N.W. Africa, Asia Minor.
A. radiatus Loisel.: ray-florets yellow, inner involucral bracts with large, fringed appendages (S. Europe, N.W. Africa, Canary Islands).

☐☐ *Chrysanthemum segetum* L. **Corn Marigold**
☐☐ 20–60cm; June–August; ☉
A hairless, blue-green, rather fleshy plant with an erect, simple or slightly branched, very leafy stem. Leaves oblong to obovate, incised or coarsely toothed, the upper ones almost undivided and somewhat stem-clasping. Flower heads solitary, 2–5cm across, with yellow disc and ray-florets. Involucral bracts ovate, pale green with a light brown, membranous margin, which is broadened on the inner involucral bracts. Fruits without pappus, those of the ray-florets with 2 lateral wings. Receptacle without bracts.
Cultivated and fallow land.
Eastern Mediterranean region, S.W. Asia, naturalised in the rest of the Mediterranean region, Canary Islands, and almost the whole of Europe.
A species formerly placed in the same genus is *Coleostephus myconis* (L.) Rchb. f. (*Chrysanthemum myconis* L.): leaves finely serrate. Fruits with a pappus consisting of a membranous crown (Mediterranean region, Canary Islands).

☐☐ *Chrysanthemum coronarium* L. **Crown Daisy**
☐☐ 30–80cm; March–September; ☉
A stout, erect, hairless plant, much-branched and very leafy. Leaves oblong to obovate, sessile and half stem-clasping, doubly pinnately divided with lanceolate, pointed lobes. Flower-heads solitary, 3–6cm across, with yellow disc and ray-florets. Involucral bracts ovate with a translucent, membranous margin, broader in the case of the inner bracts. Fruits without pappus, those of the ray-florets triangular in cross-section with the angles winged. Receptacle without scales. There are 2 varieties that occasionally occur together: one has uniformly deep yellow ray-florets, the other (var. *discolor* d'Urv.) has pale yellow ray-florets which are deep yellow only at the base.
Cultivated and fallow land, often covering large areas, also grown in gardens, sometimes escaping and growing wild.
Mediterranean region, eastwards to Iran, Canary Islands.

Daisy family *Asteraceae (Compositae)*

■□ *Otanthus maritimus* (L.) Hoffmanns. & Link (*Diotis maritima* (L.) Desf. ex Cass.)
□□ **Cottonweed**
10–50cm; June–September; ♃, ♄
A densely white-felted, aromatic, shore-plant with stout, ascending, somewhat woody stems, and numerous, oblong or spathulate, sessile leaves, broad at the base, 5–17mm long, entire or finely crenate-serrate. Flowers all tubular, yellow, in spherical heads, 8–10mm across, in shortly stalked clusters at the ends of the stems. Involucral bracts white-felted, receptacle with chaffy scales. Corolla with 2 narrow wings at the base. Fruits about 4mm, curved, without a pappus.
Sandy beaches.
Coasts of the Mediterranean and the Atlantic, northwards to Ireland, Canary Islands.

□■ *Doronicum orientale* Hoffm. (*D. caucasicum* Bieb.)
□□ 20–60cm; April–June; ♃
Rhizome with tufts of silky hairs. Basal leaves long-stalked, roundish-ovate with a broad, heart-shaped base, toothed. Stem-leaves 1 or 2(–3), sessile, clasping the stem, the lower sometimes fiddle-shaped. Flower-heads solitary, long-stalked, 2.5–6cm broad, with yellow disc-florets and narrow, yellow ray-florets. Involucral bracts linear-lanceolate, ½–¾ as long as the ray-florets, the latter without a pappus.
Deciduous woods and rocks in the mountain zone, also grown as an ornamental plant.
S.E. Europe, westwards to Italy and Sicily, Asia Minor, Caucasus.
D. columnae Ten. (*D. cordatum* auct. non Lam.) is very similar, but it has a hairless or sparsely hairy rhizome and 3 or 4 stem-leaves (S.E. Europe). Basal leaves narrowing towards the base are a characteristic of *D. corsicum* (Lois.) Poir. with 3–8 flower-heads (Corsica) and *D. plantagineum* L. with solitary flower-heads (W. Europe).

□□ *Senecio bicolor* (Willd.) Tod. ssp. *cineraria* (DC.) Chat. (*S. cineraria* DC.) **Cineraria**
■□ 25–60cm; May–August; ♄
A white-felted, much-branched subshrub. Leaves clustered at the base of the stem, the upper side of the leaves covered with cobwebby hairs, becoming hairless, the under side densely white-felted, ovate, lobed to deeply pinnately divided, the segments again divided, the terminal lobe usually longer than it is broad. Flower-heads in clusters, shortly stalked, 12–15mm across, with orange-yellow disc-florets, 10–13 pale yellow ray-florets, 3–6mm long, and white-felted involucral bracts.
Coastal rocks, also on sand, grown in various forms as an ornamental plant.
Western and central Mediterranean region, Canary Islands.
Ssp. *bicolor* has the terminal lobe of the leaf as broad as long and blunt-tipped, and the flower-heads on long stalks (central and eastern Mediterranean region). Ssp. *nebrodensis* (Guss.) Chat. has hairless or only sparsely hairy involucral bracts (Sicily).

□□ *Calendula arvensis* L. **Field Marigold**
□■ 10–30cm; April–October; ☉
An ascending to prostrate plant with a downy-hairy, usually branched stem. Leaves oblong-lanceolate, slightly undulate, entire to remotely toothed, sessile, the upper ones half stem-clasping. Flowers in terminal heads, 1–2cm across, nodding in fruit. Ray-florets orange to golden yellow, less than twice as long as the involucral bracts. In each head there are 3 different forms of fruit: the outer ones are curved and covered with spines, which assist their dispersal by animals, next come fruits with lateral wings, enabling them to be dispersed by the wind, and in the centre are slender fruits, curled and grub-like.
Cultivated and fallow land, waysides.
Mediterranean region, eastwards to Iran, rarely extending into the warmest parts of central Europe, Canary Islands.
The much more robust **Garden Marigold**, *Calendula officinalis* L. (origin unknown) has escaped and grows wild in the Mediterranean region and elsewhere. It has ray-florets 2cm long, at least twice as long as the involucral bracts, as has *C. suffruticosa* Vahl, the latter woody at the base (extreme south of Europe, Asia Minor, N.W. Africa, Canary Islands).

Daisy family *Asteraceae (Compositae)*

■☐ *Carlina corymbosa* L.
☐☐ 20–70cm; June–September; ♃
Stems of this widespread and variable species stiffly erect and much branched, hairless or covered with cobwebby hairs, and bearing flower-heads at the ends. Leaves oblong-lanceolate, up to 9×3cm, undulate, with a spiny, toothed to pinnately divided margin, the upper ones clasping the stem and broadest at the base. Flower-heads 1.2–2cm in diameter, flowers yellow. Inner involucral bracts spreading out in dry weather and resembling ray-florets, golden yellow, 10–16mm long. Outer involucral bracts not or at most 1cm longer than the inner ones (ssp. *corymbosa*). In ssp. *graeca* (Boiss.) Nym. (only in the eastern Mediterranean region) the outer involucral bracts exceed the inner by about 2cm.
Pastures, fallow land, open woods and undergrowth.
Mediterranean region.
The genus is concentrated in the Mediterranean region, and is represented here by both perennial and annual species. The more primitive, woody species are restricted to the Canary Islands.

☐☐ *Carlina macrocephala* Moris
☐■ 15–40cm; July–August; ⊙
Plant with cobwebby hairs or almost hairless. Stem stiffly erect, simple or slightly branched, with lanceolate, undulate, spiny-toothed to pinnately divided leaves, 7–11cm long. Flower-heads 1.5–3cm in diameter, the inner involucral bracts 13–17mm long and 1.5–2mm broad, spreading out in dry weather and resembling ray-florets, white above and purple beneath. Outer involucral bracts much longer than the inner in ssp. *macrocephala* and flower-heads 1–4 (Corsica, Sardinia, central Italy); in ssp. *nebrodensis* (Guss. ex DC.) D.A. Webb, they are scarcely longer than the inner ones and the flower-heads are usually more than 4 (Sicily).
Open woods in the mountain zone.
Corsica, Sardinia, central Italy, Sicily.
C. sicula Ten.: plant perennial. Inner involucral bracts 2.5–3mm broad (S.E. Italy, Sicily). *C. lanata* L.: plant annual. Leaves permanently felted beneath. Inner involucral bracts reddish purple on both sides (Mediterranean region, eastwards to Iran).

☐☐ *Carlina acanthifolia* All.
■☐ 5–10cm; July–September; ♃
A decorative, stemless plant with the leaves clustered in a rosette, 10–30cm long, pinnately divided to just over half-way into spine-toothed segments, at least the under side covered with cobwebby hairs. The solitary, sessile flower-head 3–7cm in diameter, with yellowish to reddish disc-florets, and with the inner involucral bracts 5.5cm long and shining yellow above, spreading out in dry weather and resembling ray-florets. Two subspecies occur in the Mediterranean region: ssp. *acanthifolia*, with the spines of the middle involucral bracts usually branched; and ssp. *cynara* (Pourr. ex Duby) Rouy, with the spines of the middle involucral bracts usually simple (only in the Pyrenees, S. France, and the northern Apennines).
Stony pastures, dry grassland.
S. Europe and eastern central Europe, mainly in the mountains.

☐☐ *Carlina racemosa* L.
☐■ 10–40cm; August–October; ⊙, ♃
A white-woolly plant with forked branches from the base. Leaves stiff, lanceolate, 10×2cm, remotely spine-toothed, the lower ones stalked, the upper sessile with numerous prominent lateral veins. Flower-heads with yellow disc-florets, 8–15mm across, more or less sessile at the ends of the stems and in the forks of the branches. Inner involucral bracts sulphur-yellow, 10–12mm long and 1–2mm broad, spreading out in dry weather and resembling ray-florets. Outer involucral bracts leaf-like, longer than the flower-heads.
Pasture land, often covering large areas.
Southern Iberian peninsula, Sardinia, N.W. Africa.

238

Daisy family *Asteraceae (Compositae)*

■□ *Atractylis humilis* L.
□□ 5–30cm; July–September; ⁴
Stem simple, hairless or covered with woolly hairs, with numerous oblong-lanceolate, sessile stem-leaves, pinnately divided into spiny segments, and shortly stalked rosette-leaves, 2.5–5cm long. Flower-heads solitary at the ends of the stems, 1.5–2.5cm across, with purple, tubular florets, and an involucre of outer, leaf-like bracts, bipinnately divided at the base, and entire inner bracts, cut squarely or notched at the end and tipped by a narrow spine. Fruits silky-hairy, with a pappus of feathery, white hairs, brownish at the base.
Garigue, stony pastures, on limestone.
Spain, Balearic Islands, France, N.W. Africa.
A. cancellata L.: plant an annual, flowering April–June. Outer involucral bracts divided, comb-like, arranged loosely round the flower-head, inner bracts lanceolate (Mediterranean region, Canary Islands, eastwards to Iran).

□■ *Echinops spinosissimus* Turra (*E. viscosus* DC. non Schrad. ex Rchb.)
□□ 0.5–1.5cm; June–September; ⁴
A stiffly erect, very spiny plant, the branched stem densely covered with glandular and cobwebby hairs. Leaves ovate-lanceolate in outline, usually bipinnately divided, glandular-hairy above and white-felted beneath, often with glandular hairs on the veins, the segments spiny. Heads 1-flowered, clustered into spherical, greenish blue or greyish inflorescences, 3.5–7cm across. Individual flower-heads surrounded by a ring of bristles that are as long as or slightly shorter than the spathulate, pointed and finely toothed outer involucral bracts. Spines of the middle, lanceolate, involucral bracts at least twice as long as the flower-head or absent. Pappus-hairs bristle-like, joined at base. There are several subspecies.
Fallow land, stony pastures, sandy beaches, often near the coast.
Eastern Mediterranean region, westwards to Sicily.

□□ *Echinops ritro* L. **Globe Thistle**
■□ 20–70cm; July–September; ⁴
Stem erect, usually branched, white-felted or almost hairless, often with glandular hairs. Leaves elliptic in outline, 1 or 2 times pinnately divided, with a recurved margin, the under side white-felted, the upper side varying according to the subspecies. Segments with spines 3–15mm long. Heads 1-flowered, clustered into spherical, blue inflorescences, 3.5–4.5cm across. Individual flower-heads surrounded by a ring of bristles that are ⅓–½ as long as the 12–17mm long involucre. Involucral bracts hairless but fringed with bristles, arranged in several overlapping rows, the innermost free to the base, fringed with hairs, and ending in a fine spine. Pappus-hairs bristle-like, united at least below. A variable species.
Dry grassland, stony pastures, also grown as an ornamental plant.
S. and E. Europe, S.W. Asia, absent from the Balearic Islands, Corsica, Sardinia, Crete.
E. sphaerocephalus L.: leaves densely covered with glandular and woolly hairs and scattered short bristles on the upper side, outer involucral bracts glandular-hairy on the back. Flower-heads pale blue or white (S. and E. Europe, Asia Minor, naturalised in central Europe).

□□ *Staehelina dubia* L.
□■ 10–40cm; June–July; ♄
A small, subshrub with white-felted stems, and narrowly lanceolate leaves, 1.5–4cm long and 2–4mm broad, white-felted beneath, with a somewhat recurved and undulate-toothed margin. Flower-heads very slender, singly or up to 4 together on stems leafy to the top, with purple tubular florets and the involucre 1.5–2cm long and 3–5mm broad. Involucral bracts overlapping, sparsely felted on the back and with a reddish margin, the inner ones tinged red-dish throughout. Fruit 4–5mm long, the white pappus 2–2.5cm, with branched bristles.
Garigue, stony pastures.
Western Mediterranean region, eastwards to central Italy.

Daisy family *Asteraceae (Compositae)*

■□ *Cirsium candelabrum* Gris. **Candelabra Thistle**
□□ 1.5–2m; May–August; ☉
A species of thistle conspicuous by its tall, pyramid-shaped growth. Leaves leathery and undulate, pinnately divided into triangular segments, with stiff spines 10–15mm long. Flower-heads in groups of 4–12 at the end of short branches, surrounded by 2–8 leaves of about the same length. Involucre 14–19×7–13mm, involucral bracts appressed, distinctly striped, the outer ones with stout, erect or spreading spines, 1–3mm long, the inner ones somewhat broadened, and fringed with spines at the tip. Corolla white or yellowish white, 13–17mm. Fruits 3.5–5mm, with a feathery pappus 13–16mm long.
Scree, waysides, in the mountain zone.
Balkan peninsula, S.W. Romania.

□■ *Picnomon acarna* (L.) Cass. (*Cirsium acarna* (L.) Moench)
□□ 20–70cm; July–August; ☉
A much-branched, thistle-like plant covered with grey cobwebby hairs. Leaves oblong-lanceolate, with stout, yellow spines, 4–15mm long, on the margin, and finer, shorter spines between them, the leaf-bases extending down the stem forming spiny wings. Flower-heads terminal, with purple or whitish tubular florets, in dense clusters or solitary, surrounded and exceeded by the upper leaves. Involucre cylindrical, 22–30×8–15mm, the involucral bracts tipped by a recurved, pinnately divided spine. Fruits ovate-oblong, compressed, brown and shining, with a feathery pappus 14–19mm long.
Waysides, waste ground, cultivated land.
Mediterranean region, Canary Islands, S.W. Asia.

□□ *Notobasis syriaca* (L.) Cass. (*Cirsium syriacum* (L.) Gaertn.) **Syrian Thistle**
■□ 0.3–1.5cm; April–June; ☉
A tall, thistle-like plant, usually branched above and tinged blue-purple. Leaves almost hair-less above, white-veined, the under side sparsely covered with grey cobwebby hairs, the lower ones stalked, oblong in outline, lobed and spiny-toothed, the stem-leaves sessile, the broad base clasping the stem, pinnately divided, the uppermost almost reduced to stout, stiff spines which surround and exceed the flower-heads. Heads solitary or several together with purple tubular florets and shortly spiny involucral bracts, 17–23×15–25mm, covered with cobwebby hairs. Fruits 5–6mm, dark brown, laterally compressed, hairless, with numerous feathery pappus-hairs, 13–15mm long, and an inner ring of hairs 1–2mm long united at the base.
Waysides, fallow and cultivated land.
Mediterranean region, Canary Islands, S.W. Asia.

□□ *Ptilostemon hispanicus* (Lam.) Greut. (*Chamaepeuce hispanica* (Lam.) DC.)
□■ 0.6–1m; July–September; ♃
A thistle-like plant, woody at the base and with a white-felted stem. Leaves leathery, ovate-lanceolate, lobed or sinuately toothed with stout, yellow spines, 10–20mm long, standing in lax groups of 2–4, dark green above, white-felted beneath. Flower-heads with purple tubular florets, 2.5–4cm across, stalked, forming a terminal cluster. Involucral bracts with a long, sharp, spreading spine. Fruits obliquely obovate, hardly compressed, with a feathery pappus 16–25mm long.
Waysides.
S. Spain.
There are several species in various parts of the Mediterranean region. *P. casabonae* (L.) Greut.: spines on the leaf-margin in groups of 2–4(–7) arising from the same point. Flower-heads almost sessile, forming a spike-like inflorescence (central Mediterranean region). *P. afer* (Jacq.) Greut.: leaves pinnately divided, the segments further divided into 2 or 3 parts with stout spines 5–12mm long. Flower-heads stalked, in groups of 10–16, forming racemes or flat-topped terminal clusters (Balkan peninsula, Asia Minor).

Daisy family *Asteraceae (Compositae)*

■□ *Galactites tomentosa* (L.) Moench
□□ 0.1–1m; April–August; ☉, ☉
An erect, thistle-like plant, usually branched only in the upper part, with a basal leaf-rosette.
Leaves becoming hairless above, often flecked with white, white-felted beneath, the base
extending a short distance down the equally white-felted stem, pinnately divided, with
spines 1.5–6mm long. Flower-heads 1–1.5cm across, the florets all tubular, pink, pale purple,
or more rarely whitish, the outer ones much longer and more brightly coloured, spreading,
infertile and serving only for display. Receptacle densely hairy. Involucral bracts ovate, covered with cobwebby hairs, erect, narrowing into a grooved and greenish tip 5–10mm long.
Fruits 3–5mm, with a feathery, white pappus 3–4 times as long.
Waysides, fallow land, pastures.
S. Europe, N.W. Africa, Canary Islands.

□■ *Cynara scolymus* L. **Globe Artichoke**
□□ 0.5–2m; April–August; ☉
A robust plant with pinnately divided to simple leaves, up to 80×40cm, becoming hairless
above, grey-felted beneath, soft, the segments not or only shortly spine-tipped, the lower
ones stalked, the upper sessile. Flower-heads very large, 8–15cm in diameter, with blue tubular florets. Involucral bracts fleshy below, with an ovate, blunt, notched or spine-tipped
appendage. The fleshy receptacle, together with the involucral bracts, is picked just before
flowering time and eaten as a vegetable. The active principle cynarin, which is obtained from
the leaves, is of importance in the treatment of gall-bladder disorders.
Grown in several cultivated varieties in the Mediterranean climate as a vegetable, but not
known as a wild plant. Perhaps derived from *C. cardunculus* L.
C. cardunculus L., **Cardoon**: leaves firm, pinnately divided 1–2 times, the segments with yellow spines 15–35mm long. Flower-heads smaller, involucral bracts with an erect or spreading spine, 1–5cm long. The blanched leaf-stalks are eaten as a vegetable (originally in the
western Mediterranean region, cultivated elsewhere as an economic or ornamental plant,
sometimes escaping and becoming naturalised).

□□ *Silybum marianum* (L.) Gaertn. **Holy Thistle, Milk Thistle**
■□ 0.2–1.5m; April–August; ☉
An erect, branched plant, with a large overwintering leaf-rosette. Leaves without hairs or
becoming hairless, shining green, with white veins and markings, sinuately lobed with a
spiny margin, the lower ones stalked, the upper ones stem-clasping with a heart-shaped base,
and spines up to 8mm long. Flowers red-purple, all tubular, in long-stalked, solitary heads 4–
8cm across. Outer involucral bracts broadly ovate, the appendage ending in a stout, yellow,
recurved spine, 2–5cm long. Fruits 6–8mm, shining, black with grey markings, and with a
pappus 1.5–2cm long. These fruits and the active principle that they contain, silymarin, are
used for treating disorders of the liver and gall-bladder.
Waste ground, waysides, pastures, often in fairly large numbers.
Mediterranean region, Canary Islands, S.W. Asia, occasionally naturalised further north.
S. eburneum Coss. & Dur. is similar, but the spines of the stem-leaves are 7–15mm long and
the outer involucral bracts are spineless (Spain, N.W. Africa).

□□ *Leuzea conifera* (L.) DC. (*Centaurea conifera* L.)
□■ 5–30cm; May–August; ♃
Stem erect, usually simple, felted, leafy up to the solitary, terminal flower-head. Leaves
white-felted beneath, the lower ones stalked, ovate-lanceolate, undivided or pinnately
divided and lyre-shaped, the upper ones sessile with linear-lanceolate segments. Involucre
of flower-head ovoid, 4–5cm in diameter, resembling a pine-cone. Middle involucral bracts
with round, brownish, membranous appendages, jaggedly cut at the margin, that completely
hide the lower parts of the involucral bracts. Florets purple or whitish. Fruits black, warted,
4mm long, with feathery, snow-white pappus-hairs about 6 times as long that are joined at
the base.
Garigue, pastures, open woods.
Western Mediterranean region, eastwards to Italy and Sicily.

Daisy family *Asteraceae* (*Compositae*)

■☐ *Centaurea calcitrapa* L. **Star Thistle**
☐☐ 0.1–1m; July–September; ⊙
Stem ascending or erect, much-branched from the base, rough. Young leaves grey-woolly, the older ones green, glandular and coarsely hairy, the basal ones pinnately divided, with lanceolate, pointed, remotely serrate segments, withered at flowering time, stem-leaves sessile, the uppermost lanceolate or spear-shaped, not extending down the stem. Flower-heads sessile, terminal and in the axils, surrounded by the upper leaves. Florets red or whitish, with glandular dots. Marginal florets not spreading. Involucre cylindrical-ovoid, 6–8mm across, the middle involucral bracts greenish with a membranous margin and a spreading spine, 10–18mm long, strongly thickened at the base and bearing 1–3 lateral spines 1–3mm in length. Fruits without pappus.
Fallow land, waysides, waste ground, pastures.
Mediterranean region, Canary Islands, N.W. Asia, introduced in places in central and W. Europe.
C. iberica Trev. ex Spreng.: young leaves green, slightly rough. Involucre 8–14mm across, middle spine of involucral bracts 15–30mm. Pappus 1–3m (eastern Mediterranean region, S.W. Asia). A genus of many species, very variable in form.

☐■ *Centaurea sphaerocephala* L.
☐☐ 5–70cm; April–June; ♃
Stem prostrate to erect, simple or branched, leafy up to the flower-head. Leaves covered with coarse to cobwebby hairs, spine-tipped, the lower ones stalked, pinnately divided and lyre-shaped, the upper ones entire or toothed, often with ear-like appendages at the base and stem-clasping, but not extending down the stem. Flower-heads solitary, with purple florets, the outer ones spreading and the involucre 12–35mm across. Appendage of the involucral bracts recurved, with 5–13 yellowish, palmately arranged spines, 3–6mm long, the middle one usually somewhat longer than the rest. Fruits shining, only the inner ones with a short, reddish pappus. There are several subspecies.
Sandy beaches, also on pasture-land.
Western Mediterranean region.

☐☐ *Centaurea solstitialis* L. **St Barnaby's Thistle**
■☐ 0.2–1m; July–September; ⊙, ⊙
A much-branched, grey-green, woolly or densely felted plant, the stems winged because of a downward extension of the leaves. Lower leaves pinnately divided and lyre-shaped, with-ered at flowering time, the upper ones linear-lanceolate, entire, shortly spine-tipped. Flower-heads solitary at the ends of the branches, florets pale yellow and without glands. Marginal florets not spreading. Involucre ovoid-spherical, 7–12mm across. Appendages of the middle involucral bracts not extended downwards at the base but tipped with a 10–15(–30)mm long spine that has 1–3 lateral spines, about 3mm long, at each side at the base. Pappus to 5mm long. There are several subspecies, some with a more brownish or only slightly longer middle spine on the involucral bracts.
Cultivated and fallow land, waste ground.
Mediterranean region, S.W. Asia, occasionally introduced into central and N.W. Europe.
C. melitensis L.: plant green, flower-heads solitary or 2–3 together, florets densely covered with sessile glands. Middle spine of the involucral bracts 5–8mm long, with 1–3 lateral spines in the lower half (S. Europe, Canary Islands, N.W. Africa).

☐☐ *Cnicus benedictus* L. **Blessed Thistle**
☐■ 10–60cm; April–July; ⊙
Stem erect, branched, grooved and angular, with pinnately divided, sinuate, spine-toothed, pale green leaves, the lower ones stalked, the upper ones sessile and half stem-clasping, all covered with cobwebby hairs and sticky glands, and with prominent white veins on the under side. Flower-heads with only yellow tubular florets, 3–3.5cm across, solitary at the ends of the branches, surrounded by the uppermost leaves. Outer involucral bracts with a short, simple spine, the inner ones longer with a pinnately divided spine. Pappus consisting of 10 outer bristles, about 1cm long, and 10 inner, shorter ones, all yellow. A medicinal plant, used to treat indigestion. Cultivated and fallow land, also grown in gardens.
Mediterranean region, S.W. Asia, sometimes escaping from cultivation and growing wild.

Daisy family *Asteraceae* (*Compositae*)

■☐ *Carthamus dentatus* (Forsk.) Vahl
☐☐ 15–60(–100)cm; July–September; ☉
A thistle-like, more or less glandular plant with shaggy-woolly to cobwebby hairs. Stem-leaves often grey-green, lanceolate to ovate-lanceolate, pinnately divided with a spiny margin. Flower-heads oblong-ovoid, with purple tubular florets. Inner involucral bracts with distinct, ovate-lanceolate, toothed appendages, the outer involucral bracts leaf-like, 1–2 times longer than the inner. Fruit 4-angled, broadly obpyramidal, with a conspicuous pappus, twice its length, consisting of brown, linear scales, fringed with hairs. There are 2 subspecies.
Fallow land, pastures.
Southern Balkan peninsula, S.W. Asia.

☐■ *Carthamus lanatus* L.
☐☐ 15–75cm; June–September; ☉
A glandular plant, with straw-coloured stems usually branched in the upper part, at first covered with cobwebby or woolly hairs but becoming hairless later. Leaves ovate-lanceolate, leathery, broadened at the base, the upper ones sessile and half clasping the stem, pinnately divided to sinuately toothed, with triangular, sharp-pointed segments. Flower-heads 2–3cm, solitary at the ends of the branches, surrounded by the uppermost leaves. The true involucral bracts have a spine-toothed appendage, the innermost ones are much shorter, oblong-lanceolate, with a narrow, membranous, entire or toothed appendage. Florets all tubular, golden or pale yellow. Fruits ovoid, 4-angled, dark brown, with a pappus of several rows of persistent, oblong scales, fringed with hairs. There are 2 subspecies.
Fallow land, pastures, waysides.
Mediterranean region, Canary Islands, S.E. Europe, S.W. Asia.
C. arborescens L. occurs in Spain and N.W. Africa: plant perennial, up to 2.5m high, flower-heads up to 4cm across. Inner involucral bracts without an appendage.

☐☐ *Carduncellus caeruleus* (L.) C. Presl (*Carthamus caeruleus* L.)
■☐ 20–60cm; May–July; ♃
Plant with woolly or cobwebby hairs, becoming hairless, with an erect, usually simple stem. Leaves very variable, the lower ones stalked, pinnately divided and lyre-shaped or oblong-lanceolate, the upper ones sessile and half clasping the stem, ovate-lanceolate, all coarsely toothed, the teeth having a sharply pointed, whitish, bristle-like tip. Flower-heads solitary, with blue tubular florets, and the outer, leaf-like, spine-toothed involucral bracts about 3cm broad. Inner involucral bracts equally long or shorter, glandular, with a membranous, rounded, fringed appendage. Fruits 6mm, indistinctly angled, wrinkled above, with whitish pappus-scales, 1½–2 times as long, fringed with hairs.
Garigue, fallow land, pastures.
S. Europe, N.W. Africa, Canary Islands, absent from Yugoslavia.
C. monspelliensium All.: flower-heads often stalkless, 2–4cm across. Outer involucral bracts spreading. Pappus about 4 times as long as the fruits (S.W. Europe).

☐☐ *Scolymus hispanicus* L. **Spanish Oyster Plant**
☐■ 20–80cm; June–September; ☉ ♃
A thistle-like, more or less hairy, erect and usually branched plant. Stem-leaves firm, sinuately pinnately divided with spine-toothed segments, extending only a short way down the stem so that the wings are not continuous. Flower-heads 1–2cm across, at the ends of the branches and in the leaf-axils, with golden-yellow ray-florets, exceeded by 3 spine-toothed bracts. Involucral bracts lanceolate, gradually narrowing to a point, scarcely hairy. Outer fruits enclosed by the receptacular scales and appearing winged. Pappus of 2–4 short bristles.
Waysides, waste ground, fallow land.
Mediterranean region, Canary Islands.
S. grandiflorus Desf.: stems continuously winged. Involucral bracts with numerous hairs, the outer ones abruptly narrowing to a spiny tip (central Mediterranean region). *S. maculatus* L.: Annual, leaves and stem-wings with a distinctly thickened, white margin. Pappus absent (Mediterranean region, Canary Islands).

Daisy family *Asteraceae (Compositae)*

■□ *Catananche caerulea* L. **Cupidone**
□□ 30–90cm; May–September; ♃
Plant with a tall, stiffly erect and slightly branched stem, covered with short, appressed hairs. Leaves almost entirely basal, 20–30cm long, linear, 3-veined, entire or with 2–4 teeth. Flower-heads solitary, with only blue ray-florets, on long stalks bearing several small scale-like bracts. Involucral bracts loosely overlapping, ovate, abruptly narrowing into a sharp point, silvery and membranous with a dark mid-vein. Fruits 5-angled, with a pappus of 5–7 lanceolate scales.
Garigue, open woods, especially on chalk, occasionally cultivated as an ornamental plant.
Western Mediterranean region, eastwards to N.W. Italy, except for Corsica and Sardinia.
C. lutea L.: plant annual, 8–40cm high. Ray-florets yellow, shorter than the narrow and gradually pointed inner involucral bracts (Mediterranean region).

□■ *Hyoseris radiata* L.
□□ 10–35cm; January–December; ♃
A rosette-plant, resembling a Dandelion, with leaves 5–25cm long, often long-stalked, pinnately divided into backward-pointing, toothed lobes. Flower-heads solitary, on leafless, hairless, more rarely mealy or slightly rough stalks, 6–40cm long. Outer involucral bracts arrowly ovate, 4–5mm long, the inner ones lanceolate, 10–15mm long, spreading out at fruiting time, the yellow ray-florets about twice as long. Fruits 8–10mm, brown, with a yellowish pappus of stiff hairs, and linear scales, the marginal ones compressed, the middle ones compressed and winged, and the inner ones cylindrical.
Grassy and stony pastures.
Mediterranean region, Canary Islands.
H. scabra L.: a small, annual plant, the stalks bearing the flower-heads shorter than the leaves, prostrate or ascending, usually thickened in the middle or higher up. Inner involucral bracts 7–10mm, erect at fruiting time (Mediterranean region).

□□ *Rhagadiolus stellatus* (L.) Gaertn. **Star Hawkbit**
■□ 20–50cm; April–June; ☉
Stem erect, often branched, coarsely hairy in the lower part, hairless above. Basal leaves narrowly obovate, almost entire, toothed or pinnately divided, narrowing into a short, indistinct stalk. Flower-heads with ray-florets about 8mm long, long-stalked, and grouped into a lax panicle. Involucre consisting of an outer row of small, scale-like bracts, and an inner row of usually 8 bracts, 8–9mm long, hairy at least on the outer side of the tip, erect at first, but enlarged to 1.5–2cm at fruiting time, and curved, spreading out like a star, and surrounding the marginal fruits.
Cultivated and fallow land.
Mediterranean region, Canary Islands, S.W. Asia.
R. edulis Gaertn.: inner involucral bracts usually 5 or 6, hairless outside. Fruits more or less straight, 1–1.5cm long. Basal leaves pinnately divided almost to the midrib, with a large terminal lobe and distinct leaf-stalk (Mediterranean region, S.W. Asia).

□□ *Urospermum dalechampii* (L.) Scop. ex F.W. Schmidt
□■ 20–40cm; April–August; ♃
Plant hairy, with the rosette-leaves pinnately divided into backward-pointing lobes. Stem-leaves entire or toothed, stem-clasping, the uppermost ones opposite. Flower-heads up to 5cm across, on long, stout stalks, thickened above, the central ray-florets sulphur-yellow, the marginal ones often tinged red-brown on the outer side. Involucre of one row of 7–8 lanceolate bracts, 1.5–2.5cm long, united at the base, softly hairy, and sometimes with a pale margin. Fruits with a long beak, and a pappus of reddish brown, feathery hairs.
Waysides, cultivated and fallow land.
Western Mediterranean region, eastwards to Yugoslavia.
U. picroides (L.) Scop. ex F.W. Schmidt: an annual, coarsely hairy plant. Flower-heads smaller, with stiff, long-pointed, bristly-hairy involucral bracts. Pappus white (Mediterranean region, Canary Islands, S.W. Asia).

Daisy family *Asteraceae* (*Compositae*)

■□ *Tragopogon porrifolius* L. **Salsify**
□□ 0.2–1.2m; April–July; ⊙, ⊙
A hairless to somewhat woolly-hairy plant with a cylindrical root. Leaves linear, long-pointed, broadened at the base, and half stem-clasping. Stem thickened and club-shaped below the flower-head. Involucral bracts usually 8. Ray-florets in ssp. *porrifolius* about as long as the involucral bracts, lilac or reddish purple, in ssp. *australis* (Jord.) Nym. only half as long, deep violet. Fruits beaked, all with a pappus of feathery hairs that are shorter than the fruit. Other subspecies are in existence.
Grassy pastures, fallow land, waysides, formerly grown as a vegetable like Scorzonera or as an ornamental plant, sometimes escaping and becoming naturalised.
Mediterranean region, Canary Islands.
T. hybridus L. (*Geropogon glaber* L.): plant annual, 20–60cm high, hairless. Outer fruits with a pappus of 5 simple, stiff hairs, the inner ones with feathery hairs (Mediterranean region, Canary Islands, S.W. Asia).

□■ *Reichardia tingitana* (L.) Roth (*Picridium tingitanum* (L.) Desf.)
□□ 5–40cm; April–May; ⊙, ⊙, ♃
Leaves hairless, smooth to densely white papillose, those of the basal rosette lanceolate, blunt or pointed, toothed or pinnately divided, with a short, broadly winged stalk. Stem-leaves 1–6, sessile and stem-clasping. Flower-heads 2–2.5cm across, solitary or up to 4 together on long stalks, thickened at the end, sometimes bearing bracts that resemble the involucral bracts. Ray-florets yellow, purple at the base, the marginal ones with a red stripe on the outer side. Involucre 10–15mm long and broad, consisting of several rows of hairless, ovate bracts with a broad, membranous margin. All fruits angled, with transverse wrinkles and a simple, soft, snow-white pappus.
On sand and rocks along the coasts, also in deserts.
Southern Mediterranean region, Canary Islands, S.W. Asia.
R. picroides (L.) Roth: leaves usually only sparsely papillose. Ray-florets entirely yellow. Membranous margin of the involucral bracts narrow, not more than 0.5mm. Inner fruits smooth (Mediterranean region, Canary Islands).

□□ *Lactuca viminea* (L.) J. & C. Presl **Pliant Lettuce**
■□ 0.3–1.3m; July–September; ⊙, ♃
Stem erect, whitish, with numerous rod-like lateral branches. Leaves hairless, dark grey-green, the lower ones shallowly or deeply pinnately divided, with linear-lanceolate, often toothed segments, the upper ones simple, lanceolate, with 2 characteristic linear lobes, 1–3.5cm long, at the base that extend down the stem and are united with it. Flower-heads with usually 5 pale yellow ray-florets, sessile, arranged in the form of a spike on the branches. Fruits blackish, ribbed, gradually narrowing into a beak that is shorter or as long as the fruit, the total length 7–15mm. Pappus simple, white. There are several subspecies, the one illustrated being ssp. *chondrilliflora* (Bor.) Bonnier, with fruits 7–9mm long, and the beak ¼–½ as long as the body of the fruit (western and central Mediterranean region).
Stony pastures, dry grassland, waysides.
Mediterranean region, Canary Islands, S.W. Asia, northwards to central and E. Europe.

□□ *Crepis rubra* L. **Pink Hawksbeard**
□■ 5–40cm; April–June; ⊙
Plant with a basal rosette of oblanceolate, pointed, hairy leaves, 2–15cm long, deeply toothed to pinnately divided with backward-pointing lobes. Stems solitary or several together, simple or branched once, with a few, usually bract-like leaves and 1 or 2 flower-heads about 3cm across. Ray-florets pink or white. Involucre 11–15×4–10mm. Involucral bracts in 2 rows, the outer ones hairless or slightly woolly, about half as long as the inner ones that are glandular-hairy. Fruits dark brown, ribbed and with small spines, beaked, the outer ones shorter than the inner. Pappus-hairs snow-white and soft.
Cultivated land, grassy pastures.
S. Italy, Balkan peninsula, Crete.

Posidonia family *Posidoniaceae*
Lily family *Liliaceae*

■□ *Posidonia oceanica* (L.) Delile *Posidoniaceae*
□□ Up to 55cm; October–May; ♃
Aquatic plant, growing below the surface of the water, with a stout rhizome, densely covered by the brown, fibrous remains of dead leaves. At the tip of each branch of the rhizome are 5–10 dark green, ribbon-like leaves, rounded at the end, 6–10mm broad, and with 13–17 veins. Flowers rarely formed, without an involucre, arranged in a long-stalked, compound inflorescence of spikes that is surrounded by 2 leaf-like bracts. On fine, sandy ground in 3–40m of water. The leaves, torn off and crushed by the surf and rolled up into brown balls the size of a fist, are found in the tide-zone together with the rhizomes.
Coasts of the Mediterranean, also the Atlantic coast of S.W. Europe.
Zostera marina L., **Common Eel-grass**, has thin, non-fibrous rhizomes. Leaves with up to 9 veins, widespread on the coasts of the northern hemisphere.

□■ *Asphodelus fistulosus* L. **Hollow-stemmed Asphodel** *Liliaceae*
□□ 15–70cm; March–June; ☉ or a short-lived perennial
Roots usually fibrous, not thickened. Leaves all basal, with a more or less broad, membranous margin below, semi-cylindrical and hollow, up to 35cm long and 4mm across, slightly rough on the edges. Inflorescence a lax raceme, simple or only slightly branched, on a long, smooth, hollow stalk, with membranous, whitish bracts and 6 perianth-segments. Perianth-segments spreading out like a star, 10–12mm long, white to pink with a green or red-brown mid-vein. Fruit-capsule spherical or ovoid-spherical, 5–7mm.
Waysides, cultivated land, garigue.
Mediterranean region, Canary Islands.
A. tenuifolius Cav. is often regarded as a separate species: plant annual, leaves rough on all veins, not more than 2.5mm broad, inflorescence-stalk rough below. Perianth-segments 5–12mm long, capsules 3–5mm (S. Italy, Sicily, N. Africa, Canary Islands, S.W. Asia).

□□ *Asphodelus albus* Mill. **White Asphodel** *Liliaceae*
■□ 0.5–1.2m; April–June; ♃
Roots rather fleshy and swollen. Leaves all basal, narrowly linear, up to 60cm long and 1–2.5cm broad, keeled, gradually narrowing towards the tip. Inflorescence a raceme, simple or at most branched at the base, on a stout stalk. The 6 perianth-segments open wide forming a star, white with a green or red-brown mid-vein, 1.5–2cm long. Bracts membranous, longer than the flower-stalks. In ssp. *albus* the bracts are dark brown, and the capsule 8–15×6–13mm; in ssp. *villarsii* (Verl. ex Billot) J.B.K. Richardson & Smythies, the bracts are whitish, and the capsule 16–20×18–25mm (only S.W. Europe).
Meadows, pastures, open woods, extending up into the higher zones.
S. Europe, northwards to N.W. France, Switzerland and Hungary.

□□ *Asphodelus aestivus* Brot. (*A. microcarpus* Viv.) **Asphodel** *Liliaceae*
□■ 0.5–1.5m; March–June; ♃
Roots thickened and spindle-shaped. Leaves all basal, 25–45cm long and 1–2(–4)cm broad, flat and slightly keeled. Inflorescence much-branched, pyramidal, on a stout stalk, with membranous to pale green bracts, 10–15mm long, and star-like flowers with 6 spreading perianth-segments on stalks 5–7mm long. Perianth-segments white with a red-brown mid-vein, 10–16mm long. Capsule obovate to spherical, 5–8×6–10mm, with 2–7 transverse grooves.
Garigue, pastures, often in large numbers.
Mediterranean region, Canary Islands, eastwards to Iran.
A. ramosus L. (*A. cerasiferus* Gay) is similar but the inflorescence is generally less branched or almost simple. Perianth-segments 15–20mm long. Capsules 15–20×16–22mm, with 7–8 tranverse grooves. Plants with the characters of both species have been named *A. chambeironii* Jord. (S.W. Europe).

Lily family *Liliaceae*

■□ *Asphodeline lutea* (L.) Rchb. **Yellow Asphodel, King's Spear**
□□ 0.4–1m; April–June; ♃
In contrast to species of *Asphodelus*, the stem is densely leafy to the top. Leaves 8–35cm×1.5–3(-5)mm, narrowly linear, pointed, triangular in cross-section, enlarged at the base into a membranous sheath that encloses the stem. Flowers golden yellow, in a dense raceme, 15–30cm long, that lengthens at fruiting time to as much as 50cm. Perianth-segments somewhat unequal, oblong-lanceolate, 2–2.5cm long, more or less spreading and star-like. Bracts membranous, about 1–2.5cm, ovate, pointed, longer than the flower-stalks. Capsules almost spherical, 1–1.5cm, with black, triangular seeds.
Garigue, stony pastures, also cultivated on rock-gardens as an ornamental plant.
Eastern Mediterranean region, westwards to Italy, also in N.W. Africa.
A. liburnica (Scop.) Rchb. is similar, stem 25–60cm, only leafy in the lower half, bracts not larger than 15×3mm (eastern Mediterranean region).

□■ *Aphyllanthes monspeliensis* L.
□□ 10–35cm; April–July; ♃
The only species in this characteristic genus. Plant growing in tufts, with numerous blue-green, ribbed, rush-like stems, about 1mm thick, that have at their base only red-brown sheaths 3–8cm long, the remains of modified leaves. Flowers 1–3, terminal, delicate pale blue, with 6 oblanceolate perianth-segments, about 2cm long, with a single dark vein, surrounded by 1–3 free, membranous, bristle-tipped bracts, 8–10mm long. Each individual flower with 5 blunt, sepal-like bracts, united at the base. Fruit a capsule with black seeds.
Garigue, also in open woods.
Western Mediterranean region, eastwards to N.W. Italy, Sardinia.

□□ *Colchicum bivonae* Guss.
■□ 15–30cm; August–October; ♃
Corm with a dark brown, leathery tunic. The 5–9 lanceolate, basal leaves, up to 25cm long and 8–13mm broad, develop only after flowering time. Flowers 1–6, the 6 perianth-segments pale or dark rose-purple, distinctly chequered, joined below into a long, slender tube, the oblong to broadly lanceolate free portions 5.5–6.5cm long. Anthers purple-black or purple-brown, attached at the middle, with yellow pollen. The 3 styles are recurved at their tips with the stigmas extending along them. A variable species.
Pastures, open woods, extending up into the mountain zone.
Eastern Mediterranean region, westwards to Sardinia.
There are several species found only in limited areas, mainly in the eastern Mediterranean region. Others with a wider distribution are closely related to our native Meadow Saffron in having only a suggestion of a chequered pattern or even none at all. These include *C. neapolitanum* (Ten.) Ten. with perianth-segments 3–4.5cm long and yellow anthers (S. Europe, N.W. Africa) and *C. cupanii* Guss. with 2 or 3 leaves already developed at flowering time (central Mediterranean region).

□□ *Merendera pyrenaica* (Pourr.) P. Fourn. (*M. bulbocodium* Ram.)
□■ 5–15cm; August–September; ♃
Bulb covered by a blackish, leathery tunic. Leaves all basal, linear, up to 22cm long and 4–8mm broad, folded, usually appearing only after the flowers. Flowers solitary or in pairs, rose-purple, the 6 perianth-segments with lanceolate blade, 3–4.5cm long, and long-clawed bases that differ from *Colchicum* in not being united. Anthers yellow, 8–12(-17)mm, attached at the base, longer than the filaments.
Pastures in the mountain zone.
Iberian peninsula, Pyrenees.
M. filifolia Camb.: leaves appearing during or just after flowering time, not more than 3mm broad. Anthers yellow, usually 6–8mm (western Mediterranean region). *M. attica* (Sprun. ex Tomm.) Boiss. & Sprun.: anthers dark purple, 1.5–3mm (eastern Mediterranean region). *M. sobolifera* Mey. (eastern Mediterranean region) and *M. androcymbioides* Valdés (S.W. Spain) are spring-flowering.

Lily family *Liliaceae*

■☐ *Gagea graeca* (L.) A. Terracc. (*Lloydia graeca* (L.) Endl. ex Kunth)
☐☐ 5–25cm; April–May; ♃
A delicate, hairless plant, nowadays placed in the genus *Gagea*, with a single bulb. It has 2–4 linear basal leaves and alternate, linear-lanceolate stem-leaves. Flowers usually 3–5, at first nodding, later erect, funnel-shaped, the 6 blunt, obovate-oblong, free perianth-segments white with purple veins. 10–15mm long. Anthers blunt.
Rocky places, on chalk.
S. Greece, Aegean, Crete, Cyprus, Asia Minor.
G. trinervia (Viv.) Greut.: similar, but flowers usually solitary. Anthers with a pointed appendage (Sicily, N. Africa).

☐■ *Tulipa sylvestris* L. **Wild Tulip**
☐☐ 5–45cm; April–June; ♃
The only widespread species of tulip in the Mediterranean region, often putting out stolons. In the subspecies illustrated, ssp. *australis* (Link) Pamp., the stem is at most 2mm in diameter, with 2 or 3 grey-green, grooved, hairless, narrowly lanceolate leaves, 15–20cm long, the lowest less than 1.2cm broad. Flowers almost always solitary, slightly nodding before opening, with 6 elliptic-lanceolate perianth-segments, 2–4cm long, all entirely yellow within, the outer ones tinged reddish on the outside, pointed, and 4.5–9mm broad, the inner ones 6–16mm broad, gradually pointed, and fringed with hairs at the base. Filaments broadened below, bearded on the edges, 5–8mm long, anthers 2.5–4mm. Ssp. *sylvestris* is considerably stouter: stem at least 2.5mm in diameter, the lowest leaf more than 1.2cm broad. Flowers nodding in bud, the outer perianth-segments often greenish on the outside, 3.5–6.5cm long and 8–18mm broad, the inner ones somewhat longer and 16–26mm broad. Filaments 9–14mm, anthers 4–9mm.
Ssp. *australis*: grassy and stony pastures in the mountain zone, ssp. *sylvestris*: tree plantations, vineyards, fields. Ssp. *australis*: Mediterranean region, S.E. Europe, absent from the islands, ssp. *sylvestris*: central Mediterranean region, also Corsica, Sardinia and Sicily, rarely becoming naturalised in central and northern Europe.

☐☐ *Tulipa saxatilis* Sieber ex Spreng.
■☐ 5–25cm; April; ♃
Plant with 2 or 3 oblong-lanceolate, more or less flat leaves, bright green above, up to 40cm long and 4.5cm broad. Flowers usually solitary on a stalk 5–25cm long, the perianth-segments pointed, pink to red-purple, yellow at the base inside, 3.8–5.5cm long. Filaments bearded at the base.
Stony pastures, cultivated land.
Crete.
T. cretica Boiss. & Heldr. is also endemic in Crete: perianth whitish to pink with a yellow base, greenish outside, 1.5–3.5cm long. *T. boeotica* Boiss. & Heldr.: perianth-segments scarlet, each with a black patch edged with yellow at the base (southern Balkan peninsula, Asia Minor).

☐☐ *Fritillaria messanensis* Rafin.
☐■ 15–40cm; March–April; ♃
Stem with 7–10 linear leaves, the lowest 4–9cm long and 3–7mm broad, often opposite, the others alternate or the uppermost in ssp. *messanensis* in a whorl of 3. Flowers nodding, broadly bell-shaped, the perianth-segments 22–32mm long, with an indistinct yellowish, brownish or purple chequered pattern, and a green margin on the back. Nectar-groove at the base of the perianth-segments 6–10mm long. There are several subspecies.
Open woods, thickets, grassy pastures.
N.W. Africa, Sicily, S. Italy, Balkan peninsula to Crete.
F. graeca Boiss. & Sprun. is similar: leaves 5–12, the lowest ovate to lanceolate, 3.5–11cm long and 11–25mm broad. Nectar-groove 4–6mm (southern part of the Balkan peninsula, Aegean). Numerous other species, some difficult to distinguish, occur in limited areas, particularly in the eastern Mediterranean region.

Lily family *Liliaceae*

■□ *Ornithogalum narbonense* L. (*O. pyramidale* L. ssp. *narbonense* (L.) Asch. & Gr.)
□□ 20–50(–80)cm; April–June; ♃
Plant with the inflorescence in the form of a long raceme. Flowers erect, all on stalks of about the same length, scentless, with 6 widely spreading perianth-segments, 12–16mm long, milky white on the inside, and with a green stripe running along the whole length of the back. Anthers yellow, ovary 3.5–5mm, flat at the top, with a thin style of at least the same length. Bracts about as long as the flower-stalks, but far exceeding the flower-buds. Leaves 4–6, persisting until after the flowering period.
Cultivated fields, pastures, waysides.
Mediterranean region, Canary Islands, S.W. Asia.
A species with a long, cylindrical inflorescence is *O. pyrenaicum* L.: leaves often already withered by flowering time. Bracts shorter than the flower-stalks. Perianth-segments yellowish inside, greenish with a darker green stripe outside (Mediterranean region, W. Europe).

□■ *Ornithogalum montanum* Cyr.
□□ 10–20cm; April–May; ♃
Distinguished from other species in the genus mainly by the hairless, broad (8–20mm) and flat, usually green, linear leaves without a white middle stripe on the upper surface. Inflorescence a flat-topped cluster on a short stalk. Flowers 3–20, with 6 widely spreading, white perianth-segments, 10–25mm long, that have a broad, green middle stripe on the outside. Bracts usually shorter than the flower-stalks.
Stony places, grassy pastures.
Eastern Mediterranean region, westwards to central Italy, Sicily.

□□ *Urginea maritima* (L.) Bak. **Sea Squill**
■□ 0.5–1.5m; August–October; ♃
Bulb white or red, very large, up to 18cm in diameter and often protruding above the surface of the ground. Leaves withered by flowering time in autumn, lanceolate, 0.3–1m long and 3–10cm broad. Inflorescence-stalk bearing at its end a long and dense raceme of more than 50 flowers. Flower-stalks 1–3cm long, more or less erect, perianth-segments 6–8mm, white, with a green or purple mid-vein, spreading out like a star. Anthers greenish. Bracts awl-shaped, shorter than the flower-stalks, often quickly falling. There are several subspecies. A poisonous plant, the fleshy bulb-scales being used to treat heart disease.
Pastures, stony places, garigue, sandy beaches.
Mediterranean region, Canary Islands.
The following 2 species are generally smaller and more delicate, *U. undulata* (Desf.) Steinh.: leaves 8–15cm×3–10mm, strongly undulate on the margins. Flowers pink, in a loose raceme (E. Spain, Corsica, Sardinia, N. Africa) and *U. fugax* (Moris) Steinh.: leaves not broader than 2mm. Flowers white or pink (Corsica, Sardinia, Italy [Apulia], N.W. Africa).

□□ *Scilla peruviana* L.
□■ 20–50cm; March–June; ♃
An ornamental plant with a bulb up to 8cm. Leaves all basal, lanceolate, 40–60cm long and 1–6cm broad, the margin often fringed with short hairs. Inflorescence a dense, broadly pyramidal to hemispherical raceme on a short, stout stalk, the 20–100 flowers with 6 blue to purple or whitish perianth-segments, 5–14mm long. Anthers yellowish. Bracts awl-shaped, 5–8cm long. A very variable species.
Damp places in grassy pastures, thickets and open woods.
Iberian peninsula, Sardinia, S. Italy, Sicily, N. Africa, Canary Islands.
S. lilio-hyacinthus L.: raceme ovoid with 5–15 flowers, and bracts 1–2.5cm long. Anthers bluish (France, N. Spain). *S. hyacinthoides* L.: raceme long, with 40–150 flowers. Bracts very small, 1.5mm (S. Europe, also cultivated as an ornamental plant, sometimes escaping and growing wild).

Lily family Liliaceae

■□ *Bellevalia romana* (L.) Rchb. (*Hyacinthus romanus* L.)
□□ 20–50cm; April–May; ♃
Bulbous plant, with 3–6 basal, linear-lanceolate leaves, smooth on the margin, and 5–15mm broad, that exceed the raceme. Flowers 20–30, on erect to spreading stalks 8–20mm long. Perianth white, occasionally bluish at the base, later dingy brown, 6–9mm long, united to about half-way. Fruits triangular with 3 prominent ribs.
Damp meadows and cultivated land.
Eastern and central Mediterranean region, westwards to France.
The very similar species *B. mauritanica* Pomel. occurs in N. Africa.
B. ciliata (Cyr.) Nees has lilac, more or less pendent flowers, and leaves 15–30cm broad, shorter than the inflorescence, with the margin fringed with long hairs. Flowers 9–11mm, the lower stalks 30–35mm (eastern Mediterranean region, N.W. Africa). *B. trifoliata* (Ten.) Kunth: leaves 15–25mm broad, often fringed with fine hairs. Flowers violet, 8–16mm, on spreading or slightly recurved stalks, 4–8mm long (eastern and central Mediterranean region).

□■ *Dipcadi serotinum* (L.) Med. (*Uropetalum serotinum* (L.) Ker-Gawl.)
□□ 10–40cm; March–July; ♃
All leaves basal, linear and grooved, shorter than the inflorescence-stalk. Flowers 3–10, narrowly bell-shaped, in an erect, loose raceme, often all facing the same way. Perianth-segments 12–15mm, yellowish, brownish, or greenish, sometimes orange-red, ¼–½ joined at the base, the 3 outer ones curving outwards, the 3 inner ones straight at first, later bending outwards at the tip. Bracts lanceolate, longer than the flower-stalks.
Stony pastures, also on sand.
Western Mediterranean region, Canary Islands.
Autumn-flowering, usually more robust plants, up to 1m high, are separated as *D. fulvum* (Cav.) Webb & Berth. (Spain, Morocco, Canary Islands).

□□ *Muscari comosum* (L.) Mill. **Tassel Hyacinth**
■□ 15–80cm; April–June; ♃
Leaves 3–5, all basal, 7–40cm long and 5–17mm broad, grooved, linear, gradually narrowed towards the tip and often bending down. Raceme 4–10cm long, relatively loose. The lower, brownish green, fertile flowers 5–10mm, oblong to urn-shaped with 6 teeth directed outwards, spreading horizontally, the upper flowers infertile, smaller and with longer stalks, bright blue, held erect and forming a tuft. A variable species. There are garden forms with a much-branched panicle consisting entirely of infertile flowers.
Cultivated land, dry grassland, garigue.
Mediterranean region, extending into the warm regions of central Europe.

□□ *Muscari neglectum* Guss. ex Ten. (*M. racemosum* (L.) Lam. & DC.)
□■ 10–35cm; March–May; ♃
Leaves 3–6, all basal, linear to linear-lanceolate, grooved. Flowers ovoid, in a short, dense raceme, on spreading or recurved stalks up to 5mm long, the lower ones fertile, 3.5–7.5mm long, blackish blue, with 6 white, recurved teeth, the upper ones sterile, smaller and paler. A very variable species, distinguished in some floras as follows: *M. racemosum* with loose, semi-cylindrical leaves, only 1–3mm across, narrowly grooved on the upper side, and *M. neglectum* with grooved leaves, 3–6mm broad, that are much longer than the inflorescence-stalk. Larger and broader in all parts.
Cultivated land, grassy pastures.
Mediterranean region, extending northwards into central Europe, S.W. Asia.
M. commutatum Guss. is similar: corolla deep black-purple with similarly coloured teeth (eastern Mediterranean region). The only autumn-flowering species in the genus in this region is *M. parviflorum* Desf. (Mediterranean region).

Lily family *Liliaceae*

■□ *Allium roseum* L. **Rose Garlic**
□□ 10–65cm; March–June; ♃
Bulb with small bulblets, the outer tunic dotted with small holes. Leaves 2–4, linear and flat, often finely toothed on the margin, up to 35cm long and 14mm broad, enclosing the lower part of the inflorescence-stalk like a sheath for ⅕ of its length. Umbel hemispherical, up to 7cm across, with 5–30 erect, broadly bell-shaped pink or white flowers, 7–12mm long, often with bulblets amongst them. Involucre 3 or 4-lobed, shorter than the 7–45mm long flower-stalks. A variable species. Cultivated and fallow land, often in large numbers, garigue. Mediterranean region, Canary Islands. Var. *insulare* Genn. (also treated as a separate species *A. confertum* Jord. & Fourr.) is found on Corsica and Sardinia: plant generally smaller, 10–15cm high, umbel 2–3cm across, with flowers 5–7mm long. There are numerous species of *Allium*, confined to small areas, throughout the Mediterranean region.

□■ *Allium subhirsutum* L.
□□ 20–50cm; March–June; ♃
Leaves 2–3, almost basal, 5–45cm long and up to 10mm broad, linear, flat and soft, fringed with hairs on the margin. Flowers in a loose, erect, hemispherical umbel, 2.5–7cm across, without bulblets, on a round, hairless stalk 7–30cm long. Flower-stalks up to 4cm, 3–5 times as long as the white perianth-segments, 7–9mm long, that spread out like a star. Stamens with usually brown, more rarely yellow anthers. Involucre shorter than the flower-stalks.
Cultivated and fallow land, garigue, on sand or rock.
Mediterranean region, Canary Islands.
A similar species, regarded by some authors as a subspecies of *A. subhirsutum*, is *A. trifoliatum* Cyr.: umbel 2.5–4cm across. Flower-stalks up to 2cm, 1½–3 times as long as the pink or pink-veined perianth. Anthers yellow (eastern Mediterranean region, westwards to S.E. France). *A. neapolitanum* Cyr.: flowers white, lustrous, cup-shaped, perianth-segments 7–12mm long, bluntly elliptic, the outer ones somewhat broader than the inner. Inflorescence-stalk with 2 sharp and 1 blunt edge, the lowest ⅕–¼ enclosed in a sheath formed by the leaves, that are 0.5–2cm broad, hairless or finely toothed on the margin (Mediterranean region).

□□ *Allium triquetrum* L.
■□ 10–50cm; December–May; ♃
Plant with 2 or 3 hairless, keeled leaves, forming a short sheath above the ground, up to 17mm broad and about as long as the sharply triangular inflorescence-stalk. Flower 3–15, nodding and long-stalked, in a one-sided umbel with an involucre of 2 bracts. Bulblets absent, perianth-segments white with a green mid-vein, 10–18mm long, pointed, curved and making the perianth bell-shaped, stigma 3-lobed.
Damp, shady margins of woods and thickets, ditches, river-banks.
Western Mediterranean region, eastwards to Italy and Tunisia.
A. pendulinum Ten. also has a triangular inflorescence-stalk: umbel with 2–9 flowers, at first erect, later hanging down on all sides. Perianth-segments with 3 green veins, only drooping after flowering (Corsica, Sardinia, Italy, Sicily).

□□ *Allium nigrum* L.
□■ 0.4–1m; March–June; ♃
A stately plant with 3–6 basal leaves, up to 50cm long and 8cm broad, flat, and somewhat rough on the margin. At the end of the tall, stout inflorescence-stalk is a hemispherical or almost spherical umbel, 5–10cm across, surrounded by a membranous involucre, later becoming 2 to 4-lobed, usually without bulbils. Flowers very numerous, their stalks 2.5–4.5cm long. Perianth spreading out like a star, later becoming recurved. Perianth-segments 6–9mm, narrowly oblong, blunt, pink-purple or white, with a greenish mid-vein. Filaments about 5mm long, broadening to 1.5mm at the base.
Cultivated and fallow land.
Mediterranean region, Canary Islands.

Lily family *Liliaceae*

■□ *Asparagus albus* L.
□□ 0.5–1m; August–October; ♄
Stems woody, whitish, overhanging, bent from side to side, smooth or only shallowly grooved. Leaves modified into stout, projecting spines, 5–12mm long and very broad at the base, in the axils of which are tufts of 10–20 short shoots (phylloclades), 5–25mm long, not sharply pointed and soon falling. Flowers scented, on stalks 3–6mm long, in groups of 6–15, with a white, 6-lobed, spreading perianth, 2–3mm long. Berries at first red, later black, 4–7mm.
Maquis, garigue, hedges.
Western Mediterranean region, eastwards to Italy and Sicily, absent from France.

□■ *Asparagus acutifolius* L.
□□ 0.4–2m; July–October; ♄
A much-branched, climbing subshrub, with whitish or grey, woody stems. In the axils of small, scale-like leaves are 5–30 or more short shoots, very similar in appearance, 2–8mm long, stiff and sharply pointed. Flowers on stalks 3–7mm long, solitary or up to 4 together, with bell-shaped, 6-lobed, yellow-green perianth, 3–4mm long. Berries red, later black. The young, green shoots that appear in spring are picked and eaten as Wild Asparagus.
Woods, maquis, garigue.
Mediterranean region, Canary Islands.
A. aphyllus L.: short shoots in clusters of 3–7, distinctly unequal, 10–20mm long (southern Mediterranean region). Two species flowering in May–July, with herbaceous stems, short shoots not sharply pointed, and red berries are *A. tenuifolius* Lam. with very numerous, slender short shoots (S.E. Europe, Asia Minor) and *A. maritimus* (L.) Mill. with thicker short shoots in groups of 4–7 (Mediterranean region).

□□ *Asparagus stipularis* Forsk. (*A. horridus* L.f.)
■□ 0.5–1m; March–May; July–October; ♄
An apparently leafless, grey-green, bushy plant with finely grooved stems and stout short shoots, 1–5cm long, modified into green spines that are usually solitary but sometimes form spreading groups of 2 or 3. At their base are 0–2 small leaves reduced to membranous scales, and 2–8 flowers on stalks 1–3mm long with a 6-lobed, yellowish to purple perianth 4mm long. Berries bluish black, 5–8mm.
Garigue, waysides.
Southern Mediterranean region, Canary Islands, absent from France, Corsica and Yugoslavia.

□□ *Ruscus aculeatus* L. **Butcher's Broom**
□■ 10–80cm; October, February–April; ♄
Evergreen, branched subshrub, with stiff, leaf-like, broadly ovate to lanceolate branches about 2.5cm long, arranged in 2 rows, ending in a spiny tip, and situated in the axils of small scale-leaves. Inconspicuous, greenish white flowers, solitary or few in a cluster are produced in the axil of a small bract on the upper side of these flattened shoots, giving the impression that the flowers arise from 'leaves', the male and female flowers on separate plants. Fruit a shining red berry, about 1.5cm across. Rhizome used in medicines for blood circulation problems in veins. The young shoots, like those of Asparagus, are edible, and the stems are often found in dried flower arrangements.
In the undergrowth of maquis, evergreen and deciduous woods, extending up into the mountain zone, also grown as an ornamental shrub.
Mediterranean region, W. Europe, Canary Islands, S.W. Asia.
R. hypoglossum L.: stems not branched, only 20–40cm high. Flattened shoots leathery, not sharply pointed, tongue-shaped, 3–10×1–3.3cm, with herbaceous bracts, 3.5–13mm broad, usually on the upper side (S.E. Europe, Asia Minor). *R. hypophyllum* L.: usually not branched, 10–70cm high. Flattened shoots not sharply pointed, 3–14×1.5–5cm. Bracts 1–2mm broad, often membranous, situated on the under side (western Mediterranean region).

Lily family Liliaceae
Agave family Agavaceae
Daffodil family Amaryllidaceae

■☐ *Smilax aspera* L. *Liliaceae*
☐☐ Climbing up to 15m high; August–November; ♄
Evergreen, hairless, climbing shrub, the male and female flowers on separate plants. Leaves leathery and shining, narrowly to broadly heart-shaped or spear-shaped, up to 11×10cm long and broad, with hooked spines on the margin and on the main veins beneath, also on the stems which are bent in a zigzag form (in ssp. *mauritanica* (Poir.) Arc. the leaves are broadly heart-shaped, and are almost or entirely without spines). At the base of the leaf-stalk, which is up to 2cm long, are 2 tendrils. Delicate, fragrant flowers, in clusters of 5–30, are produced on terminal and axillary branches. Perianth-segments whitish, greenish or pink, 2–4mm long. Berries red, later black. The young shoots, like those of Wild Asparagus, are eaten as a vegetable.
Maquis and woods, also on walls.
Mediterranean region, eastwards to India.

☐■ *Agave americana* L. **Century Plant** *Agavaceae*
☐☐ 5–8m; June–August; ♄
Leaves of the 1–2m high basal rosette thick, fleshy and grey-green, 15–25cm broad, linear-lanceolate, compressed above the broad, sheathing base, remotely spine-toothed along the margin and tipped with a brownish spine, 2–3cm long, closely appressed in bud and leaving impressions. After 10–15 years a single flowering-stem, up to 8m high, is produced, bearing stem-clasping bracts and a terminal panicle. Flowers fragrant, 7–9cm long, greenish yellow, clustered at the ends of the horizontal branches of the panicle. After the fruits have ripened, the plant dies, but easily propagates itself vegetatively by suckers.
Cultivated since the 16th century in the Mediterranean region and the Canary Islands as an ornamental plant, also in forms with yellow-edged leaves, often escaping and growing wild near the coast. Native in Mexico.
In contrast to the agaves, the large genus *Aloe*, which belongs to the Lily family, has the leaves spreading in bud. Cultivated in gardens as ornamental plants, rarely also escaping and growing wild (native mainly in S. Africa).

☐☐ *Sternbergia lutea* (L.) Ker-Gawl. ex Spreng. *Amaryllidaceae*
■☐ 10–30cm; September–October; ♃
Leaves linear, blunt, 4–15mm broad, entire or indistinctly toothed, appearing at the same time as the flowers. The golden yellow, crocus-like flowers are held erect on a stem 4–10cm long. They have a short tube, and 6 ovate-elliptic perianth-segments 3–4cm long and 7–15mm broad. At the base is a membranous spathe. Stamens 6, the filaments much longer than the anthers. Ssp. *sicula* (Tineo ex Guss.) D.A. Webb has leaves 3–5mm broad, distinctly toothed on the margin, and more pointed perianth-segments only 4–8mm broad.
Garigue, rocky places, pastures, also cultivated as an ornamental plant.
S. Europe, S.W. Asia, Tunisia, elsewhere sometimes escaping from cultivation and growing wild.
S. colchiciflora Waldst. & Kit.: leaves appearing after the flowers. Flower-stem only 1–2cm high, most of it underground. Perianth-tube almost as long as the segments (sporadic from Spain to Asia Minor).

☐☐ *Narcissus serotinus* L. *Amaryllidaceae*
☐■ 10–30cm; September–November; ♃
Leaves of this delicate species solitary or in pairs, cylindrical, 1mm across, usually only on non-flowering bulbs. Flower-stem thin, 10–25cm, bearing a single, erect, scented flower, more rarely 2 or 3. Perianth-tube 12–20mm long, the 6 free segments oblong-lanceolate, 10–16mm, spreading and white, the orange corona very short, about 1mm, lobed. Spathe 1.5–3.5cm, membranous.
Garigue, pastures.
Mediterranean region, absent from France.
Also autumn-flowering is *N. elegans* (Haw.) Spach: leaves 2–4.5mm broad, present at flowering time. Flowers in groups of 2–7 (Balearic Islands, Italy, Sicily, N. Africa).

Daffodil family *Amaryllidaceae*
Yam family *Dioscoreaceae*

■☐ *Narcissus tazetta* L. **Polyanthus Narcissus, Rose of Sharon** *Amaryllidaceae*
☐☐ 20–60cm; February–May; ♃
The 3–6 blue-green leaves are linear, bluntly keeled, 5–24mm broad, and about as long as the stout, compressed, 2-edged flower-stem. Flowers in an umbel of (2–)3–15, scented, on stalks of unequal length, with the tube 12–18mm long and 6 widely spreading, white, cream or yellow segments, the latter 8–22mm long, broadly ovate, usually touching or overlapping. The cup-shaped corona is 3–6mm long, yellow or orange. At the base of the inflorescence is a membranous spathe, 3–5cm long. There are several subspecies.
Meadows, pastures, cultivated land, often cultivated and sometimes escaping and growing wild.
Mediterranean region, Canary Islands.
N. papyraceus Ker-Gawl.: similar, but flowers pure white. Sometimes regarded as a subspecies of *N. tazetta* (S. Europe, N.W. Africa).

☐■ *Narcissus poeticus* L. **Pheasant's Eye Narcissus** *Amaryllidaceae*
☐☐ 20–60cm; April–June; ♃
Leaves 3–5, linear and flat, 5–14mm broad, and about as long as the compressed, 2-edged flower-stem. Flowers scented, usually solitary and nodding, with a greenish tube 2–3cm long, and 6 widely spreading, white segments, the latter 1.5–3cm long, ovate to roundish, the margins overlapping (ssp. *poeticus* with 3 protruding stamens) or obovate to wedge-shaped, more or less distinctly clawed (ssp. *radiiflorus* (Salisb.) Baker: all 6 stamens protruding). The cup-shaped corona only 1–3mm long, yellow, with a red, curly rim. Spathe 3–5cm, membranous, longer than the flower-stalk. A variable species.
Mountain meadows, deciduous woods, frequently grown as an ornamental plant.
S. Europe, absent from the islands, further north escaping from cultivation and in places becoming naturalised.
There are numerous species with a yellow perianth, mainly in the Iberian peninsula. *N. bulbocodium* L.: perianth-segments almost linear, pointed, 6–15mm long. Corona very large, cup-shaped, 7–25×9–35mm (Spain, Portugal, S.W. France, Morocco).

☐☐ *Pancratium maritimum* L. **Sea Daffodil** *Amaryllidaceae*
■☐ 20–60cm; July–September; ♃
Plant with a large bulb, 5–7cm across, and 5 or 6 twisted, linear leaves, 1–2cm broad and up to 75cm long. Inflorescence-stalk stout, compressed, with a red-brown spathe, 5–7cm long, divided into 2 parts, and 3–15 flowers clustered into an umbel on stalks 0.5–1cm long. The white, fragrant flowers are noticeably large, with a tube 6–8cm long, and spreading, linear-lanceolate segments 3–5cm long. The funnel-shaped corona is about ²/₃ as long, 12-toothed, with the stamens protruding from it. Fruit-stalks bending downwards, the capsule with pitch-black seeds.
Coastal dunes.
Mediterranean region.
P. illyricum L.: flowers only 6–9cm, the corona deeply divided into 6 2-toothed lobes, less than half as long as the perianth-segments. Leaves up to 3cm broad. Flowering in early summer (rocky places in Corsica, Sardinia and Capraia).

☐☐ *Tamus communis* L. **Black Bryony** *Dioscoreaceae*
☐■ 1–4m; April–June; ♃
Plant with a large underground tuber. Stem grooved, twining clockwise. Leaves alternate, shining dark green, deeply heart-shaped with 3–9 curved and branched veins, and with 2 small, firm stipules at the thickened leaf-base. Male and female flowers on separate plants, with an inconspicuous, yellowish green, 6-lobed perianth, the male in many-flowered panicles, the female forming a few-flowered raceme in the leaf-axils. Fruit a fleshy, red berry, 10–15mm. A poisonous plant, containing a substance that acts as a strong skin-irritant.
Woods, undergrowth, and hedges.
Mediterranean region, W. Europe, extending into the warmest areas of central Europe, Canary Islands, S.W. Asia.

Iris family *Iridaceae*

■□ *Hermodactylus tuberosus* (L.) Mill. (*Iris tuberosa* L.) **Snake's Head Iris, Widow Iris**
□□ 20–40cm; February–April; ⚄
Plant iris-like, with 2–4 finger-shaped tubers on the root-stock. Leaves 1.5–3mm broad, 4-angled, longer than the thin flower-stem. Flowers terminal, solitary, greenish yellow, the 3 outer perianth-segments 4–5cm long, obovate at the base, with a recurved dark brown-purple blade, not bearded, the 3 inner ones erect, 2–2.5cm long, narrow and with a long point. The 3 broadened and petal-like style-branches have 2 pointed lobes. Bracts 1 or 2, herbaceous, lanceolate, as long as or longer than the flower. Ovary 1-celled.
Fallow land, stony pastures, garigue.
Mediterranean region, westwards to S.E. France, elsewhere sometimes escaping from cultivation and growing wild.

□■ *Iris unguicularis* Poir.
□□ 10–50cm; December–April; ⚄
Plant with a stout rhizome, leaves narrowly linear, 10–50cm×1–5mm, persisting after they have withered, light brown. Flowers solitary, scented, stemless, with a very slender perianth-tube, 6–20cm long, the lower part usually surrounded by herbaceous, pointed bracts, 6–13cm long. Outer perianth-segments recurved, with an oblong-elliptic, beardless blade, deep purple at the tip, elsewhere purple with white and yellow veins, the inner segments erect, purple, 45–55×7–10mm. The broadened and petal-like style-branches have yellow glandular hairs near the edges. A variable species, of which the subspecies found in Crete is often regarded as a separate species (*I. cretensis* Janka). Plants in N. Africa are larger in all parts.
Open woods, maquis, garigue.
N.W. Africa, Greece, S.W. Asia.

□□ *Iris pseudopumila* Tineo
■□ 5–30cm; March–May; ⚄
A small species of iris with a stout rhizome. Leaves persisting throughout the winter, not broader than 15mm. Stem up to 25cm long. Flowers solitary, purple, or only the 3 outer perianth-segments purple-brown in colour, the latter 5–7.5cm long, with a yellow beard, the tips bent outwards, the inner segments erect, of about equal length, with a broadly elliptic blade. Bracts up to 12cm long, almost completely enclosing the 5–7.5cm long perianth-tube, partly hidden by the leaves.
Garigue, grassy pastures.
W. Yugoslavia, S.E. Italy, Sicily.
Similar species include *I. lutescens* Lam. (including *I. chamaeiris* Bertol.): bracts not enclosing the upper part of the perianth-tube and not hidden by the leaves. Leaves persisting throughout the winter, 5–25mm broad (S.W. Europe), and *I. pumila* L.: plant leafless in winter. Stem at most 1cm long (S.E. Europe, Siberia: ssp. *attica* (Boiss. & Heldr.) Hay. with sickle-shaped leaves, 8cm×9cm, in Greece and Macedonia).

□□ *Gynandriris sisyrinchium* (L.) Parl. (*Iris sisyrinchium* L.) **Barbary Nut**
□■ 5–50cm; March–May; ⚄
Distinguished from species of *Iris*, amongst other characteristics, by a corm growing deep in the ground and surrounded by fibrous tunics. Leaves 1 or 2, limp, grooved, with a long sheath and a free blade 10–50cm long that is longer than the inflorescence. Flowers 1–6, each in the axil of a dry, membranous, brown bract 4–6cm long. Perianth pale blue, united below into a short tube, the 3 outer segments 3×1cm, recurved, with a white patch that is yellow in the centre, the 3 inner ones erect, lanceolate. Stamens and style-branches adhering and forming a column (hence the name of the genus). Each flower opens for only half a day.
Garigue, grassy pastures, also on sand, especially near the coast.
Mediterranean region, S.W. Asia, absent from France and Yugoslavia.

Iris family *Iridaceae*
Rush family *Juncaceae*

■□ *Crocus corsicus* Vanucci ex Maw *Iridaceae*
□□ 10–20cm; February–June; ♃
Corm with fibrous tunic, finely netted in the upper part. Leaves present at flowering time, narrowly linear, 0.5–1.5mm broad, usually longer than the 1–3 purple flowers with dark veins. Bract undivided, membranous, often with brown markings. The 6 segments of the perianth usually 2–3.5cm, joined at the base into a long tube. Anthers orange, longer than the filaments, stigmas scarlet.
Garigue, stony pastures, at an altitude of 300–2600m.
Corsica, Sardinia.
A closely related species is *C. minimus* DC. with perianth-segments only 1.7–2.7cm long and a bract divided into 2 parts at its tip. Anthers pale yellow, about as long as the filaments. Stigmas yellow. Flowering somewhat earlier and only found up to an altitude of 600m (S. Corsica, Sardinia). There are many other species found only in small areas.

□■ *Gladiolus illyricus* Koch *Iridaceae*
□□ 20–60cm; April–June; ♃
A delicate plant compared with our garden gladiolus. Leaves rather narrow, lanceolate, 10–40cm×4–10mm. Flowers, each with 2 bracts, in a fairly loose, 3 to 10-flowered, one-sided spike, large plants sometimes having a side-branch. Perianth-segments 6, rose-red, united below into a short, slightly curved tube, the unequal, more or less bluntly pointed blades 25–40×6–16mm. Anthers spear-shaped at the base, as long as or shorter than the filaments. Seeds winged.
Stony pastures, maquis, open woods.
S. and W. Europe, Asia Minor.
G. communis L. (including ssp. *byzantinus* (Mill.) Ham.) is very simiar: Plant larger, 0.5–1m high. Leaves 30–70cm×8–22mm. Spike 10 to 20-flowered, often branched. Seeds winged (S. Europe, N. Africa). *G. italicus* Mill. (*G. segetum* Ker-Gawl.) occurs mainly in cornfields, often in large numbers: Anthers longer than the filaments, seeds not winged. Leaves 10–16mm broad, the lowest bract longer than the flowers (Mediterranean region, Canary Islands, to central Asia).

□□ *Juncus maritimus* Lam. **Sea Rush** *Juncaceae*
■□ 0.3–1m; June–September; ♃
A tuft-forming rush with a short, creeping rhizome. Stem 1.5–2mm broad, with 2–4 cylindrical, sharply pointed leaves of about the same length, all basal. Lower leaves dark brown to purple, the uppermost with a small blade. Inflorescence branched, loose, elongated, with 2 or 3-flowered heads, usually exceeded by the lowest, cylindrical, sharply pointed bract, which forms a conspicuous extension to the stem. Individual flowers straw-yellow, of 6 segments, without bracteoles. Inner perianth-segments without appendages at the tips and somewhat shorter than the more pointed outer ones. Capsule triangular-ovoid, pointed, 2.5–3.5mm, as long as or slightly longer than the perianth.
Saltmarshes and meadows on the coast, also, rarely, inland.
Mediterranean region, Canary Islands, coasts of W. and N. Europe to Sweden, S.W. Asia.

□□ *Juncus acutus* L. **Sharp-pointed Rush** *Juncaceae*
□■ 0.3–1.5m; April–July; ♃
A large rush forming dense tufts, with stiff, sharply pointed, cylindrical leaves. Flowering stem 2–4mm in diameter, often made longer by the lowest, sharply pointed, stem-like bract. Perianth-segments 6, about equal in length, the 3 inner ones broader, with membranous appendages at the tips. Capsule 5–6mm, shortly pointed, about twice as long as the perianth.
Sandy beaches, saltmarshes, more rarely inland.
Mediterranean and Atlantic coasts (northwards to Ireland), Canary Islands, coasts of the Black Sea, Caspian Sea, etc.
J. littoralis Mey. (*J. acutus* ssp. *tommasinii* (Parl.) Asch. & Gr.) is similar, with capsules 2.5–4mm (northern and eastern Mediterranean region, Black Sea and Caspian Sea).

Grass family *Poaceae (Gramineae)*

■☐ *Desmazeria rigida* (L.) Tutin (*Scleropoa rigida* (L.) Griseb., *Catapodium rigidum* (L.) Hubb.)
☐☐ **Fern Grass**
5–35(–60)cm; May–July; ☉
A small, hairless, grey-green grass, often tinged purple, branched at the base and forming a tuft. Stems prostrate or ascending to erect. Leaves flat or rolled up, up to 2mm broad and 10cm long, and narrowing to a point. Ligule 1–3mm. Panicle stiff, one-sided, 1–12cm, ovoid-oblong, branches arranged in 2 ranks, the lower ones branched and usually some distance apart, the upper ones simple. Spikelets 4–10mm, narrowly oblong, flat, awnless, with 5–12 florets, shortly and comparatively thickly stalked.
Grassy pastures, waysides, cultivated land; ssp. *hemipoa* (Delile ex Spreng.) Stace is found only on sandy coasts.
Mediterranean region, W. Europe, rarely extending into Germany, Canary Islands, S.W. Asia.

☐■ *Cynosurus echinatus* L. **Rough Dog's-tail**
☐☐ 0.1–1m; April–July; ☉
A grass with thin, smooth stems that grows as an individual plant or forms clumps. Leaf-blades 3–10mm broad, flat, and rough especially above. Ligule 2–10mm, the upper leaf-sheaths slightly inflated. Panicle dense, ovoid, one-sided, condensed into a spike, awnless, 1–4cm long and up to 1.5cm across, 'prickly' all over, with 2 kinds of spikelets: fertile ones 1 to 5-flowered, with membranous, pointed glumes and a rough lemma bearing an awn twice its own length, and sterile spikelets consisting of several equally narrow, awned scales, arranged in 2 distinct rows.
Cultivated land, grassy pastures, open woods, occasionally grown as an ornamental grass.
Mediterranean region, Canary Islands, S.W. Asia.
C. elegans Desf.: plant usually smaller, leaves only 1–3mm broad. Panicle mostly loose. Upper scales of the sterile spikelets much shorter and broader than the lower ones (Mediterranean region, Canary Islands, S.W. Asia).

☐☐ *Lamarckia aurea* (L.) Moench **Golden Dog's-tail**
■☐ 5–25cm; March–July; ☉
Stems of this low-growing grass erect or ascending. Leaves 2–6mm broad, flat and soft, pale green, with a ligule 5–10mm long. Panicle spike-like, oblong-ovoid, up to 6×2.5cm, green at first, later golden yellow, with spikelets of 2 kinds on hairy stalks, spreading out on one side. Fertile spikelets with the lemma 6–10mm long, composed of one fertile and one rudimentary floret, surrounded by 2–4 sterile spikelets, 5–8mm long, consisting of 2 lanceolate glumes and 6–9 awnless and flowerless lemmas arranged in 2 rows.
Waysides, fallow land, crevices in walls.
Mediterranean region, Canary Islands, S.W. Asia.

☐☐ *Briza maxima* L. **Large Quaking-grass**
☐■ 10–60cm; April–June; ☉
Forms loose tufts or grows erect as an individual plant. Leaves with the blade 5–20cm long and 3–8mm broad, flat and thin, slightly rough on the margins, the sheath smooth, and the ligule 2–5mm long. Panicle loose, consisting of 1–12 pendent, ovoid to oblong spikelets, flattened at the sides, on hair-like stalks 6–20mm long, each spikelet with 7–20 florets and 14–25mm in length. Glumes awnless, deeply concave, spreading out almost horizontally from the axis of the spikelet.
Garigue, pastures, cultivated land, waysides, also grown as an ornamental plant.
Mediterranean region, Canary Islands, introduced elsewhere.
Briza minor L.: flower-spikelets much smaller, 3–5mm long, 4 to 8-flowered, on stalks 4–12mm long. Ligule 3–6mm (grassy pastures, especially in damp places, Mediterranean region, W. Europe, S.W. Asia). *Briza media* L., a species also native in Britain, is perennial, and is further distinguished by the ligule, which is only 0.5–1.5mm long, and by the 4 to 12-flowered spikelet, which is 4–7mm in length.

Grass family *Poaceae (Gramineae)*

■□ *Melica minuta* L.
□□ 10–60(–100)cm; April–July; ♃
Leaves of this slender, erect, more or less grey-green grass rolled, up to 4mm, or when flat up to 8mm, broad, hairless or sparsely hairy above, with a ligule up to 5mm long, deeply incised or cut off squarely. Panicle very loose, pyramidal, 4–20cm, the branches often spreading horizontally. Spikelets 5–9mm, ovoid, often pendent on curved stalks, hairless and awnless, with 2 fertile florets and 2 or 3 rudimentary ones that are joined into a club-shaped structure. Glumes membranous, often brown-purple, the upper, larger lemma with a membranous tip and 9–11 distinct veins. A variable species.
Rock-crevices, stony pastures, open woods.
Mediterranean region.

□■ *Elymus farctus* (Viv.) Runem. ex Meld. (*Agropyron junceum* (L.) Beauv.)
□□ 30–80cm; June–August; ♃
A stout grass with a long, creeping rhizome. Leaf-blade grey-green, stiff, up to 5mm broad, more or less strongly rolled up towards the tip, the upper side densely velvety on the thick leaf-veins. Flowering stem erect, stiff and fairly thick, with a spike 15–35cm. Spikelets 8–12, usually 5 to 9-flowered, 10–25mm long, flattened at the sides, arranged some distance apart in 2 ranks and appressed to the hairless axis that breaks up at maturity. Glumes keeled asymmetrically, 6 to 12-veined, blunt and awnless like the other bracts.
Sand dunes.
Ssp. *farctus* occurs throughout the Mediterranean region, often in the parentage of hybrids, ssp. *rechingeri* (Runem.) Meld., which is without a creeping rhizome and is found on coastal rocks in the Aegean, and ssp. *boreali-atlanticus* (Sim. & Guin.) Meld. is distributed on the coasts of N. and W. Europe.

□□ *Aegilops geniculata* Roth (*A. ovata* L.p.p.)
■□ 10–40cm; April–July; ☉
Stems numerous, curving upwards. Leaves with a small, narrow and flat, hairy or hairless blade, and a hairless, somewhat inflated sheath. Lobes at base of blade sometimes fringed with hairs. Flower-spikes awnless, 1–2cm long, ovoid, with 1 or 2 rudimentary spikelets at the base, usually consisting of 2 fertile spikelets and above them 1 sterile spikelet on a flat, broad axis. The 2 coarsely leathery and rough glumes equal, rounded on the back and green-striped, with 4–5 long awns. Awns of the lemma about the same length.
Dry, open, grassy pastures, waysides, fallow land.
Mediterranean region, Canary Islands, S.W. Asia.
Two species with 2 or 3 awns on the glumes, distinctly longer than those of the lemma, are *A. neglecta* Req. ex Bertol. (*A. ovata* L.p.p.): spike abruptly contracted above the 2 fertile spikelets, the 1 or 2 sterile ones separated from them, and *A. triuncialis* L.: all 4–6 spikelets fertile, awns of the terminal spikelet longer than those of the lateral ones (both species in the Mediterranean region and S.W. Asia).

□□ *Lagurus ovatus* L. **Hare's tail**
□■ 5–60cm; April–June; ☉
Leaves of this erect or ascending grass grey-green, the blades 2–10mm broad, flat, and velvety. Leaf-sheaths loose, the upper ones somewhat inflated, ligule about 3mm, blunt and membranous, hairy. A characteristic feature is the softly hairy, erect, spherical, ovoid or shortly cylindrical inflorescence, up to 6×2cm, from which individual awns protrude. Spikelets very shortly stalked, 1-flowered, 7–9mm long, the glumes with spreading hairs and a slender bristle, the lemma narrowing into 2 bristles, with a bent awn, 8–18mm long, on the back.
Sandy soils near the coast, fallow land, waysides, also grown as an ornamental plant, and a favourite grass for dried flower arrangements.
Mediterranean region, Canary Islands.

Grass family *Poaceae* (*Gramineae*)

■□
□□ *Ammophila arenaria* (L.) Link ssp. *arundinacea* Lindb. f. **Marram Grass**
0.5–1.2m; May–August; ♃
A common coastal grass with stout, branched, creeping rhizomes that form dense tufts. Leaves with a stiff, grey-green blade, up to 6mm broad, the upper part curled inwards, finely hairy on the ribs, the ligule 1–3cm long and deeply divided, and the leaf-sheath hairless. Panicle erect, pale, condensed into a spike-like inflorescence 7–25cm long. Spikelets 10–16mm, compressed at the sides, 1-flowered, awnless. Glumes lanceolate, persistent, about as long as the lemma, which has fine, white hairs, 4–5mm long, at the base.
Sandy beaches, dunes, also planted to consolidate sandy areas.
Coasts of the Mediterranean region and the Atlantic coast of Portugal.
Ssp. *arenaria* occurs on the Atlantic coast of N. and W. Europe southwards to N.W. Spain.

□■
□□ *Parapholis incurva* (L.) Hubb. (*Pholiurus incurvatus* Hitchc., *Lepturus incurvatus* Trin.)
Curved Sea Hard-grass
5–25cm; April–July; ☉
A low-growing grass, branched at the base and forming tufts. Leaves with a short blade, flat or curled inwards, 1–2mm broad, rough on the upper side, the ligule 0.5–1mm long, and the uppermost sheath inflated. Spikes stiff, slender, and strongly curved, 1–10cm long. Spikelets 1-flowered, 4.5–7mm, arranged alternately, each in a separate indentation of the axis, longer than the internodes, and falling together with these when ripe. Glumes equal, stiff, the keel not winged.
Saline meadows, on sandy or stony ground, usually near the coast.
Mediterranean region, W. Europe.
P. filiformis (Roth) Hubb.: flower-spikes straight or only slightly curved, keel of the glumes distinctly winged (Mediterranean region).

□□
■□ *Stipa capensis* Thunb. (*S. tortilis* Desf.)
10–60cm; March–June; ☉, ☉
A low-growing, rather tufted grass with jointed, ascending, hairless stems. Leaves blue-green, slender, curled inwards, the uppermost with a broadened sheath, which at first encloses the lower part of the inflorescence. Ligule very short, squarely cut at the end and fringed with hairs like the opening of the sheath. Panicle 3–10(–15)cm, condensed into a spike, spirally twisted at maturity. Spikelets 1-flowered, glumes long-pointed, translucent, much longer than the 6–7mm long, hairy lemma, which bears a 2-jointed awn, 7–10cm long. The latter is twisted and hairy up to the second joint, but straight and rough beyond that.
Grassland, pastures, garigue.
Mediterranean region, Canary Islands, S.W. Asia.

□□
□■ *Stipa tenacissima* L. (*Macrochloa tenacissima* (L.) Kunth) **Esparto Grass**
0.6–1.5m; April–July; ♃
A grass that forms large tufts and is often dominant over wide areas. Leaves very tough, only flat and green during the period of growth, otherwise curled inwards and grey, with dense, fine hairs on the strongly ribbed upper surface. Ligule very short, fringed, the mouth of the sheath with long hairs, and with 2 projections, feathery tipped, 2.5–3cm long, with spreading hairs, on non-flowering shoots. Panicle 25–35cm, dense, with 1-flowered spikelets. Glumes membranous, long-pointed, 2.5–3cm long, lemma membranous, deeply divided into 2 at the tip, about 1cm long, with an awn 4–6cm long. The latter twisted about as far as the joint and bearing hairs 1–4mm long, but with only minute, appressed hairs beyond that. Of importance in rope-making and in the manufacture of high-quality paper.
Steppes, pastures, open pine-woods.
Southern Iberian peninsula, Balearic Islands, N.W. Africa.
S. gigantea Link: stems to 2.5m. Panicle 30–50cm, very loose. Awn of the lemma 7–12cm long, rough, hairless (southern Iberian peninsula, Morocco).

Grass family Poaceae (Gramineae)

■☐ *Ampelodesmos mauritanica* (Poir.) T. Durand & Schinz (*A. tenax* (Vahl) Link)
☐☐ 1–3m; April–June; ♃
A tall grass, growing in large tufts, and often dominating large areas. Leaves coarse, up to 1m long and 7mm broad, very rough and strongly ribbed, the margins later curled inwards. Ligule lanceolate, 8–15mm long, fringed at the margin. Panicle on a long, stout stalk, much-branched, somewhat inclined to one side, with stalked, 2 to 5-flowered spikelets, laterally compressed, and 10–15mm long. Glumes somewhat unequal in length, keeled, shorter than the spikelets, often purple. Lemma 2-toothed at the tip and with an awn 1–2mm long, hairy on the back in the lower half. Used in the manufacture of paper and in rope-making.
Garigue, maquis, often spreading after the destruction of woods.
Western Mediterranean region, sporadic from Spain to Italy, N. Africa.

☐■ *Arundo donax* L. **Giant Reed**
☐☐ 2–6m; August–December; ♃
The largest European grass, resembling bamboo. Vigorous vegetative reproduction by far-creeping rhizomes. Stem woody, overwintering, and only flowering the second year, 2–3.5cm in diameter. Leaf blade flat, grey-green, up to 60×6cm, with rough margins. Flowers in dense panicles, 30–60cm long. Spikelets 12–18mm, usually with the florets tinged purple. Glumes membranous, hairless, the lemma with 2 tips, and long silky hairs on the back that give a shining, silvery appearance to the whole inflorescence in autumn. Used for a variety of purposes, planted as wind-breaks, dried for making baskets, mats, fishing rods, etc.
Ditches, river-banks, damp places.
Throughout the Mediterranean region and the Canary Islands; elsewhere cultivated and becoming naturalised. Probably native in Asia.
A. plinii Turra is similar: plant only up to 3m high, leaves 1–2cm broad. Spikelets 8–10mm, with 1–2 florets, lemma not divided at the tip, with long silky hairs (Mediterranean region).
The **Common Reed**, *Phragmites australis* (Cav.) Trin. ex Steudel (*P. communis* Trin.) occurs throughout the whole of Europe and elsewhere: up to 3.5m high, spikelets with 2–10 florets, lemma hairless.

☐☐ *Lygeum spartum* L. **Albardine**
■☐ 20–80cm; March–May; ♃
A tuft-forming grass, often covering large areas. Leaves curled inwards and rush-like, up to 1.5mm broad, tough, arching over at the end, the ligule about 7mm. A characteristic feature is the white, ovate, pointed, sheath-like bract, 3–4(–9)cm long, that encloses a usually 2-flowered spikelet. Glumes absent. Lemmas about 2cm, united into a tube in the lower half with long, spreading, silky hairs, the upper half free and hairless. Palea 3–4cm, much longer than the lemma. Spikelets falling in their entirety when ripe. Used in the manufacture of paper and in rope-making.
Grassy steppes, especially on clayey and saline soils.
Southern Mediterranean region, northwards to Spain, Sardinia, S. Italy, Crete.

☐☐ *Sporobolus pungens* (Schreb.) Kunth
☐■ 10–30cm; July–September; ♃
A far-creeping grass with long, wiry rhizomes. Numerous ascending or erect, flowering and non-flowering shoots. Leaves in 2 distinct rows, with a short, sharply pointed, grey-green blade, 2–8cm×2–5mm, hairy on the upper side and with the margins curled inwards, in place of the ligule a row of hairs. Leaf-sheaths overlapping. Panicle much-branched and dense, 3–6cm long, ovoid or narrowly ovoid, greenish or violet. Spikelets 1-flowered, 1.5–2.5mm, shortly stalked, without hairs and awns. Glumes unequal, the upper one longer, resembling the lemma and palea.
Sandy beaches.
Mediterranean region.

Grass family Poaceae (Gramineae)
Sedge family Cyperaceae

■☐ *Cynodon dactylon* (L.) Pers. **Bermuda Grass** *Poaceae*
☐☐ 10–40cm; almost throughout the year, in the northern part of the distribution zone June–October; ⚃
A grass with long, above-ground rhizomes, rooting at the nodes. Leaves arranged in 2 ranks, the blade linear-lanceolate, 2–15cm long and 2–4mm broad, usually with scattered hairs and rough on the margins, the ligule with a tuft of long hairs on each side. Flowering-stem erect or ascending, with 3–7 finger-like spikes, 1–5cm long, that bear 2 rows of closely set, almost sessile, 1-flowered spikelets, about 2mm long, on one side. All scales awnless, often tinged violet.
Pastures, cultivated and fallow land, waysides, footpaths.
Probably originating in the Mediterranean region, but nowadays found in all the warm and dry regions of the world.

☐■ *Hyparrhenia hirta* (L.) Stapf (*Andropogon hirtus* L., *Cymbopogon hirtus* (L.) Thoms.)
☐☐ *Poaceae*
0.4–1.2m; April–September; ⚃
A tuft-forming grass with erect, often branched stems. Leaves grey-green, 2–4mm broad, with a short ligule fringed with hairs. The whole inflorescence up to 30cm long, consisting of 2–10 pairs of spikes, 2–4cm long, that are enclosed by leaf-sheaths at their base. Each spike with 4–7 pairs of silky-hairy, 2-flowered spikelets, one of each pair of spikelets sometimes sessile, 4–6.5mm long, with a slender, jointed awn, 1–3.5cm long and hairy below, the other stalked and awnless.
Grassy pastures, garigue, fallow land.
Mediterranean region, Africa, Canary Islands, S.W. Asia.
Andropogon distachyos L. is also widely distributed: Stem simple with a terminal inflorescence of 2 finger-like spikes, 4–14cm long, with hairless awns.

☐☐ *Cyperus rotundus* L. *Cyperaceae*
■☐ 10–60cm; August–November; ⚃
Underground rhizomes hardly more than 1mm thick, with distant, narrow scales, occasionally with tubers. Stem triangular, with keeled leaves at the base, 2–6mm broad, and at the end an inflorescence of 4–10 unequal rays, surrounded by 2–6 bracts, at least the outer one exceeding the inflorescence. Spikelets in groups of 3–12 at the end of the rays, 1–2cm long and 1–2mm broad, with 6–32 florets arranged in 2 rows. Axis of the spikelet winged, the scales ovate, red-brown with a green keel, overlapping. Stigmas 3, fruit triangular.
Damp, sandy places, often near the coast.
Mediterranean region, Canary Islands, subtropical and tropical regions of the world.
C. longus L. is similar and also widespread: underground rhizomes 3–10mm thick, covered with broad scales, without tubers. Inflorescence often more than 10-rayed, much exceeded by the bracts. Because of its impressive height (2–5m) and historical significance (manufacture of paper from the pith of the stem) the **Papyrus**, *Cyperus papyrus* L., is often visited in its single location in Europe, near Syracuse in Sicily: Inflorescence up to 0.5m broad, composed of over 100 rays, 10–30cm long.

☐☐ *Cyperus capitatus* Vand. (*C. kalli* (Forsk.) Murb., *C. mucronatus* (L.) Mab. non Rottb.)
☐■ *Cyperaceae*
10–50cm; April–July; ⚃
A shore plant with long, creeping, scaly rhizomes, and woolly hairs on the roots. Stem solitary, round and grooved, with grey-green, grooved leaves, 1–6mm broad at the base. Inflorescence terminal, 15–30mm across, consisting of a head of very closely set, 4 to 12-flowered spikelets. Scales broadly lanceolate, red-brown, ending abruptly in a stiff point, 1–3mm long. Stigmas 3. Fruits triangular. Also characteristic of this species are the usually 3 grooved bracts of the inflorescence, up to 15cm long, that are broadened at the base and arch over towards the ground.
Sandy beaches, dunes.
Mediterranean region, Canary Islands.

Palm family *Arecaceae (Palmae)*

■☐ *Chamaerops humilis* L. **Dwarf Fan Palm**
☐☐ 0.5–4m; even taller in cultivation; April–June; ♄
Often bushy because of grazing, only in inaccessible places or in cultivation with a tall trunk
that is covered with grey or whitish fibres. Leaves clustered at the top, with a circular, fan-
shaped blade, 70–80cm across, divided for up to ²/₃ into 10–20 pointed, lanceolate segments,
the leaf-stalk spine-toothed on its edges. Flowers in dense, yellow panicles with a sheathing
bract, the male and female flowers on the same or on separate trees. Fruits 1–3cm, yellow,
later reddish brown, unpalatable. The leaf-fibres are used as padding and in making brooms.
The leaf-buds are eaten as a vegetable.
Garigue, stony pastures, sandy places, also grown as an ornamental plant.
Western Mediterranean region, eastwards to Italy.

☐■ *Trachycarpus fortunei* (Hook.) Wendl. **Chusan Palm**
☐☐ 4–12m; April–June; ♄
Trunk densely covered with dark brown fibres. Leaves bright green, the blade 50–60cm in
diameter, divided fan-like almost to the base into many narrow, stiff segments. Stalk 40–
100cm long, with fine spines along the edges. Leaf-sheath with a fibrous layer on the inner
side. Flowers in stout panicles 30–60cm long, the male and female on the same tree. Fruits
blue-black, 12–14mm, resembling grapes.
An ornamental tree, relatively hardy in the Mediterranean region (native in S.E. Asia).
Other cultivated palms with fan-shaped leaves include *Washingtonia robusta* Wendl. (above
left in the illustration): the smooth trunk with diagonal furrows has its upper part enclosed
by withered leaves, *W. filifera* (J.A. Linden) Wendl.: leaves with white threads hanging from
them (both species native in California), and *Livistona australis* (R.Br.) Mart. which has a tall,
slender, ringed trunk (native in Australia).

☐☐ *Phoenix dactylifera* L. **Date Palm**
■☐ Up to 30m; February–June; ♄
Tree with a slender trunk bearing the scars of the fallen leaves in a mosaic-like pattern. At the
top is a cluster of spreading, curved, grey-green, pinnate leaves, 3–5m long. Leaflets
arranged in a V-shape, linear-lanceolate, long-pointed and keeled, the middle ones 30–40cm
long. Inflorescences at first in sheath-like bracts, much branched. Fruits 2.5–7.5cm, oblong,
fleshy, variable in form. In order to obtain good crops of fruit, branches of male flowes are
tied to the female inflorescences to assist pollination by the wind, so that in cultivation only a
few male trees are required. An important food in the dry regions of N. Africa and S.W. Asia.
Alcoholic drinks are made from the sap in the trunk. The palm frond is used in religious
ceremonies on Palm Sunday.
Irrigated plantations have been established in N. Africa, S.W. Asia and S. Spain (Elche); in
the rest of the Mediterranean region it is found as an ornamental plant. Probably originating
in the region of Iran and Arabia.
P. theophrasti Greut.: trunk slender, not more than 10m high, putting out suckers like the true
Date Palm. Leaves grey-green, the middle leaflets 30–50cm, the lower ones spiny, yellowish.
Fruits to 16 × 10mm, yellow-brown at first, later blackish, unpalatable (native in Crete).

☐☐ *Phoenix canariensis* hort. ex Chabaud **Canary Palm**
☐■ Up to 20m; February–June; ♄
Trunk stouter than that of the true Date Palm, always solitary. Crown more leafy, with less
rigid and more graceful green fronds, 5–6m long, the middle leaflets 40–50cm long. Fruits
1.5–2.3cm, oblong, orange, later dark red-brown, unpalatable. More quick-growing and less
sensitive to cold than the true Date Palm, and therefore planted in preference throughout the
Mediterranean region as a park and avenue tree. Native in the Canary Islands.
Jubaea chilensis (Molina) Baill. is also frequently cultivated, with shorter leaves and a
smooth, stout, grey trunk (native in Chile).

Arum family Araceae

■☐ *Arum italicum* Mill. **Italian Arum**
☐☐ 20–70cm; April–May; ⁂
Leaves appearing in late autumn, long-stalked, with an arrow-shaped or spear-shaped blade 15–35cm long. Flowers unisexual on a cylindrical axis (spadix), with sterile flowers above and below the male ones, the uppermost, flowerless portion usually yellow. The bract (Spathe) surrounding the inflorescence 15–40cm long, usually pale greenish yellow. Berries red. Ssp. *italicum*: leaves white-veined, lateral lobes spreading (distributed throughout almost the whole of the region), ssp. *neglectum* (Towns.) Prime: leaves of one colour or rarely with dark markings, lateral lobes converging (W. Europe and western Mediterranean region), ssp. *byzantinum* (Blume) Nym.: spathe tinged purple (eastern Balkan peninsula, Crete). Other subspecies also occur.
Undergrowth, hedges, tree plantations.
Mediterranean region, W. Europe, Canary Islands.
Two striking species are *A. creticum* Boiss. & Heldr. with a white to yellowish spathe, without sterile flowers (Crete), and *A. dioscoridis* with the spathe yellow-green, flecked dark purple or tinged dark purple throughout, and the spadix similarly coloured (Rhodes, Chios, Near East). An autumn-flowering species with a dark purple spathe is *A. pictum* L. (Balearic Islands, Corsica, Sardinia).

☐■ *Biarum tenuifolium* (L.) Schott
☐☐ 10–20cm; October–March; ⁂
Leaves 5–20cm long, linear to narrowly lanceolate, flat or undulate, only appearing after the main flowering time. Inflorescence-stalk very short, below the ground. Spathe united below into a short tube, the free part 3–5 times as long, tongue-shaped, dark purple, tinged green outside. Spadix with the flowerless portion dark purple and worm-like, often longer than the spathe. Flowers unisexual, with sterile flowers above and below the male ones.
Garigue, stony and grassy pastures.
S. Europe, Morocco, Asia Minor, absent from France and the islands of the western Mediterranean region.
B. carratracense (Haens. ex Willk.) Font Quer: sterile flowers only below the male ones (S. Spain) and *B. davisii* Turrill: spathe hood-shaped, greenish white, flecked pink-brown (Crete).

☐☐ *Arisarum vulgare* Targ.–Tozz. **Friar's Cowl**
■☐ 20–40cm; March–May and October–November; ⁂
Leaves basal, long-stalked, with an ovate to arrow-shaped blade. In the widely distributed ssp. *vulgare* the inflorescence-stalk is about as long as the leaf-stalks. Spathe 3–5cm, united below into a tube striped brown-purple, the upper part helmet-shaped and arching over the protruding and forward curving spadix. Spadix with 4–6 female flowers at the base, and above them about 20 male flowers, all fertile and sessile, the flowerless portion greenish. Berries greenish. Many subspecies occur, especially in N. Africa.
Cultivated and fallow land, garigue.
Mediterranean region, Canary Islands.
A. proboscideum (L.) Savi: spathe with a long, upward pointing, thread-like appendage at the tip (Italy, S.W. Spain).

☐☐ *Dracunculus vulgaris* Schott **Dragon Arum**
☐■ 0.6–1.2m; April–June; ⁂
Plant with strong smell of carrion at flowering time. Leaves pedate, divided into 9–15 elliptical or oblong-lanceolate, pointed segments. Leaf-stalks with their sheaths enveloping the inflorescence-stalk. Spathe large, with an undulate margin, dark purple and hairless within, greenish on the outer side. Spadix with a stout, flowerless portion, coloured like the spathe and often extending beyond it, the male and female flowers separated by only a few sterile flowers.
Woods, undergrowth, nutrient-rich, damp places, also grown as an ornamental plant.
Eastern Mediterranean region, westwards to Corsica and Sardinia, cultivated elsewhere and in places becoming naturalised.
D. muscivorus (L.f.) Parl.: spathe hairy within, the tip of the spadix completely covered with thread-like structures (Balearic Islands, Corsica, Sardinia).

Orchid family *Orchidaceae*

■☐   *Limodorum abortivum* (L.) Swartz **Limodore**
☐☐   30–80cm; April–July; ♃
An orchid without green leaves, the stout, steel-blue to dingy purple stem only having
sheathing scale-leaves. Inflorescence loose, 4 to 25-flowered, 10–30cm long. Bracts longer
than the ovaries. Flowers pale violet with darker veins, 1.5–2.5cm long, the outer perianth-
segments spreading out wide, the 2 lateral inner ones narrower and somewhat shorter. Lip
undivided, curved upwards and undulate-crenate on the margin, later often yellowish. Spur
1.5–2.5cm, about as long as the ovary, slender, curving upwards. Ssp. *trabutianum* (Batt.)
Rouy has a spur only 2mm long (N.W. Africa, rarely in the Iberian peninsla).
Open deciduous and evergreen woods, thickets, grassland, extending into the mountain
zone, mainly on chalk.
Mediterranean region, northwards to the warmest areas of central Europe and eastwards to
Iran.

☐■   *Neotinea maculata* (Desf.) Stearn (*N. intacta* (Link) Rchb.f.) **Dense-flowered Orchid**
☐☐   8–25(–40)cm; March–May; ♃
Leaves 3–6, blue-green, usually with lines of dark brown spots, the lower ones clustered in a
rosette, oblong, pointed, spreading, 3–12×1–3cm, the upper ones smaller and erect. Flowers
in a dense, slender spike, 2–6cm long. Bracts whitish, shorter than the ovaries. Perianth-
segments dingy pink to yellowish or greenish white, 3–4mm long, converging to form a
helmet-shaped flower. Lip scarcely longer, extending horizontally, flat, 3-lobed, the middle
lobe often longer than the linear lateral lobes. Spur very short, up to 2mm, blunt. Evergreen
and deciduous woods, thickets, grassland, extending into the mountain zone.
Mediterranean region, W. Ireland, Canary Islands.

☐☐   *Dactylorhiza sulphurea* (Link) Franco ssp. *pseudosambucina* (Ten.) Franco (*Orchis romana*
■☐   Seb. & M.)
15–35cm; March–June; ♃
Leaves narrowly oblong, not spotted, up to 12, most of them in a loose rosette. Inflorescence
4–10cm, bracts green or purple, extending beyond the flowers. Flowers yellow or pale to dark
red-purple, the lateral outer perianth-segments spreading, the middle one erect or inclined
forwards, up to 13mm long, the lateral inner ones smaller and converging, broadened near
the base. Lip more or less 3-lobed, without markings, broadly ovate to roundish, up to
10×15mm, the red form sometimes yellow at the base. Spur slender, 12–25mm, distinctly
longer than the ovary, horizontal to nearly vertical. In ssp. *siciliensis* (Klinge) Franco the
spur is fairly thick and shorter than to as long as the ovary (Iberian peninsula, Sardinia, Sicily, N.W. Africa).
Evergreen and deciduous woods, bushy places.
Italy, Sicily, eastwards to the Crimea and Asia Minor.

☐☐   *Orchis papilionacea* L. **Pink Butterfly Orchid**
☐■   20–40cm; February–May; ♃
Leaves 6–10, clustered at the base, narrowly lanceolate, erect, not spotted, the uppermost
ones sheathing the stem up to the inflorescence. Inflorescence ovoid, 3 to 15-flowered, often
with purple bracts that are about as long as the ovaries. Perianth-segments brown-purple
with dark veins, the outer ones 10–15mm long, loosely converging to form a helmet-shaped
structure. Lip 12–16mm, undivided, spreading out like a fan at the end, often with an undulate or irregularly toothed margin, whitish or pink to carmine-red, often with dark red
markings. Spur horizontal or sloping downwards, somewhat shorter than the ovary. Variable
in form, e.g. in Spain there are plants with the lip 20–25mm: var. *grandiflora* Bois.
Grassland, maquis, open woods, mainly on chalky soils.
Mediterranean region, Caucasus.
O. boryi Rchb.f.: lip weakly 3-lobed, pale pink, edged with violet, with 4–6 violet dots at the
base (S. Greece, Crete).

Orchid family *Orchidaceae*

■□
□□ *Orchis morio* L. **Green-winged Orchid**
10–30cm; March–May; ♃
Leaves 6–9, lanceolate, pointed, not spotted, the lower ones in a rosette. Inflorescence 5 to 25-flowered, the lower flowers opening before the upper ones. Bracts about as long as the ovaries. The 5 perianth-segments converging into a helmet shape, pink, white, or purple-red with greenish veins. Lip paler in the middle, with dark spots, 3-lobed, the middle lobe often notched, without teeth in the middle, smaller than the lateral lobes which are broad, folded downwards, and often slightly recurved. In ssp. *picta* (Lois.) Arc. (the plant illustrated), the outer perianth-segments are 6–8mm, and the spur usually as long as the ovary (S. Europe to the Caucasus, N.W. Africa), in ssp. *morio* the perianth-segments are 8–10mm long, and the spur shorter than the ovary (found almost throughout the whole distribution area of the species), and in ssp. *champagneuxii* (Barn.) Cam. the lip is usually unspotted and only shallowly 3-lobed, and the spur broader towards the end (S. France, Iberian peninsula, Morocco).
Grassy pastures, garigue, open woods.
Almost the whole of Europe, Asia Minor, eastwards to the Caucasus, N.W. Africa.

□■
□□ *Orchis coriophora* L. **Bug Orchid**
15–40cm; April–June; ♃
Leaves 4–10, narrowly lanceolate, folded. Inflorescence 5–15cm, oblong, with 1-veined bracts. Flowers in the plant illustrated, ssp. *fragrans* (Pollini) Sudre, usually scented, brown-red and green. Perianth-segments pointed, forming a spiked helmet. Lip spotted, 8–10mm long, 3-lobed, more or less flat, the middle lobe distinctly longer than the lateral lobes. Spur pale, directed downwards, as long as or longer than the lip. In ssp. *coriophora* the flowers smell of bugs, lip 6–8mm, the middle lobe hardly longer than the lateral lobes. Spur only half as long as the lip.
Grassy pastures, maquis, open woods.
Mediterranean region, northwards to central and E. Europe, and eastwards to Iran. Ssp. *fragrans* predominates in the Mediterranean region.
Orchis sancta L., **Holy Orchid**, is similar: perianth-segments long-pointed, the outer ones 9–12mm. Lip unspotted, lateral lobes serrate at the margin. Spur hook-shaped, curving downwards. Lower bracts 3 to 5-veined (Aegean to Palestine).

□□
■□ *Orchis lactea* Poir. **Milky Orchid**
7–20cm; February–April; ♃
Leaves 6–8, pale green, the basal ones broadly ovate-lanceolate. Inflorescence 2.5–5cm long. Bracts about as long as the ovaries, membranous. Perianth-segments pale rose or whitish, converging to form a helmet-shaped structure, the outer ones long-pointed and curving outwards, with dark red or greenish veins. Lip spotted with red, deeply 3-lobed, the middle lobe much longer and broader, undivided or only slightly notched, with a small tooth in the middle. Spur 6mm long, pointing downwards.
Grassy pastures, maquis, open woods, extending into the mountain zone.
Throughout the Mediterranean region, but only local.
O. tridentata Scop., **Toothed Orchid**, is similar: plant larger, 15–45cm. Middle lobe of lip more deeply divided. Spur half as long as the ovary. Flowering time March–June (S. France to the Caucasus, Asia Minor and Palestine, rare in central Europe).

□□
□■ *Orchis simia* Lam. **Monkey Orchid**
20–45cm; March–June; ♃
Leaves 3–6, broadly lanceolate, shining pale green, the lower ones in a basal rosette. Inflorescence 3–7cm long, the upper flowers opening before the lower ones. Bracts up to half as long as the ovaries. With some imagination the flowers can look like tiny monkeys. Perianth-segments pale purple, sometimes streaked or spotted and tinged with green, pointed, forming a helmet, the outer ones about 10mm long. Lip 14–16mm, white to pink, with red spots, deeply 3-lobed, the middle lobe again divided with a long tooth between the 2 segments. All 4 segments linear, rounded at the tip, usually dark red. Spur somewhat thickened at the end, pointing downwards, about half as long as the ovary.
Grassy pastures, bushy places, open woods.
Mediterranean region, S.W. Asia, extending locally to S. England and central Europe.

Orchid family *Orchidaceae*

■☐ *Orchis italica* Poir. (*O. longicruris* Link) **Naked Man Orchid**
☐☐ 20–40cm; March–May; ♃
Leaves 5–8, mostly clustered in a basal rosette, oblong-lanceolate with an undulate margin, spotted or unspotted. Inflorescence ovoid, 3.5–6.5cm long, dense, the lower flowers opening before the upper ones. Bracts 1-veined, membranous, at most ⅓ as long as the ovary. Perianth-segments pink with darker lines, pointed, converging to form a helmet-shaped structure, the outer ones 9–12mm long. Lip 12–16mm, white or pink with red spots, deeply 3-lobed, the middle lobe again divided, with a long, pointed tooth between the 2 segments. All the segments linear and pointed. Spur slender, pointing downwards, about half as long as the ovary.
Grassy pastures, maquis, open woods, mainly on chalk.
Mediterranean region, absent from France, Corsica and Sardinia.

☐■ *Orchis quadripunctata* Cyr. ex Ten. **Four-spotted Orchid**
☐☐ 10–30cm; March–May; ♃
Basal leaves 2–4, oblong-lanceolate, spotted or unspotted, clustered in a rosette. Inflorescence loose, 8 to 35-flowered, the lower flowers opening first. Bracts almost as long as the ovaries. Flowers 9–13mm, white, pink to purple-violet, the outer perianth-segments 3–5mm, rounded and spreading, the 2 lateral inner ones smaller and convex, converging. Lip 5–7mm, about equally 3-lobed, pale at the base, usually with 4 dark red spots. Spur slender and long, 10–12mm, pointing more or less downwards. In Sardinia and Sicily plants with smaller flowers and often only 1 dark red mark at the base of the lip have been called ssp. *brancifortii* (Biv.) Cam.
Stony and grassy pastures, garigue.
S. Europe, from Sardinia to Greece, Crete and Cyprus.
Orchis anatolica Boiss.: inflorescence only 2 to 15-flowered. Spur pointing more or less upwards, 1.5–2.5cm long (eastern Mediterranean region, from the Aegean and Crete eastwards).

☐☐ *Orchis purpurea* Huds. **Lady Orchid**
■☐ 25–80cm; April–June; ♃
A stately plant with 3–6 very large basal leaves, broadly lanceolate to ovoid, 6–17×2–6cm. Inflorescence 5–20cm long, many-flowered, the membranous bracts much shorter than the ovaries. Perianth-segments brown-purple on the outside, sometimes spotted, converging to form a rounded helmet, the outer ones 12–14mm long. Lip white or pink, spotted with purple, 10–15mm, usually deeply 3-lobed, the middle lobe much larger and broader than the narrower lateral lobes, again divided and with a small tooth in the middle. Spur pointing downwards, 4mm, ⅓ as long as the ovary.
Open woods, thickets, tree plantations, on chalky soils, in the Mediterranean region mainly in the mountain zone.
S. Europe, rare in southernmost parts, extending into W. and central Europe, Algeria, Asia Minor, eastwards to the Caucasus.

☐☐ *Orchis provincialis* Balb. ssp. *provincialis* **Provence Orchid**
☐■ 15–35cm; March–June; ♃
Leaves lanceolate, distinctly spotted, 2–5 of them forming a basal rosette. Inflorescence cylindrical, 5–7cm long, with 5–20 pale yellow flowers, and bracts that are as long as the ovaries and are appressed to them. Outer perianth-segments 9–14mm, the lateral ones curving backwards, the middle ones erect, the 2 lateral inner ones smaller and converging. Lip 8–12mm long and broad, 3-lobed, convex, somewhat darker in the middle and with purple-red spots. Spur curved upwards, thickened at the end, about as long as the ovary.
Deciduous woods in the mountain zone, grassy pastures, maquis.
S. Europe, Asia Minor.
O. provincialis ssp. *pauciflora* (Ten.) Cam., often regarded as a separate species: Leaves unspotted, inflorescence with only 3–7 flowers, lip orange-yellow, with fine red-brown spots in the middle, spur curving upwards, more slender, about 1½ times as long as the ovary (S. Europe from Corsica to the Aegean). *O. laeta* Steinheil, a very similar species, is native in N.W. Africa.

Orchid family *Orchidaceae*

■□ *Aceras anthropophorum* (L.) Ait.f. **Man Orchid**
□□ 10–40cm; April–June; ♃
Lower leaves 5–12cm long, broadly lanceolate, rounded at the end with an abrupt point. Up to 60 greenish yellow flowers, often streaked and edged red-brown, in an elongated, narrow spike up to 20cm long. The upper 5 perianth-segments converge to form a helmet. Lip without a spur, 12–15mm, with 2 narrow lateral lobes, and a middle lobe about twice as long that is deeply divided into 2 narrow segments, giving the impression of a tiny hanging man.
Grassy pastures, maquis, open woods, mainly on chalk.
Mediterranean region, W. Europe, rare in central Europe.

□■ *Barlia robertiana* (Lois.) Greut. (*Aceras longibracteatum* Rchb.f., *B. longibracteata* Parl.)
□□ **Giant Orchid**
25–80cm; January–April; ♃
Lower leaves up to 25×10cm, ovate to oblong, clustered in a rosette at the base of the stout stem. Flowers strongly scented, greenish to reddish or brownish, with red markings, in a dense, cylindrical spike, 8–25cm long. Bracts about twice as long as the ovaries. Outer perianth-segments 2–2.5cm, converging with the 2 lateral, narrower and shorter inner ones to form a helmet-shaped structure. Lip up to 2cm long, 3-lobed, the 2 lateral lobes often undulate on the margin, broad, curving inwards and sickle-shaped, the middle lobe 1½–2 times as long and divided into 2 broad segments. Spur short, 3–6mm, bag-shaped and pointing downwards.
Grassy pastures, maquis, open woods.
Mediterranean region, Canary Islands.

□□ *Serapias lingua* L. **Tongue Orchid**
■□ 10–35cm; March–May; ♃
An orchid often growing in fairly large groups. Leaves pointed, lanceolate, 4–8. Flower-spike loosely 2 to 9-flowered. Bracts purple, more rarely greenish, scarcely exceeding the flowers. The 5 perianth-segments combine to form a helmet-shaped structure, 15–25mm long, which stands out horizontally. The front part of the lip is purple-red, pink, yellowish or whitish, lanceolate, pointed, and extends at an angle forwards or downwards from a slightly narrowed base, at most only slightly hairy, 10–18mm long and 5–10mm broad. Clearly visible at the base is a dark coloured, undivided or furrowed swelling. Lateral lobes protruding only slightly from the helmet.
Dry and damp grasslands, maquis, open woods, tree plantations.
S. Europe, N.W. Africa.
S. parviflora Parl.: leaf-sheaths often spotted with red at the base. Flowers small, the front part of the lip 5–10mm long and 3–5mm broad, usually strongly bent back. At the base are 2 dark-coloured, parallel swellings (S. Europe, S.W. Anatolia, N.W. Africa).

□□ *Serapias vomeracea* (Burm.) Briq. **Long-lipped Serapias**
□■ 10–55cm; April–June; ♃
Leaves 4–9, linear to broadly lanceolate, pointed, the 2 uppermost ones tinged brown-purple like the floral bracts. Inflorescence in ssp. *vomeracea* 3 to 10-flowered, flowers large. Bracts much longer than the erect helmet-shaped structure, 20–30mm long, formed by the 5 perianth-segments. Front part of the lip 20–30mm long and 8–12mm broad, brownish purple, with dense, long hairs where it adjoins the lower part, and with 2 parallel swellings at the base. In the plant illustrated, ssp. *orientalis* Greut., the inflorescence is shorter, 3 to 6-flowered, the flowers very large; the front lobe of the lip bears long hairs from its point of attachment to the middle, and the lateral lobes protrude further from the helmet. In ssp. *laxiflora* (Soó) Goelz & Reinh. the inflorescence is longer, up to 12-flowered, and the front part of the lip is only up to 15mm long and 5mm broad with scarcely any hairs.
Grassy and stony pastures, fallow land, open woods.
S. Europe, Asia Minor; ssp *orientalis* and ssp. *laxiflora* are found particularly in the eastern Mediterranean region. In *S. cordigera* L. the front part of the lip is heart-shaped, 20–35mm long and 20–25mm broad (Mediterranean region, eastwards to Crete).

Orchid family *Orchidaceae*

Ophrys L. **Bee Orchids**
A variable genus, consisting of about 50 species and subspecies, which has the Mediterranean region as its centre of distribution. numerous hybrids occur. There has also been extensive writing on the subject (see Bibliography).
Plants perennial, with 2 spherical to ovoid, undivided tubers. Leaves lanceolate to ovate, the lower ones in a rosette, the upper ones smaller and sheathing. Flowers 2–10(–15), forming a loose spike in the axils of green bracts. Outer perianth-segments more or less spreading, oblong or ovate, the inner lateral ones smaller and narrower, often hairy. Lip very variable in form, insect-like, its form connected with an interesting biological mechanism for transference of pollinia (pollen-masses).

■□□   *Ophrys speculum* Link ssp. *speculum* (*O. vernixia* Brot.) **Mirror Orchid, Mirror of Venus**
□□□   10–25cm; February–May. Outer perianth-segments green, usually with 2 brown-purple
□□□   stripes, the upper segment curving forwards. Lip 11–15mm, 3-lobed, with a roundish middle lobe, the edge densely covered with spreading, brown hairs, and in the middle a hairless, shining, metallic blue area with a yellow margin (Mediterranean region).

□■□   *Ophrys speculum* Link ssp. *regis-fernandii* Acht. & Kell.
□□□   Like the previous subspecies, but with the middle and lateral lobes of the lip much narrower
□□□   and the edges recurved (S. Aegean, W. Turkey). In Portugal there is a similar plant, ssp. *lusitanica* O. & E. Danesch.

□□■   *Ophrys lutea* (Gouan) Cav. **Yellow Bee Orchid**
□□□   7–30cm; February–June. Outer perianth-segments olive-green, the upper one curving for-
□□□   wards. Lip roundish to oblong, 3-lobed, with small pointed tubercles, brown with a grey-blue patch; in ssp. *lutea* the hairless yellow margin is 2–3mm broad and the length of the lip is 12–18mm (central and eastern Mediterranean region), in ssp. *murbeckii* (Fleischm.) Soó (Mediterranean region) and ssp. *melena* Renz (Greece) the margin is 1–2mm broad, and the lip only 9–12mm in length.

□□□   *Ophrys fusca* Link ssp. *fusca* **Sombre Bee Orchid**
■□□   10–40cm; March–May. Outer perianth-segments very broad, yellowish green, the upper one
□□□   curving forwards. Lip oblong, 13–23mm, 3-lobed, dark red-brown with a narrow, yellow margin, velvety-hairy, with 2 blue-grey or blue-purple patches (Mediterranean region); in ssp. *iricolor* (Desf.) Schwarz these patches are a bright steel-blue (only eastern Mediterranean region). *O. pallida* Rafin. is similar, but the perianth-segments are pale green, and the lip only 7–9mm, recurved at the tip (Sicily).

□□□   *Ophrys fusca* Link ssp. *omegaifera* (Fleischm.) Nelson
□■□   10–25cm; March–April. Similar to ssp. *fusca*, but the lip only up to 20mm long, recurved,
□□□   hairy on the margins, the brown patch with a grey-blue margin and an omega-shaped mark (Crete, Rhodes, S.W. Turkey). *O. dyris* Maire (Iberian peninsula, N.W. Africa) is very similar.

□□□   *Ophrys sphegodes* Mill. ssp. *sphegodes* **Early Spider Orchid**
□□■   10–45cm; February–June. Outer perianth-segments yellowish green, the middle one curved
□□□   or erect. Lip roundish to ovate, with small basal protuberances, 8–16mm, the inside hairless, pale to dark brown, usually with a bluish to violet H-shaped mark, the outside hairy (S. Europe, Asia Minor, northwards to S. England and central Europe).

□□□   *Ophrys sphegodes* Mill. ssp. *atrata* (Lindley) E. Mayer
□□□   20–40cm; March–May. Similar to ssp. *sphegodes*, but with large basal protuberances, and
■□□   with the usually blue mark extending towards them in 2 parallel lines which become joined at the base (western and central S. Europe). Other subspecies occur.

□□□   *Ophrys spruneri* Nym. **Grecian Spider Orchid**
□□□   10–40cm; March–May. Perianth-segments all spreading, often tinged purple. Lip extended,
□■□   10–15mm, 3-lobed, the middle lobe having an appendage at the tip and marked with 2 long, blue-violet, parallel lines with a paler edge (Greece, Aegean, Crete).

□□□   *Ophrys ferrum-equinum* Desf. **Horseshoe Orchid**
□□□   10–35cm; March–May. Perianth-segments pink to purple-violet, more rarely greenish or
□□■   whitish, spreading to recurved. Lip 10–14mm, roundish to ovate, velvety-hairy, with a small, downward-pointing appendage at the tip, and with 2 blue-violet parallel lines, often joining to form a horseshoe-shaped mark, sometimes with a paler edge (Greece to S.W. Turkey).

Orchid family *Orchidaceae*

■□□
□□□ *Ophrys bertolonii* Moretti. 15–35cm; March–early June. Outer perianth-segments pale to
□□□ dark rose-purple, occasionally whitish, spreading to recurved. Lip 10–15mm, oblong-ovate,
usually undivided, curved upwards and saddle-shaped, black-purple, densely hairy, with a
yellowish, upward-curved appendage at the tip. Near the tip is a shining, more or less shield-
shaped mark (central Mediterranean region).

□■□
□□□ *Ophrys lunulata* Parl. **Crescent Ophrys**. 15–30cm; March–May. Outer perianth-segments
□□□ pink, occasionally whitish, spreading, the lateral ones extending under the lip, the inner ones
of almost equal length. Lip 10–12mm, ovate, deeply 3-lobed, with strongly recurved margins,
brown or black-purple, hairy, with a small, upward-pointing appendage at the tip. The bluish
mark is in the form of a crescent, the concave side facing the tip (S. Italy, Sicily).

□□■
□□□ *Ophrys argolica* Fleischm. **Eyed Bee Orchid**. 15–35cm; March–May. Outer perianth-seg-
□□□ ments pale to deep lilac, rarely greenish, spreading. Lip 12mm, roundish, usually undivided,
red-brown, with dense white hairs on the upper margin, and a downward-pointing appendage at the tip. Two separate bluish marks, sometimes united to form a clasp-shaped mark
(Greece, Crete, Aegean).

□□□
■□□ *Ophrys reinholdii* Sprun. ex Fleischm.. 15–40cm; March–May. Outer perianth-segments
□□□ rose-purple, also whitish or green, spreading to recurved. Lip 3-lobed, black-purple, the lateral lobes recurved, densely hairy. Middle lobe ovate, with an appendage at the tip. Markings
consisting of 2 separate or combined spots, white or violet edged with white (Greece,
Aegean, S.W. Turkey).

□□□
□■□ *Ophrys scolopax* Cav. ssp. *cornuta* (Steven) Camus (*O. oestrifera* M. – Bieb. ssp. *oestrifera*)
□□□ **Woodcock Orchid**. 20–50cm; March–June. Outer perianth-segments pink to violet, also
green or white, spreading. Lip 8–14mm, 3-lobed, dark brown, the lateral lobes drawn out into
a pointed horn, up to 12mm long, the middle lobe ovate, convex, with a yellow-green,
upward-pointing appendage at the tip. Markings in the upper part of the lip variable, consisting of brownish or bluish spots with whitish edges (eastern Mediterranean region, westwards to Mt. Gargano). Ssp. *scolopax*, in the western and central Mediterranean region, has
smaller, blunt horns. Two other subspecies occur.

□□□
□□■ *Ophrys fuciflora* (F.W. Schmidt) Moench (*O. holosericea* (Burm.f.) Greut.) **Late Spider**
□□□ **Orchid**. 10–50cm; April–May. Outer perianth-segments broad, pink or whitish, spreading to
recurved. Lip 9–16mm, almost square, with protuberances at the base and a yellowish green,
upward-pointing appendage at the tip, velvety in the middle and with longer hairs on the
margins, brown or dark brownish purple. The markings are very variable and are distributed
across the lip (central and eastern Mediterranean region, rarely extending into central
Europe). There are 4 subspecies.

□□□
□□□ *Ophrys tenthredinifera* Willd. **Sawfly Orchid**. 10–45cm; March–May. Outer perianth-seg-
■□□ ments broad, pink to rose-purple, rarely whitish, spreading, concave. Lip 11–14mm, square,
with 2 small protuberances at the base, and a hairless upward-pointing appendage at the tip
with a tuft of hairs at its point of attachment, red-brown in the middle, shortly hairy, with a
broad, yellow, densely hairy marginal zone. The fairly small patch at the base of the lip is
shield-shaped and dark blue or brown-violet in colour (Mediterranean region).

□□□
□□□ *Ophrys apifera* Hudson **Bee Orchid**. 20–60cm; end of March–July. Outer perianth-segments
□■■ fairly large, spreading to recurved, deep pink or whitish. Lip 10–12mm, broadly ovate, 3-
lobed, distinctly convex, the lateral lobes with basal protuberances and densely hairy. The
middle lobe usually with a long, yellow, recurved appendage. The shield-shaped mark is violet or reddish brown on a brownish ground with yellowish margins or spots (Mediterranean
region, rarely extending into W. and central Europe).

□□□
□□□ *Ophrys bombyliflora* Link **Bumble Bee Orchid**. 10–25cm; March–May. Outer perianth-seg-
□□■ ments pale green, spreading. Lip fairly small, 8–10mm, 3-lobed, brown to dark brown. Lateral lobes with basal protuberances, densely hairy, the middle lobe distinctly convex, without an appendage but with a bluish-violet mark with a paler edge, shield-shaped or divided
into 2 parts (Mediterranean region, Canary Islands, eastwards to S.W. Turkey).

Bibliography

BARONI, E., *Guida Botanica d'Italia*, 4th Edition, reprinted in Bologna, 1975

BAUMANN, H., *Griechische Pflanzenwelt in Mythos, Kunst und Literatur*, Munich, 1982

BAUMANN, H., and S. KÜNKELE, *Die wildwachsenden Orchideen Europas*, Stuttgart, 1982

BONAFÈ, F., *Flora de Mallorca*, 4 Vols., Palma de Mallorca, 1977–1980

BONNIER, G., *Flore complète illustrée en couleurs de France, Suisse et Belgique*, 13 Vols., Neuchâtel, 1912–1934

BONNIER, G. and G. DE LAYENS, *Flore complète portative de la France, de la Suisse et de la Belgique*, Paris, 1975

BOUCHARD, J., *Flore pratique de la Corse*, 2nd Edition, Bastia, 1974

CEBALLOS, A., J. F. CASAS and F. M. GARMENDIA, *Plantas silvestres de la Peninsula Iberica*, Madrid, 1980

COSTE, H., *Flore descriptive et illustrée de la France, de la Corse et des Contrées limitrophes*, 3 Vols., 2nd Edition, Paris 1937, and Suppl. 1–5, Paris, 1972–1979

DANESCH, E., and O., *Orchideen Europas, Südeuropa*, Berne and Stuttgart, 1969

DAVIS, P. H. (ed.), *Flora of Turkey and the East Aegean Islands*, 10 Vols., Edinburgh 1965–1988

EBERLE, G., *Pflanzen am Mittelmeer*, 2nd Edition, Frankfurt, 1975

ERIKSSON, O., A. HANSEN and P. SUNDING, *Flora of Macaronesia, Checklist of Vascular Plants*, 2nd Edition, Oslo, 1979, 3rd Revised Edition, Hansen and Sanding, 1985

FENAROLI, L., *Flora Mediterranea*, 2 Vols., Milan, 1962, 1964

FIORI, A., *Nuova Flora analitica d'Italia*, 2 Vols., reprinted Bologna, 1969

FIORI, A., and G. PAOLETTI, *Iconographia Florae Italicae.*, reprinted Bologna, 1970

FOURNIER, P., *Les quatre flores de la France, Corse comprise*, Paris, 1961

GÖTZ, E., *Die Gehölze der Mittelmeerländer*, Stuttgart, 1975

GUINOCHET, M., and R. DE VILMORIN, *Flore de France*, 4 Vols., Paris, 1973–1982

HAEUPLER, H., and I., *Mallorca in Farbe*, Stuttgart, 1983

HARRIS, T., *Pareys Mittelmeerführer*, Hamburg and Berlin, 1982

HAYEK, A., *Prodromus Florae Peninsulae Balcanicae*, 3 Vols., Dahlem bei Berlin, 1927–1933

HEGI, G., *Illustrierte Flora von Mitteleuropa*, 1st–3rd Editions, Vol. 1–7, Munich and Berlin, 1906–1982

HORVAT, J., V. GLAVAC and H. ELLENBERG, *Vegetation Südosteuropas*, Stuttgart, 1974

HUXLEY, A., and W. TAYLOR, *Flowers of Greece and the Aegean*, London, 1977

KOHLHAUPT, P., *Mittelmeerflora*, Bozano, 1980

MAIRE, R,., *Flore de l'Afrique du Nord*, 13 Vols., Paris, 1952–1967

NACHTIGALL, W., *Tiere und Pflanzen an Mittelmeerküsten*, Munich, Vienna, Zurich, 1983

PIGNATTI, S., *Flora d'Italia*, 3 Vols., Bologna, 1982

POLUNIN, O., *Flowers of Europe*, London, 1969

POLUNIN, O., and A. HUXLEY, *Flowers of the Mediterranean*, 3rd Edition, London, 1987

POLUNIN, O., and B. E. SMYTHIES, *Flowers of South-West Europe*, London, 1973

POLUNIN, O., *Flowers of Greece and the Balkans*, Oxford, 1980

QUEZEL, P., and S. SANTA, *Nouvelle Flore de l'Algérie et des régions désertiques méridionales*, 2 Vols., Paris, 1962–1963

RECHINGER, K. H., *Flora Aegaea*, reprinted Vienna, 1973

RECHINGER-MOSER, F., O. WETTSTEIN and M. BEIER, *Italien*, Stuttgart, 1967

Rikli, M., *Das Pflanzenkleid der Mittelmeerländer*, 3 Vols., 2nd Edition, Berne, 1943–1948

Reisigl, H., E. and O. Danesch, *Mittelmeerflora*, Berne and Stuttgart, 1977

Schönfelder, P., and I., *Das Blüht am Mittelmeer*, 3rd Edition, Stuttgart, 1982

Täckholm, V., *Students' Flora of Egypt*, 2nd Edition, Beirut, 1974

Vedel, H., *Trees and Shrubs of the Mediterranean*, Penguin, 1978

Tutin, T. G., *Flora Europaea*, 5 Vols., Cambridge, 1964–1980

Williams, J. G., A. E. Williams and N. Arlott, *A Field Guide to the Orchids of Britain and Europe with North Africa and the Middle East*, London, 1978

Willkomm, M., and J. Lange, *Prodromus Florae Hispanicae*, 4 Vols., Stuttgart, 1870–1893

Zangheri, P., *Flora Italica*, Padua, 1976

Zohary, M., *Flora Palaestina*, Jerusalem, 1966–1978

Index of English names

Index of scientific names